ADVANCED COASTAL NAVIGATION

AN-1

SECOND EDITION   U. S. COAST GUARD AUXILIARY

Library of Congress Catalog Card Number: 86-51655
ISBN 0-930028-0-5

Printed in the United States of America at no cost
to the United States Government or
United States Coast Guard.

We thank the following
for their support of this publication:

Aldus Corporation, Seattle, WA
Autodesk, Incorporated, Sausalito, CA
Hewlett-Packard Company, Palo Alto, CA
MicroAge of Melbourne, FL
Eric Price, Computer Consultant, Vero Beach, FL.

THE COMMANDANT OF THE UNITED STATES COAST GUARD
WASHINGTON, D.C. 20593-0001

ADVANCED COASTAL NAVIGATION, Second Edition

FOREWORD

This second edition of the Advanced Coastal
Navigation textbook has been completely revised to
include the most up-to-date methods and tools used
in modern coastal navigation. An innovative
chapter on fuel planning has been added, as well as
detailed explanations on radar plotting that should
be very useful to the recreational boater.

This text is used as the nucleus for both the
Advanced Coastal Navigation and Basic Coastal
Navigation courses offered by the U. S. Coast Guard
Auxiliary.

The Coast Guard Auxiliary is composed of civilian
volunteers who give freely of their time in many
ways to assist the U. S. Coast Guard in its mission
of boating safety. I commend the Auxiliary for the
development of this course, and I salute all
students who put in the time and effort necessary
to learn the time-honored art of navigation.

Sincerely,

J. W. KIME
Admiral, U. S. Coast Guard

OFFICE OF THE
NATIONAL COMMODORE

This second edition of ADVANCED COASTAL NAVIGATION has been produced by the Department of Education of the United States Coast Guard Auxiliary.

This text and supporting materials have been completely revised and updated to provide you with a comprehensive knowledge of the latest in coastal navigation techniques. This text has been developed for use with two public education courses offered by Coast Guard Auxiliary flotillas - BASIC COASTAL NAVIGATION and ADVANCED COASTAL NAVIGATION.

Although the talents of many Auxiliarists have been utilized in the development of this course, the combined expertise, hard work and devotion to this project of L. Daniel Maxim, the principal author, and Virginia L. Knudsen, Chief of the Department of Education's Support Division, have resulted in an excellent course for navigation students. We think you will agree.

We hope you not only enjoy this course, but that it will help you to become confident in your navigation skills as you explore the coasts and inland waters of our great country.

May your winds be fair, your currents favorable and may the sun always shine upon you.

Henry G. Pratt III
National Commodore
U. S. Coast Guard Auxiliary

TABLE OF CONTENTS

Introduction

Welcome to the exciting world of marine navigation! This is the second edition of the text, *Advanced Coastal Navigation* (ACN), designed to be used in concert with the Student Study Guide (SSG), and the 1210-Tr chart in the Public Education course of the same name taught by the United States Coast Guard Auxiliary (USCGAUX). In abridged version, this text is also used for the Basic Coastal Navigation (BCN) course.

This second edition builds upon the first edition of this same text but has been substantially rewritten to reflect the helpful advice of numerous dedicated USCGAUX instructors, student feedback, and recent technical developments in the field--particularly in the area of electronic navigation.

The ACN course is not intrinsically difficult, nor does it have advanced educational requirements. Students from many walks of life and of widely varying educational backgrounds have successfully completed the course. But it does require a professional attitude, careful attention to classroom presentations, and diligence in working out the homework problems. To provide the necessary practice in solving navigation problems, a comprehensive Student Study Guide has been developed, containing an ample supply of homework problems. *Not all of these homework problems need to be worked out by each student.* Once you have mastered one type of problem, the balance of this type can be skipped. Teaching experience has indicated that most students require four to five hours per week on average to complete the homework and prepare for the next weekly session.

The ACN course has been designed to utilize the 1210-Tr nautical chart. It is suggested that this chart be readily at hand as the text is read to follow the examples. It is recognized that students from all areas of the United States enroll in the course, and that a better geographic "balance" to the examples might be attractive. Where necessary, as for example, in the discussion of polyconic charts of the Great Lakes in Chapter 3, illustrations from other areas of the country are included. But the 1210-Tr chart contains a wide variety of features of interest to the navigator and, moreover, contains a useful summary of chart symbols printed on the reverse side for ready reference. In short, this is an ideal training chart.

The ACN text has been designed, for the most part, to teach you the "classical" methods of coastal navigation that are applicable to small vessels. Shortcuts, such as might be taken for routine cruises in very familiar waters, are not considered. Experience, sometimes called the "seaman's eye," teaches the navigator which shortcuts can be taken and under what circumstances. But the basis for shortcuts should rest on a firm foundation/mastery of "the textbook solution," and not simply arise from laziness or lack of knowledge.

Over the past few years there have been revolutionary developments in the field of marine electronics. Modern loran, the fluxgate compass, radar, RDF, fuel meters and computers, "electronic charts," and autopilots serve as examples. These devices, tied together with on-board navigational computers, have revolutionized both the art and science of marine navigation. Today it is literally true that, by merely pressing a few buttons, you can program in an entire voyage and simply sit back, watch for traffic and be prepared to dock the vessel at the conclusion of the voyage. Alarms warn of the approach of vessels within a predefined exclusion zone, passage into shallow water, and arrival at waypoints or the final destination. Once, such an "electronic voyage" would have smacked of the writings of Jules Verne, or been impossibly out of reach for most boaters. But, recent advances in the "state of the art" of marine electronics have brought science fiction into the realm of the possible and affordable.

These modern miracles have led some students to question the role of "classical" methods of coastal navigation, such as visual fixes, dead reckoning plots, and the like. Why, after all, learn the tedious calculations of tide height or tidal current, for example, when an hour-by-hour calculation requires only seconds on a laptop computer? The answer is very simple. First, not all vessels are equipped with the latest in marine electronics; students come to the ACN course owning everything from runabouts equipped with little more than a compass to large yachts equipped with the entire contents of one of the numerous catalogs of purveyors of marine electronics. The ACN course is designed for skippers of both of these types of vessels. Second, and perhaps more important, even if a vessel is equipped with the latest in navigation systems, the reliability of seaborne electronics is still far from perfect. The "classical" methods of navigation are required to monitor the performance of even the best found ship. And, should these systems fail, classical methods can be used to bring you home safe and sound.

The ACN course does include material on more sophisticated marine electronics, such as RDF, loran-C, and radar, not to teach you how to operate any particular model, but rather to acquaint you with the general principles and techniques so that you can make better use of whatever brand of equipment you own or elect to purchase.

The ACN course also contains a novel chapter on fuel planning, a subject usually given short shrift or omitted entirely in the typical text on navigation.

Several sections of this text are identified as "more technical." This material is included for those readers who have a more technical background and are interested in a more complete and detailed exposition. Students who lack the necessary background or interest can omit these sections without loss of continuity. Material so identified is not included in the final examination, however. Additionally, a list of references is appended to chapters for those who wish to learn yet more.

Perhaps surprisingly, several aspects of navigation (generally those relating to the "art" of navigation) are controversial. For example, there are those who advocate that all plotting should be done with respect to magnetic, rather than true north. Although this text takes a position on many of these points of controversy, books or articles that espouse a contrary point of view are often cited among the references. Therefore, the student should not assume that either the United States Coast Guard or the Coast Guard Auxiliary specifically endorses any work cited in the references. These are included to lend balance, perspective, and interest. Likewise, any mention or inclusion of pictures of particular makes or models of equipment does not imply that these are judged to be superior, or even recommended brands.

It is appropriate to thank the many firms that have supplied pictures and/or illustrations for use in this text. Acknowledgements are included in the caption to each illustration.

Although theory is not slighted, the emphasis in the text is on practical, time-tested approaches to navigation. The text and accompanying SSG contain numerous discussions of practical methods and numerical examples to provide a firm foundation in the art and science of coastal navigation.

This text contains a glossary of terms, given in Appendix A, and a list of acronyms and abbreviations, given in Appendix B. Readers encountering an unfamiliar term or abbreviation may wish to consult these appendices for a brief explanation.

Each page of the log book of Christopher Columbus was headed with the title *Como Dios Manda* (As God Ordains), which was testimony both to his religious faith and to the primitive state of the art of navigation at the time. This book is dedicated to the notion that you should also have a hand in the outcome of a voyage.

May you always have fair skies, calm seas, fair currents, and following winds. But, more important, may you learn how to navigate safely and efficiently regardless of sea or wind conditions.

Chapter 1

Introduction to Coastal Navigation

What is coastal navigation? In simple terms, marine navigation is "getting your vessel from where you are to where you want to go, safely and efficiently." More formally, it is the "process of directing the movement of a vessel from one point to another." It is derived from the two Latin words, *navis* (ship), and *agere* (to move). *Coastal navigation* refers to navigation in coastal (sometimes termed pilot) waters, where the opportunity exists to determine or check the vessel's position by reference to navigational aids and observations (by either visual or electronic means) of the coast and its features. Coastal navigation is distinguished from "blue water" or ocean navigation, terms used to describe navigation out of sight of land and/or coastal Aids to Navigation (ATONs). Although blue-water navigation may appear to require more sophisticated techniques and equipment, such as the employment of methods to fix the vessel's position from observation of the sun, moon, or stars, coastal navigation often demands a greater degree of accuracy and attention to detail. On a long ocean passage, for example, it may suffice to determine the vessel's position only once or twice a day, and to within a margin of uncertainty of several square miles. A well found oceangoing vessel may afford the navigator a dry workstation, and numerous electronic aids, such as SATNAV/GPS, or Omega. A passing vessel would be a curiosity in seldom traveled waters, rather than an object for collision-avoidance maneuvers. In coastal waters, particularly in narrow channels, position fixes might be required every 5 to 15 minutes, and required accuracy limits could well be measured in yards. The navigator's workspace could be cramped, and the vessel's navigational gear limited to a hand-bearing compass. All this is to be done while dodging "heavy iron" (large vessels) in busy shipping channels.

AN OVERVIEW OF THE COURSE

This section provides an overview of the *Advanced Coastal Navigation* (ACN) course in the context of the navigator's tasks on a typical voyage in coastal waters. To make the discussion concrete, suppose that you are the navigator for the 42 ft. trawler, *Verloren*, on a voyage from Tiverton, on the Sakonnet River in the state of Rhode Island, to Woods Hole, Massachusetts, approximately 40 miles distant. This area is covered by the 1210-Tr chart, which is distributed with the course materials. Reach for this chart now (the first of many times that you will be called to do this in the chapters ahead) and locate the place of departure on the voyage, Tiverton (roughly in the middle of the chart, near the top), Rhode Island, and the destination, Woods Hole, Massachusetts, on Vineyard Sound (at the far right of the chart).

It is convenient to subdivide navigation into two distinct, but related phases: *voyage planning* and *underway navigation*. The planning phase covers the initial shoreside paper-and-pencil or (increasingly) computer chores, and ends when the vessel's anchor is weighed or the mooring lines are slipped. Underway navigation covers navigation and decision making on-the-water. The overall steps in each phase are discussed below.

STEPS IN VOYAGE PLANNING

Figure 1-1 highlights the principal steps in voyage planning. It starts with the *assembly of required reference materials and trip and vessel data.* Such materials include up-to-date (and corrected) nautical charts at the right scale (discussed in Chapter 3), *Tide and Tidal Current Tables* and related materials (discussed in Chapter 8), and other navigation reference materials, such as the *Light List, US Coast Pilot,* and cruising guides to the area (discussed in Chapter 10).

The nautical charts are used to lay out the voyage, measure distances and courses, identify landmarks or ATONs that will be used to fix the vessel's position, ensure that the course avoids hazards to navigation, and for many other purposes.

The *Light List* is consulted to determine the characteristics of the relevant ATONs (such as color or light characteristics and horn sequences that are important for recognition and identification purposes), while the *Coast Pilot* provides useful "local knowledge" in narrative form. For example, following a route from Tiverton through Buzzards Bay would require a transit of the channel between Buzzards Bay and Vineyard Sound. The *1988 U.S. Coast Pilot* offers the following comments: "The passage through Woods Hole, between numerous ledges and shoals, is marked by navigational aids. However, tidal currents are so strong that the passage is difficult and dangerous without some local knowledge. Buoys in the narrowest part of the channel sometimes are towed under, and a stranger should attempt passage only at slack water." Such information is obviously invaluable for planning purposes.

Tide Tables are used to estimate the height of the tides that would be encountered on the voyage to ensure that a safe route is chosen. *Tidal Current Tables* provide information on the strength and direction of the currents, information which is important to estimate the vessel's

ground speed, and to the selection of the correct course to compensate for these currents.

Other information requirements include operating data for the vessel, such as the relation between engine revolutions per minute (RPM) and the speed through the water (discussed in Chapter 5), and fuel capacity and consumption data (presented in Chapter 11). For example, at 2250 RPM, *Verloren* might make 8 knots (nautical miles per hour), and burn 7 gallons of fuel per hour from tanks that can hold 400 gallons when topped off (filled).

The second step in voyage planning is to consult the materials assembled and *formulate voyage options for later evaluation.* Voyage options relevant for this trip would include the overall route to follow (east through Buzzards Bay, or south, then east through Vineyard Sound are obvious alternatives), departure time (which affects the water currents and tide heights that will be encountered and also how much of the voyage will be conducted during daylight hours), the speed to be run (which affects the estimated enroute time, fuel consumption, and arrival time), and planned stopovers for amenities, recreation, or fuel. Even for this "simple" trip, there are several alternatives that might be considered. Time spent developing thoughtful voyage options is time well spent. *A good navigator thinks and plans ahead, so that he/she doesn't have to exercise extraordinary seamanship!* If, for example, the more northerly route through Buzzards Bay is chosen, the trip schedule has to be worked out to minimize the hazards of transiting the channel between Buzzards Bay and Vineyard Sound. To someone unfamiliar with these waters, the *Coast Pilot* indicates that it would be prudent to make this transit during daylight hours at or near slack current. This can and should be figured out in advance, rather than "come upon" in failing light.

The third step in voyage planning is to *evaluate systematically the alternatives identified* in

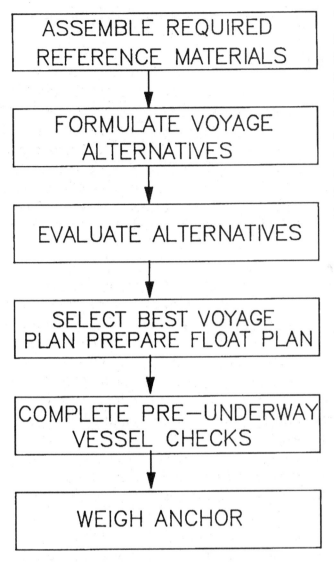

Fig. 1-1. Steps in Voyage Planning.

The flowchart contains the following boxes connected by downward arrows:

ASSEMBLE REQUIRED REFERENCE MATERIALS

FORMULATE VOYAGE ALTERNATIVES

EVALUATE ALTERNATIVES

SELECT BEST VOYAGE PLAN PREPARE FLOAT PLAN

COMPLETE PRE—UNDERWAY VESSEL CHECKS

WEIGH ANCHOR

step two. Obviously, two important factors relevant to the voyage are *Verloren's* speed, and the distance to be covered along each of the alternative routes. This distance is determined from a rough plot of the alternate routes on the nautical chart by techniques revealed in Chapter 3. In this case, the route through Buzzards Bay (approximately 37.5 miles for one possible route layout) is slightly shorter than that through Vineyard Sound (approximately 40 miles). Speed and distance determine the en route time required for the voyage (5 hours estimated time enroute (ETE) to cover 40 miles at 8 knots assuming no current), and the fuel consumption (35 gallons required assuming 5 hours enroute at

7 gallons per hour). Simple time-speed-distance (TSD) calculations are reviewed in Chapter 5, fuel consumption calculations in Chapter 11, and the somewhat more complex task of allowing for, and compensating for, currents in Chapter 7. Estimation of the probable currents is discussed at length in Chapter 8. As it happens, the currents in Buzzards Bay and Vineyard Sound are often moving in opposite directions, at speeds ranging from less than one knot to 2 knots or more. So, depending upon the current patterns prevailing on the day and time of the voyage, the two routes identified above would have significantly different ETEs. Moreover, as illustrated in Chapter 8, it is entirely possible that the longer distance route would also be the shorter time route. As noted, the length of the Buzzards Bay route is approximately 37.5 miles, compared to 40 miles for the Vineyard Sound route. But if the average current along Vineyard Sound were, say 2 knots in the direction of intended travel (a so-called *fair current*), and that in Buzzards Bay were 0.6 knots against the direction of travel (a so-called *foul current*), the time required for the trip through Vineyard Sound would be approximately 4 hours, compared to nearly 5 hours on the "shorter" route. (This calculation must be refined to take account of the fact that the first leg is common to both routes. Even a more exact calculation, however, shows that the longer distance route is the shorter time route.) This example is not hypothetical--the assumed currents are, in fact, the estimated currents at one point in the tidal current cycle. Additionally, the Vineyard Sound route avoids the trip through the channel next to Woods Hole.

For this voyage in *Verloren*, fuel certainly won't be a problem, assuming that the tanks are even near to being filled prior to departure. But for longer trips, or in vessels with higher fuel consumption or lower fuel capacity, fuel planning is often a singularly important activity. For vessels with "short legs" (limited fuel capacity), fuel stopovers would need to be considered, and/or the engine throttle setting altered to stretch fuel reserves.

Option evaluation is not limited to questions of time, speed, or fuel consumption. Many other factors need to be considered. For example, the difficulty of transiting channels or inlets, availability of *"bolt holes"* (safe places to anchor or moor in the event of mechanical problems or adverse weather), and the availability of suitable landmarks or ATONs to fix the vessel's position or to mark channels, all need to be considered. Discussion of these important matters can be found scattered throughout this text in the examples used to illustrate key points.

The fourth step in voyage planning is to *select a plan* that is "best" in some sense, considering the vessel, navigational equipment aboard, skill and local knowledge of the navigator and crew, and other relevant factors. Included here is the important task of making a *"float plan"* that describes the route and estimated time(s) of arrival so that the Search and Rescue (SAR) personnel can be promptly alerted if you become overdue. (The float plan should also include a description of the vessel, number of persons on board, available safety and radio equipment, and other relevant information.) The float plan is left in the care of a responsible person, with instructions to notify the Coast Guard in the event that the vessel becomes overdue. The navigator often prepares a more detailed voyage plan in this step, identifying checkpoints and turnpoints for each leg of the trip, courses to steer, time estimates, and fuel consumption estimates.

In this fourth step, the navigator also plots the first "legs" (route segments) of the voyage on a *tactical (underway) dead reckoning plot* (DR plot). Dead Reckoning (DR), presented in Chapter 5, is the name given to the process of predicting the future position of a vessel from knowledge of its present (or starting) position, the course steered, and the speed maintained. A tactical DR plot shows course legs (including direction, speed, and occasionally distance) and future positions (termed dead reckoning posi-

tions) at various times in a stylized format. The DR plot is maintained and updated throughout the underway portion of the voyage.

The fifth step in voyage planning is to *complete prevoyage checks* on the vessel and its equipment--much as aircraft pilots do in the preflight inspection. For example, the navigator would verify that all communications and navigation equipment were functioning properly and that the correct charts and other reference materials were aboard. Weather information should be gathered and used as part of the "go/no-go" decision. If all goes well in this step, it is time to start engines, slip *Verloren's* dock lines, note the departure time in the navigator's or ship's log, and get underway.

STEPS WHILE UNDERWAY

Figure 1-2 shows a simplified summary of the key underway activities. As noted above, the navigator estimates the future position of the vessel at various times using DR (see Chapter 5). But, these estimates are not error-free. Neither wind nor current, for example, is considered in the determination of DR positions--for reasons that are apparent on reading Chapter 5. Therefore, it is very important to check and update the actual progress of the voyage at frequent intervals in coastal waters. This is done with a series of "fixes," points in time at which the vessel's position is accurately determined.

The vessel's position can be fixed by three principal methods. First, its position can be determined by *visual observation* of the range or bearing of landmarks or ATONs. For example, the navigator could determine the magnetic bearing of the abandoned light house on Sakonnet Point, and that of the tower on Gooseberry Neck, which could fix *Verloren's* position by triangulation if the Buzzards Bay route were taken. This method for position-fixing is termed *piloting*, and is discussed in Chapter 6. Second, the vessel's position can be fixed by use of *electronic navigational systems*, such as radio direction finding (RDF), loran, or radar. For example, the RDF could be tuned to the frequency for Buzzards Light and a RDF bearing obtained on this object. Another bearing (either visually or by RDF), or range (e.g., from radar) would be sufficient to determine a fix. This is termed *electronic navigation,* and is discussed in Chapters 6 and 9. Finally, the position of the ship can be fixed by *observation of the angle (elevation) of heavenly bodies* (here meant to mean the sun, moon, or stars). This process is termed *celestial navigation.* For various reasons, including the limited opportunities for fixes, and the possible error of celestial fixes, celestial navigation is not extensively used in coastal waters, and is not presented in this text. From the above discussion, it should be clear that piloting, electronic navigation, and celestial navigation are not distinct *systems of navigation.* These are, in fact, only names given to the *means* used to check on (fix) the vessel's position.

Once a fix is determined, this is plotted on the tactical DR plot (see Chapter 5) and the plot is updated by this fix. (The data for this fix are also entered into the navigator's or ship's log.) A comparison of the fix with the vessel's DR position can be used as a "plausibility" or "reality" check on the fix and the DR position. Absent blunders, any discrepancy between the fix and the DR position is due to current, so a comparison of these two positions can be used to estimate the actual currents (the term *set* refers to the direction toward which the current is flowing, and *drift* refers to the speed of the current) encountered (the method for estimating set and drift is discussed in Chapter 7).

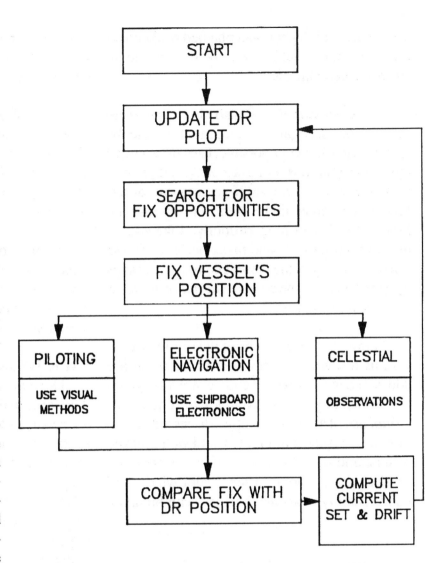

Fig. 1-2. Steps in Underway Navigation

For introductory purposes, Figure 1-2 has been simplified considerably. In practice, the navigator's underway tasks could be more complex and varied. For example, instead of merely estimating the set and drift of the current, the navigator would usually estimate a course (by the methods discussed in Chapter 7) to compensate for these effects and ensure that the vessel stays in safe water. On such a short voyage as is illustrated here, en route decision making may be relatively simple. But on other trips, the navigator would be continually revising fuel consumption estimates and the estimated time of arrival (ETA). These revised estimates could signal the need to change the voyage plan. For example, the discovery that fuel consumption was significantly higher than planned could mean that the vessel would have to be diverted to an alternate destination.

The navigator should also check the accuracy of the navigation equipment in use by comparing, whenever possible, fixes determined by various methods. For example, a comparison between an accurate visual fix and one determined by loran could be used to verify that the loran was functioning properly. Likewise, a prudent navigator would make periodic checks on the accuracy of the vessel's compass, perhaps by spot checks of the compass *deviation table*, as explained in Chapter 2.

There you have it--a brief illustration of the various navigator's tasks and where these are addressed in this text. Of course, not all voyages are sufficiently long or complex to require the *formal* use of all the techniques discussed above. For short voyages in familiar and well-marked waters, and when weather conditions are close to ideal (e.g., moderate seas, calm winds, and good visibility), various short cuts can be taken

to simplify the navigator's duties. This is termed navigation by *seaman's eye* and is addressed in Chapter 11.

In the above discussion, the contents of two subsequent chapters of this text were omitted. Chapter 2 covers the marine magnetic compass, and Chapter 4 provides a summary discussion of the navigator's tools (other than the vessel's compass).

Before moving on to some of the interesting topics in the chapters ahead, it is necessary to address two important introductory topics: the earth's coordinate system, and measurement of direction.

BACK TO BASICS: THE PLANET EARTH

The earth is approximately spherical, as illustrated in Figure 1-3. Technically, the earth is termed an *oblate spheroid* (a sphere flattened at the poles, as opposed to a *prolate spheroid* which resembles a football, but don't go calling it prolate spheroid-ball, or you will wind up being called an odd ball!), but the difference between the earth's actual shape and that of a perfect sphere is not important for this course. The average diameter of the earth is approximately 6,880 nautical miles, and its circumference is approximately 21,614 nautical miles. Since there are 360 degrees (denoted with the degree symbol °) of angular measure in a circle, 1 degree of angular measure along the earth's surface is approximately 60 nautical miles. Degrees are further subdivided into minutes (denoted with an apostrophe, e.g., 30 minutes is written 30'), and seconds (denoted with two apostrophes, e.g., 40 seconds is written 40"). There are 60 minutes in a degree (and 60 seconds in a minute), so 1 minute of angular measure is approximately equal to 1 nautical mile.

The earth rotates about a straight line called the *axis of rotation*, or *polar axis*. The earth completes one rotation every 24 hours *(the solar day)*. The axis of rotation passes through the center of the earth, intersecting the surface at

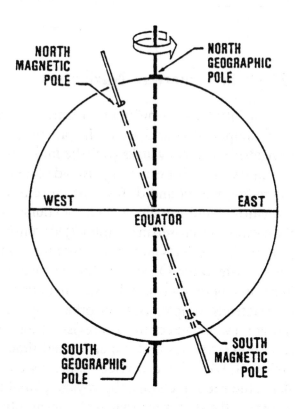

Fig. 1-3. The Earth and Its Poles

two points, termed the *north and south geo-graphic poles* (denoted Pn and Ps, respectively). The earth rotates from west to east, i.e., counter-clockwise when viewed from a point in space atop the north pole. The west-to-east rotation makes the sun appear to rise in the east, and set in the west. The earth is also a magnet--dis-cussed below--and has *north and south magnetic poles,* also shown in Figure 1-3 which are not co-incident with the geographic poles, an important point explored below.

GREAT AND SMALL CIRCLES

A plane passed through the center of the earth separates the earth into two *hemispheres,* and intersects the surface of the earth to pro-duce a geometric figure termed a *great circle*. On the surface of a sphere, the shortest distance between any two points lies on the great circle that connects these two points. (On the slightly flattened surface of the earth, the shortest dis-tance between two points is technically termed a geodesic, but for the purposes of this course a great circle and a *geodesic* are one and the same.)

If the plane is passed so that it is perpendicu-lar to the earth's axis of rotation (i.e., equidistant from the geographic poles), the resulting great circle is termed the *equator*, as shown in Figure 1-4, and the two hemispheres formed are named the *northern and southern hemispheres*.

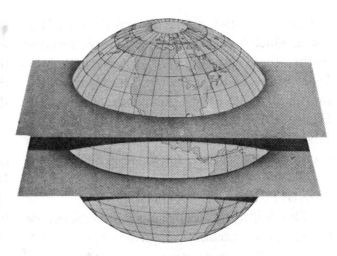

Fig. 1-5. A Parallel of Latitude

A *small circle* results if a plane is passed through the earth that does not touch the earth's center. Small circles parallel to the equator (termed *parallels*) are one of the two reference coordinates used to define position on the earth's surface. Figure 1-5 shows the equator and an-other parallel of latitude.

A great circle that passes through the polar axis or axis of rotation is termed a *meridian*. It

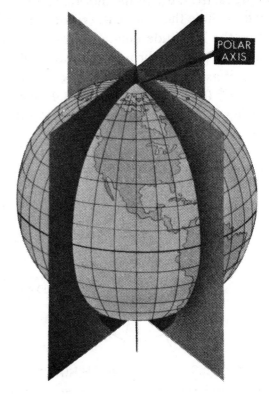

Fig. 1-6. The Planes of the Meridians Meet at the Polar Axis

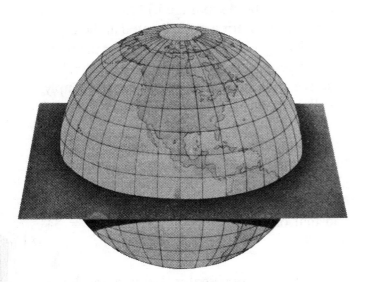

Fig. 1-4. The Equator

has two parts--that on the observer's side of the earth, which is called the *upper branch*, and one on the other side of the earth, which is called the *lower branch* of the meridian. The planes of the meridians meet at the polar axis, as shown in Figure 1-6. Meridians are used to define the other major coordinate for specifying position on the earth's surface--*longitude*.

LONGITUDE AND LATITUDE

The prime meridian (more specifically its upper branch) passes through the original site of the Royal Observatory in Greenwich, England. Also called the *Greenwich Meridian*, it is used as the origin of measurement of longitude. More precisely, longitude (abbreviated Lo, or sometimes written, λ, the Greek letter lambda) is the angular distance (in degrees, minutes, and seconds, or degrees and decimal minutes) between a position on the earth and the prime meridian measured eastward or westward through 180 degrees along the arc of the equator to the meridian of the position. Because longitude is measured only through 180 degrees, rather than 360 degrees, from the prime meridian, it is necessary to include the word east (E) or west (W) to define the longitude uniquely. For example, the meridian passing through the Naval Observatory in Washington, DC, would be identified as Lo = 77° 03.9' W (77 degrees, 3.9 minutes, west of the prime meridian) or, equivalently as

77° 03' 54" (77 degrees, 3 minutes, 54 seconds west of the prime meridian). In some writings, the E or W may be omitted, when it is clear that the longitude is east or west, but this practice should be discouraged.

As other examples, the longitude of the Griffin Observatory in Los Angeles, CA, is Lo = 118° 18.1' W, and that of the Tokyo Astronomical Observatory at Mitka, Japan, is Lo = 139° 32.5' E. Remember, longitude is always specified as east or west of the prime meridian. Figure 1-7 shows the longitudes of these three locations on the earth's surface as viewed from atop Pn.

It is not sufficient to identify a position on the earth's surface by its longitude alone, because there are an infinite number of points on any meridian. Another coordinate is necessary to specify position uniquely.

As noted, this second coordinate is termed *latitude*. More formally, latitude (abbreviated L or Lat) is the angular distance between a position on the earth's surface and the equator measured northward or southward from the equator along a meridian and labeled with a "N" or an "S" to denote whether the point is located in the northern or southern hemispheres respectively. (Sometimes, when the hemisphere is clearly implicit, the N or S will be omitted, but this practice is to be discouraged.) Latitude ranges from 0 degrees (for a point located at the equator) to 90 degrees N or S (for a point at the north or south geographic pole). Lines of constant latitude are called parallels of latitude, or simply, parallels.

Continuing the earlier examples, the latitude of the Naval Observatory in Washington, DC, is L (or Lat) = 38° 55.2' N, that of the observatory in Tokyo, Japan, L = 35° 40.4' N, and that of the Griffith Observatory, L = 34° 06.8' N.

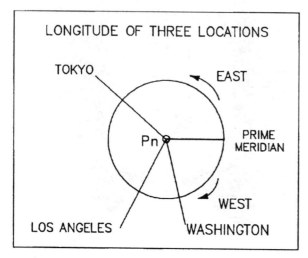

Fig. 1-7. Longitude for Three Locations on the Earth's Surface.

These two coordinates, latitude and longitude, are used to define locations on the earth's surface, as shown in Figure 1-8. By convention, a point's latitude is written first, and its longitude second, so if there are no labels, the first number written in latitude, the second longitude (the notation E or W, versus N or S also define the coordinate).

One important attribute of latitude (noted implicitly above) is the fact that one degree of latitude, measured up or down (north or south) any meridian, is equal to 60 nautical miles, and one minute is equal to 1 mile. *Note, however, that this does not hold for longitude. Although one minute of longitude does equal 1 nautical mile along the equator,* as the latitude increases, the distance along any parallel, between two meridians, becomes smaller, reaching 0 miles at either pole. (The length of one degree of longitude is approximately equal to 60 cos Lat. For example, at a latitude of 41° 30' north, approximately the mid-point of the latitudes given on the 1210-Tr chart, the length of one degree of longitude is approximately 45 nautical miles rather than 60 nautical miles on the equator.) Remember, latitude is measured along a meridian (running north or south), while longitude is measured along a parallel (running east or west) from the prime meridian.

DIRECTION
Latitude and longitude are all that are required to specify *location* on the earth's surface. But, it is also necessary to have some means for specifying *direction* on the earth's surface.

Direction is not absolute, but must be keyed to some reference point. Three common reference points are: *true north, magnetic north* (discussed below), and to the *ship's heading* (relative bearings, discussed below).

If direction is referenced to true north (geographic north or the north pole), it is defined relative to the local meridian passing through the point of interest (also called the local geographic meridian). The local geographic meridian passes through the north geographic pole, so

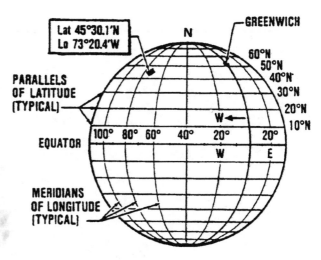

Fig. 1-8. Grid System of Latitude and Longitude.

this direction is relative to the north geographic pole or to "true north." The direction of true north, or northward along the upper branch of the local geographic meridian, is defined as zero degrees, and becomes the reference direction. By convention, the precision of angular measurement for courses or bearings is to the nearest degree. Degrees are reported to three digits, so, for example, true north has the direction 000 degrees. Direction is specified clockwise from true north. Thus, east is 090 degrees, south is 180 degrees, west 270 degrees, etc. The direction 360 degrees, and 000 degrees are one and the same and, by convention this direction is written 000 degrees. Therefore, it is said that direction is measured clockwise from north, and ranges from 000 degrees to 359 degrees.

With a suitable device for measuring angles (see Chapter 4), directions can be read off the local meridian. However, for reasons that will become apparent in later chapters, it is useful to have additional sources of directional information provided on the nautical chart. One common directional reference is termed a *compass rose*, which provides directional information relative to true north and to magnetic north (discussed below). Figure 1-9 shows a dual compass rose taken from the 1210-Tr chart. Directions relative to true north are given on the *outer circle* of the rose shown in Figure 1-9-- true

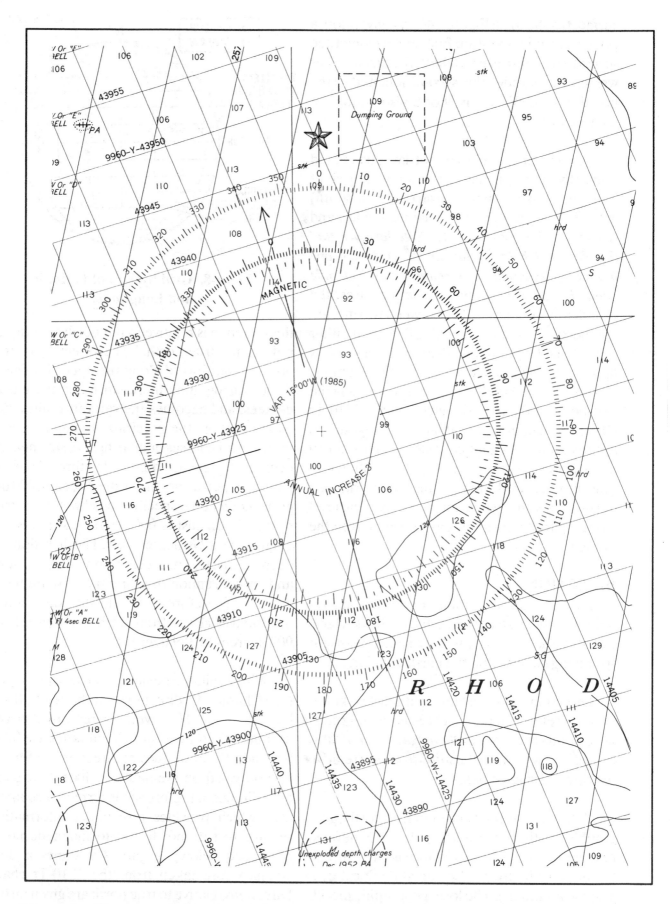

Fig. 1-9. True and Compass Rose as Presented on the 1210-Tr Chart

north is generally indicated with a *star symbol* (presumably a reference to Polaris, the star that is, to within a degree or so, aligned with true north). The principal advantage of printing compass roses on nautical charts is that it is relatively easy to *transfer* (i.e., measure) these directions with parallel rulers or a paraline plotter (see Chapter 4).

When a direction other than exactly north, south, east, or west is specified on the earth, and followed for any distance, such that each subsequent meridian is passed at the same angle relative to the direction of the geographic pole, a line is formed that "spirals" around the globe, continually edging either northward (for directions between 270 degrees and 359 degrees or 000 degrees and 090 degrees) or southward (for directions between 090 degrees and 270 degrees). This line, termed a *rhumb line* or *loxodrome*, approaches either pole, as shown in Figure 1-10. This line drawn on the surface of a sphere, such as the earth, is actually *curved*, not straight. (However, as noted in Chapter 3, it will plot as a straight line on the mercator chart typically used for coastal navigation.)

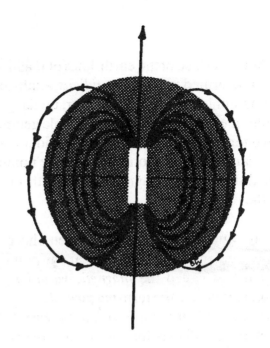

Fig. 1-11. The Earth Is a Magnet

MAGNETIC REFERENCES

The earth has a weak magnetic field, thought to be generated by the flow of the liquid iron alloy core of the planet. This field, termed a *dipole field*, is similar to the magnetic field that would be generated by a large bar magnet located near the center of the earth. The magnetic flux lines, diagrammed in the stylized and simplified representation of Figure 1-11, flow out from the core through the auroral zone of the south pole, around the earth, and return through the auroral zone of the north pole. *More important to the mariner, the magnetic poles of the earth differ from the geographic poles.* In 1984, the north magnetic pole, for example, was located in Canada's Northwest Territories, at approximately a latitude of 78.9 degrees north, and longitude 103.8 degrees west, several hundred miles removed from the geographic north pole.

According to records dating back to the 1700s, the apparent position of the north magnetic pole has shifted from a position north of Scandinavia across Greenland to its present position in the Parry Islands in northern Canada. Over geologic time, the shifts have been even more dramatic; it is believed that 200 million years ago the magnetic poles were near the equator!

Fig. 1-10. A Rhumb Line or Loxodrome as Given in Bowditch.

At the surface of the earth, lines of magnetic force are termed *magnetic meridians*, analogous to geographic meridians. However, unlike geographic meridians, which have a simple geometrical interpretation, the magnetic meridians are irregular, a phenomenon caused by the nonuniform distribution of magnetic material throughout the earth.

The angular difference between the geographic and magnetic meridians at any point on the earth is called the *magnetic variation*, or simply *variation*. (The term *magnetic declination* is also used.) Variation is said to be east if the magnetic meridian points eastward of the north geographic pole, or west if (as shown in Figures 1-12 or 1-13) the north magnetic pole is westward (to the left) of the north geographic pole as seen by the observer.

Incidentally, diagrams such as Figures 1-12 and 1-13, are very helpful in understanding the concept of variation, but are not, strictly speaking, accurate. This is because they suggest that a compass (free of shipboard magnetic influences) would always point toward the north magnetic pole. In fact, a freely suspended magnetic compass needle acted upon by the earth's magnetic field alone will lie in a vertical plane known as the magnetic meridian. These magnetic meridians, however, do not necessarily point towards the magnetic poles, because the earth's magnetic field is irregular. This technicality aside, it still follows that variation is the angular difference between true north and the direction that the vessel's compass would point, absent shipboard magnetic influence. Lines of constant variation are termed *isogonic* lines, and the line where the variation is exactly zero degrees is called the

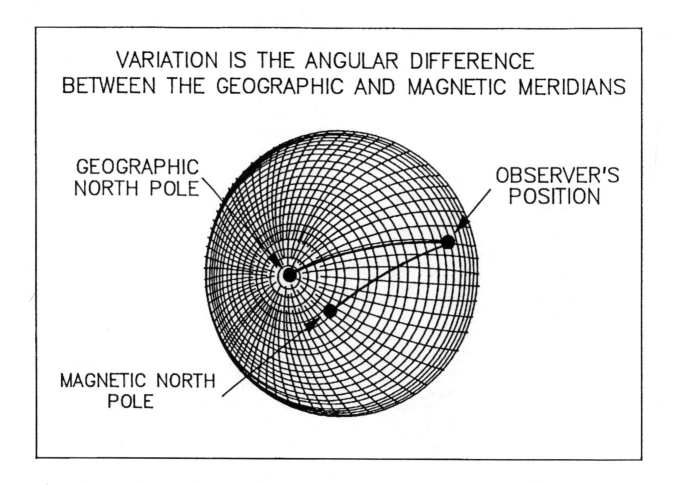

Fig. 1-12. Variation: The Approximate Difference Between the Directions to the North Geographic Pole and theMagnetic Meridian.

agonic line. These isogonic lines are charted by the Defense Mapping Agency and are published on Chart #42.

The relevance of all this to the mariner is that the magnets in the vessel's compass (discussed in Chapter 2) tend to align with the magnetic meridians, rather than the true or geographic meridians. (It is actually slightly more complicated than that, but Chapter 2 straightens out the details.) Therefore, it is necessary to know the variation to be able to convert from true to magnetic directions or the reverse.

Variation data can be found in several sources. Perhaps most convenient, variation data are printed on the compass rose, found on nautical charts, such as is illustrated in Figure 1-9. There, the *inner circle of the compass rose shows mag-netic directions,* while the outer circle shows true directions. In this illustration, the magnetic meridian points to the left of the local geographic meridian--and the variation is approximately 15 degrees *west.* (As noted above, the magnetic meridians shift around, and have daily (diurnal) and longer term (secular) changes, so, for this reason the important shifts are identified on the chart. Reference to Figure 1-9, for example, shows that the variation at this location was 15 degrees west in 1985, and that it is increasing at the rate of three minutes per year.)

Within the continental United States, variation ranges from about 20° W in northern Maine, through 0° in portions of Florida, to 21° E in northern Washington state. (On the northern border between Alaska and Canada, it is approximately 35° E as of this writing.)

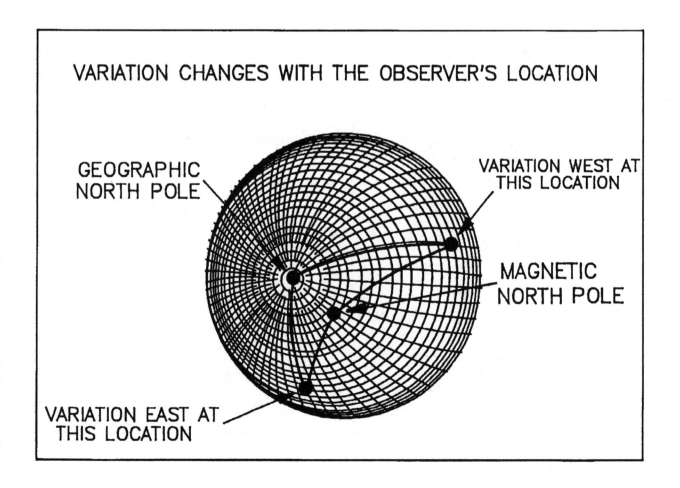

Fig. 1-13. Variation is the Angular Difference Between the Geographic (True) Meridian and the Magnetic Meridian. Variation Changes with Locality.

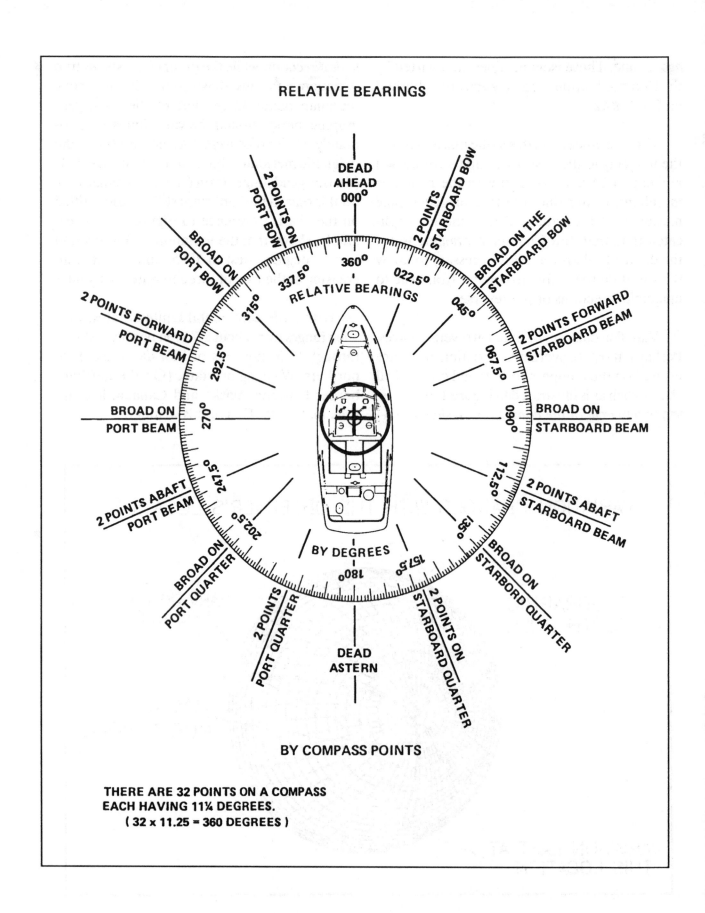

Fig. 1-14. Relative Bearings by Degrees and Points.

CONVERSION FROM TRUE TO MAGNETIC AND VICE VERSA

As noted, it is often necessary to convert from direction expressed relative to magnetic north to direction expressed relative to true north or vice versa. For example, a hand-bearing compass, discussed in Chapter 4, might be used to take a bearing on a shore-based object, and the navigator may wish to convert this to a true bearing for plotting on the nautical chart. Alternatively, a mariner may measure a true course on the chart (discussed in Chapter 3) and wish to convert this to a magnetic course.

Conversion from one reference point to another is relatively simple. Suppose, for example, that the variation is 15 degrees west, as is shown in Figure 1-9, as would apply to one portion of the area covered by the 1210-Tr chart. An object located in the direction of magnetic north from the perspective of the observer (said to have bearing 000 magnetic) would actually bear 345 degrees true. This is because, at this location, the variation is 15 degrees west, or to the left of true. A glance at the compass rose shows that all bearings have this fixed difference between magnetic and true. *Conversion from magnetic to true is, therefore, a simple matter of subtraction of a westerly variation, or addition of an easterly variation.* Thus, for example, an object bearing 090 magnetic, would bear 090 - 015 or 075 true. (Chapter 2 provides some handy memory aids to keep the addition and subtraction straight, but a simple one to remember is "magnetic or compass to true, add east.") As discussed in other chapters, magnetic courses or bearings are identified as such by the use of the word "magnetic," as the writing of an "M" after the number. If no such prefix or suffix is added, it is assumed that the course or bearing is "true."

RELATIVE DIRECTIONS (BEARINGS)

It is convenient, from time to time, for mariners to indicate directions referenced to objects other than the true and/or magnetic meridians. In fact, one of the most used direction systems is that referenced to the fore-and-aft line parallel to, or directly over, the keel of the observer's vessel.

If a direction "rose" were superimposed over the vessel (plan view) with the 000° line directly forward, at the vessel's bow, 090° on the vessel's starboard beam, 180° directly aft, on the vessel's stern, and 270° on the port beam, the *relative bearing* system is developed as illustrated in Figure 1-14. Objects relative to the instantaneous direction of the bow of the boat are indicated in degrees of angular measure, clockwise, just as directions are indicated for the true and magnetic direction systems. Shown also in Figure 1-14 are relative bearings in the older "*point system*," in which the 360 degrees are subdivided into 32 *points*. (The older "point system" is included for historical interest only, and is not used in this text.)

An object 45° off the bow on the *starboard* side (broad on the starboard bow in the older system) would have a relative bearing of (or would bear) 045° R (here the "R" denotes "relative"). If the object were 45° off the bow on the *port* side, it would have a relative bearing of: 360° - 045° = 315° R. A vessel dead ahead, directly off the bow, would bear 000° R. Note that relative bearings relate to the fore-and-aft or bow direction of the boat and change direction as the boat changes direction (heading) or position. If the boat is underway, and the object observed is stationary, the relative bearing will change as the boat approaches, passes, and continues on. The relative bearing would also change if the boat is turned, increasing in a clockwise manner as the boat turned counter-clockwise, to port.

To convert from relative bearing to either a true or magnetic bearing, all that is necessary is to remember the equation; ship's heading + relative bearing = bearing of object. Thus, for example, if the vessel were heading 070 true, and observed an object bearing 135 R, the object would bear 070 + 135 = 205 true. Of course, because there are only 360 degrees of arc measure in a circle, it may be necessary to subtract 360 degrees from the calculated bearing of the object. For example, if the ship's heading were 315 degrees true and the object's relative bearing were 135 degrees, the true bearing would be 315 + 135 = 450; subtracting 360 gives the correct answer of 090 degrees.

The concept of relative bearings is fundamental in the practice of navigation. The concept should be thoroughly understood. The three direction systems will be linked together in the use of the magnetic compass and the practice of piloting.

RECIPROCAL BEARINGS

Finally, this chapter concludes with brief mention of reciprocal bearings. A *reciprocal bearing* is one that differs from the original by 180 degrees. For example, if a fixed navigational aid, such as a lighthouse were to bear 000 degrees true from your vessel (i.e., be directly *north* of your vessel), it could equally be said that your vessel is directly *south* of the lighthouse. That is,

your vessel would be on a reciprocal bearing from the lighthouse. To calculate a reciprocal bearing, all that is necessary is to add or subtract 180 from the given bearing. In this example, the reciprocal of 000 degrees is 180 degrees (obtained by adding 180). (Helpful hint: in calculating a reciprocal by addition or subtraction, it may also be necessary to add or subtract 360 degrees to the result to ensure that the answer lies between 000 and 360.) The reciprocal of 270 degrees is 090 degrees, the reciprocal of 315 degrees is 135 degrees, etc. (With a little practice, you can do these in your head quickly by first adding 200, and taking away 20, or subtracting 200 and adding 20! Thus, for example, the reciprocal of 121 degrees is 301 degrees, obtained by quickly adding 200 to 121 to get 321, and then subtracting 20 to get 301.)

Bearings, whether with respect to true north (true bearings) or magnetic north (magnetic bearings) are all bearings from the vessel *to* an object. Reciprocal bearings are bearings *from* an object to the vessel.

REFERENCES

Bowditch, N. *American Practical Navigator, An Epitome of Navigation*, Vol. 1, Defense Mapping Agency, Washington, DC, 1984.

Budlong, J. P. *Shoreline and Sextant, Practical Coastal Navigation*, Van Nostrand Reinhold Co., New York, NY, 1977.

Departments of the Air Force and the Navy. *Air Navigation*, AFM 51-40, NAVAIR49, 00--80V--49, US Government Printing Office, Washington, DC, 1983.

Kielhorn, W. V. *A Piloting Primer*, privately printed, Naples, FL, 1988.

Maloney, E. S. *Dutton's Navigation and Piloting*, 14th edition, Naval Institute Press, Annapolis, MD, 1985.

Ministry of Defense (Navy). *Admiralty Manual of Navigation*, BR 45 (1), Volume 1, Her Majesty's Stationary Office, London, England, 1987.

Moody, A. B. *Navigation Afloat, A Manual for the Seaman*, Van Nostrand Reinhold Co., New York, NY, 1980.

Naval Training Command. *A Navigation Compendium*, NAVTRA 10494-A, US Government Printing Office, Washington, DC, 1972.

Norville, W. *Coastal Navigation, Step by Step*, International Marine Publishing Co., Camden, ME, 1975.

Queeney, T. E. "The Wandering Magnetic Pole," *Ocean Navigator*, No. 9, September/October 1986, pp. 3 et seq.

Saunders, A. F. *Small Craft Piloting and Coastal Navigation*, Alzarc Enterprises, Scarborough, Ontario, Canada, 1987.

Schufeldt, H. H., and G. D. Dunlop. *Piloting and Dead Reckoning, 2nd edition*, Naval Institute Press, Annapolis, MD, 1981.

Tver, D. F. *The Norton Encyclopedic Dictionary of Navigation*, W. W. Norton & Company, New York, NY, 1987.

U.S. Coast Guard Auxiliary. *Coastal Piloting*, U.S. Coast Guard Auxiliary National Board, Inc., Washington, DC, 1983.

Walsh, G. "Coastal Navigation, The Basics: Course and Direction," *Ocean Navigator*,

Chapter 2

The Marine Magnetic Compass

This second chapter of the Advanced Coastal Navigation Course explores the marine compass and its use. The compass is one of the simplest and most useful navigation instruments to be carried aboard a vessel. A competent navigator, well-found vessel, up-to-date charts, and a good compass are the only real requirements for a safe and efficient voyage. Columbus was able to do this even without good charts!

This chapter provides a brief history of the compass, a discussion of the types and parts of the modern compass, an exposition of the principle of operation of the compass, and finally, a discussion of possible compass errors and their measurement so that the mariner can compensate for these errors and steer correct courses. In particular, so-called TVMDC computations, named for the sequence *true-variation-magnetic-deviation-compass* with which compass courses are determined, are discussed.

One topic omitted in this chapter (and, indeed, the entire text) is that of compass adjustment. Compass adjustment refers to the process of adjusting small magnets contained in the compass to remove as much error as possible. Most modern textbooks devote considerable space to compass adjustment, and the reader may wonder why this topic is omitted here. The reason is simple. Although compass adjustment is not impossibly complex, it is not trivial, and needs to be done right! Professional compass adjusters are available at reasonable cost to perform this service and, unless the mariner is willing to devote time and intellectual effort, this is a job best left to experts. In addition to adjusting the compass, a professional can provide good advice on the placement of the compass, shipboard electronics, and other gear that may affect the compass. For those who disagree with this assessment and have the time and inclination to master the intricacies of compass adjustment, the references included at the end of this chapter provide a useful starting point for home study.

The material in this chapter is not difficult. But teaching experience indicates that considerable practice is required in order to rapidly and reliably solve the problems in the Study Guide.

BRIEF HISTORY

The exact origin of the compass is lost in antiquity. Although some accounts claim that the compass was invented well before the birth of Christ, documentary evidence of its use in Europe and China dates back only to approximately 1100 A.D. (Incidentally, by convention the early Chinese compasses were said to point south, as this was considered a more noble aspect.) The modern compass card (as opposed to needles used on the earliest compasses) apparently originated with Flavio Gioja of Amalfi in southern Italy sometime around 1300 A.D.

By the time of Columbus, the compass was well-developed and there is evidence (from the diaries of Columbus) that the phenomenon of magnetic variation was at least partially understood. By the early 1700s charts showing the locations of lines of equal variation (isogonic lines) were available. Likewise compass deviation, an important subject discussed below, was understood in qualitative terms at about this same time, although practical means for compensating for deviation were not developed until 1801 by Captain Matthew Flinders (from which the Flinders bar used in compass adjustment takes its name).

The modern liquid-filled compass similar to those used on yachts today dates back to the period 1850 to 1860 when it was developed and patented by E. S. Richie of Boston, Massachusetts. (The company founded by Richie is still in business today.) Since that time there have been evolutionary rather than revolutionary developments in the magnetic (mechanical) compass. For example, new lightweight materials are used for compass cards, improved magnets are available, and many other incremental improvements have been made to increase the accuracy, stability, and utility of the magnetic compass.

The modern gyrocompass, an instrument capable of indicating true rather than magnetic north, was developed by Elmer Sperry, an American, and Anschutz-Kampfe, a German, during the early part of the 20th century. Gyroscopes were widely used in naval and merchant ships since the end of World War I. Heretofore, gyroscopes have been electromechanical devices, but laser gyros are now in development that may revolutionize this field. (Gyroscopes are not discussed in this text as these are not presently available at reasonable cost to the typical boater.)

During the mid-1920s an *electronic* compass --termed a fluxgate compass--was developed for aircraft to provide better directional information in turns and during maneuvers. In recent years this technology has become available at a reasonable cost to the mariner, and for this reason is given passing mention.

The "electronics revolution," a phrase used frequently in this text also includes directional systems. Outputs from a fluxgate compass can be "processed" by a wide variety of computer systems and used for automated steering (autopilots), and navigational computers (e.g., to compute current set and drift as discussed in Chapter 7). Yet more sophisticated developments are likely in the near future.

For all these newer developments, the traditional magnetic compass remains one of the most important navigational tools, as evidenced by the fact that even the most sophisticated ship or aircraft in service today still has at least one magnetic compass aboard. Its relative simplicity, reliability, and lack of dependence on electrical power sources will probably ensure its survival well into the future.

PARTS OF THE COMPASS

Over the years, the marine magnetic compass has evolved into a functional easy-to-read, convenient, and relatively inexpensive navigational tool. The major parts of a modern, spherical, liquid-filled marine magnetic compass are shown in Figure 2-1. In this compass a lightweight *dial or compass rose* is graduated in degrees increasing in a clockwise direction from 000 degrees to 359 degrees to indicate the compass heading. The increments shown on the compass dial can be 1 degree, 2 degrees, or, more typically for compasses used on small vessels, 5 degrees. (Studies conducted just prior to World War II indicated that graduations every 5 degrees were significantly easier to read than finer graduations, and, in practical terms, nearly as accurate.) Numbers are typically spaced every 30 degrees, and the *cardinal points* (north, south, east, and west, or abbreviated N, S, E, and W) are also indicated on the dial. Arrows or other marks are sometimes used to designate the *intercardinal points* (e.g., NE, SE, SW, and NW). Older compasses were traditionally graduated in the mariner's "point" system, mentioned in Chapter 1, in which the circle was divided into 32 compass points, each of 11.25 degrees. These are named, in clockwise order from north; north, north by east, north-north east, north-east by

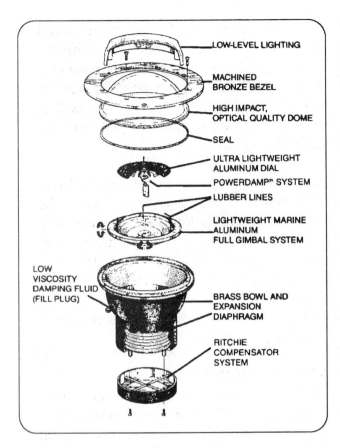

**Fig. 2-1. Exploded View of Marine Compass
(Photograph courtesy of E. S. Ritchie & Sons)**

north, north-east, north-east by east, east-north-east, east by north, east, etc. Naming these points, termed "boxing" the compass, was an unpleasant and confusing task sometimes used in hazing rituals for midshipmen and other would-be mariners. Fortunately, mariners have rediscovered the joy of numbers and the older point system is now of historical interest only. (If you have such a compass, mount it in your den, not on your vessel!)

Attached to the dial are the "north-seeking" compass magnets. The dial is supported on a jewelled bearing, which turns on a pivot. In turn, the pivot is mounted in a *gimbal system*, designed to keep the dial level with the horizon if the vessel pitches or rolls. Fastened to the gimbal is one (or more) *lubber line(s)*. The *lubber line* is the index mark against which the dial graduations are read to determine the direction of the

vessel relative to that of the card. The lubber line (or principal lubber line if there are more than one) should be aligned with the fore-and-aft axis of the vessel.

The gimbals, card, and magnets are enclosed in a bowl with a clear, transparent, hemispherical glass (or plastic) top, within which the card and gimbals are free to rotate, independent of the attitude of the container. The top (dome) may be impregnated with inhibitors to reduce any discoloration of the card or fluid from ultraviolet radiation and may also magnify the readings, so that the apparent card size is larger. The bowl is filled with a nonfreezing liquid to damp (slow down) the motion of the dial for increased stability and to support much of the weight of the card and the magnets so as to reduce wear on the pivot. The ultra-lightweight dials in use can be damped with fluids that are not viscous (thick), a combination that provides stability and accuracy without a tendency to "overshoot" and oscillate as the vessel is turned to a new heading. The compass also contains an expansion diaphragm to allow for the expansion and contraction of the damping fluid with temperature or pressure changes. A fill plug is used to replace or "top off" the damping fluid. (It is important that there are no air bubbles in the compass fluid.)

The bowl is supported by a case or holder, generally called a binnacle. Somewhere near the bowl (beneath it in the illustration in Figure 2-1) are found the compensating magnets, used to adjust the compass to compensate for the vessel's magnetic environment.

Most compasses are lighted for night use. A low intensity red lamp is preferred to avoid or minimize adverse effects on the night vision of the helmsman or crew. (Incidentally, the wires to the compass light should be twisted to minimize magnetic effects.)

Many compasses come with a hood (adjustable on some models) to reduce glare and improve readability.

Fig 2-2. Top-Reading Compass
(Photograph courtesy of E. S. Ritchie & Sons Inc.)

Removable protective covers (not shown in Figure 2 - 1) are also recommended if the compass is installed in a location where it is exposed to the elements.

COMPASS DIAL DESIGN

There are two principal designs for the compass rose or dial. These are discussed briefly below.

The first design, shown in Figure 2-2, is termed a *top-reading compass* (also a *flat card compass* by some manufacturers). With this design, the mariner reads the heading or bearing "across the card." The lubber line is located behind the card. In the photograph in Figure 2-2, for example, the vessel is headed north, or 000 degrees. The numbers indicating heading or bearing increase in a clockwise direction--a correct geometric representation. A heading of 030 degrees is to the right of a heading of 000 degrees, for example, and the compass provides the same representation. If the helmsman is asked to turn to 030 degrees from a heading or

north, it is clear that this must be a turn to the right. It is also relatively easy to read compass bearings over this compass dial. The compass dial itself is unobstructed through 360 degrees, although its placement aboard the vessel usually limits this range. A top-reading compass is installed forward of the steering mechanism and beneath the helmsman's eye level.

The second design, shown in Figure 2-3, is termed a *front-reading compass* (also called a *direct reading compass* by some manufacturers). This compass dial design is typical of most aircraft compasses and is also used for marine compasses. With this design the lubber line is in front of the dial and indicates the direction toward which the vessel is heading. In the photograph in Figure 2-3, for example, the vessel is also headed north, or 000 degrees. However, the dial is graduated in a counter-clockwise direction. Thus, for example, the 30-degree graduation on the front-reading dial is located to the left of 000. This apparent reversal in direction is made necessary because the lubber line is located in front of the dial. The mounting of a front-reading compass usually precludes its use for obtaining bearings. This is not a real detriment, since a hand-bearing compass, discussed in Chapter 4, is a ready substitute.

Fig. 2-3. Front-Reading Compass with Flush Mount
(Photograph courtesy of E. S. Ritchie & Sons Inc.)

Either design correctly shows the vessel's actual heading, but the front-reading compass design is slightly more confusing and requires a bit more practice before familiarity is assured. A helmsman, asked to come to a heading of 030 degrees from north could glance at the front-reading dial and see that this heading is to the left, and, therefore, begin a turn in the wrong direction before discovering the error. From the perspective of ease of interpretation, the top-reading compass dial is greatly to be preferred. But, it is also important to consider how the compass will be viewed once installed. In the typical powerboat installation (and in sailboats where the compass binnacle is integrated with the wheel), the compass is located on a panel immediately in front of the helmsman, and so a top-reading compass is easy to see. However, in a typical light aircraft the compass is installed at the top of the cockpit (where it is least likely to be affected by magnetic interference from radios or other electronics), at or above the eye level of the pilot, necessitating a front-reading design. Similarly, in certain sailboats the compass is mounted on the outer cabin bulkhead--nearly at eye level for the helmsman seated several feet away--and a front-reading compass is necessary.

Fig. 2-5. Easy To Read Top-Reading Compass (Photograph courtesy of C. Plath and Company)

Some compass designs, such as that shown in Figure 2-4, combine both types of compass display in one unit. The model shown in Figure 2-4 also includes an *inclinometer*, to measure the angle of roll of the vessel. Yet other compass displays, typically those used with fluxgate compasses, feature a *direct digital readout of the heading*. Digital readouts are generally shown to the nearest degree, rather than 5 degrees as is common on magnetic compasses. Although many prefer digital displays, these also have limitations or disadvantages. (For example, it is impossible to take a bearing on any object that is not aligned with the vessel's heading.)

Finally, some compasses are designed to be mounted upside down (overhead mount). This is usually installed in the ceiling of the navigator's berth, so that the navigator can read the vessel's heading when not on duty. Overhead-mount compasses are a favorite of "single handlers," and can double as a backup compass.

Fig. 2-4. Front- and Top-Reading Compass Integrated with Inclinometer (Photograph courtesy of C. Plath and Company)

Whatever display is chosen, it is important that the numerals on the dial be large and easy-to-read. Ornate displays, such as were found on older marine compasses, are less readable than the simple, clean designs of today as shown in Figure 2-5.

BRIEF ADVICE ON COMPASS SELECTION

The best advice on compass selection is not to be miserly. With compasses, as with other items of equipment, you get what you pay for. Because a compass is such an important navigational tool, it is essential that it be of high quality. Incidentally, this comment applies with particular force to small vessels. On average, small vessels are significantly more "lively" than larger vessels. Larger and more expensive compasses have better gimbals and have larger and easier to read dials. The saying "bigger is better" almost always applies to the selection of a compass. Finally, it is recommended that a vessel be equipped with at least two compasses as a precaution against compass failure. A hand-held compass (discussed in Chapter 4) can serve this purpose.

COMPASS MOUNTING

Ideally, the compass should be mounted where it can easily be read, protected from the elements, and free of any magnetic influences aboard the vessel (see below). The lubber line should be precisely aligned with the fore-and-aft axis of the vessel. On larger vessels, these requirements are easy to meet, but this is sometimes more of a problem in smaller craft. Consult a compass adjuster and read the owner's manual (or product literature) for advice on this important topic.

PRINCIPLE OF OPERATION:
DEVIATION

The modern magnetic compass is highly sensitive and is able to align itself with weak magnetic fields, such as the earth's magnetic field. The magnets underneath the compass card will align with the magnetic field and indicate direction relative to this field. But, the magnetic field aboard a ship is actually a combination (resultant) of two magnetic fields--that of the earth, and that of the vessel and its equipment.

Were the earth's magnetic field acting alone, the compass would indicate direction in the magnetic direction system -- that is, the compass would point in the direction of magnetic north. (Please refer again to Chapter 1.) Determination of the direction with respect to true north would involve nothing more than adding or subtracting the local magnetic variation from the indicated compass direction (more below).

However, the magnetic field aboard a vessel is not solely due to the earth's magnetic field. Shipboard electronics, windshield wiper motors, compressed-gas horns, tachometers, electrical motors, television sets, and other equipment also generate magnetic fields. Indeed, flashlights, camera light meters, tools, and even some kitchen utensils can also affect the compass. (For skeptics, a simple experiment proves this and is highly instructive. For example, note the compass reading, then place a flashlight near the compass and observe how the reading changes.) The vessel itself--particularly steel vessels--may have magnetic fields oriented in a variety of ways. (The vessel's magnetic field may even depend upon the direction the vessel was facing when it was constructed or last laid up for the winter!) These additional fields also affect the compass, with the result that the *compass heading* of the vessel may differ from its *magnetic heading*. The difference between these is termed *deviation*. There are actually three "norths" that the mariner need be concerned with, true north, magnetic north, and *compass north. Simply put, deviation is the difference between the direction that the compass actually points and the direction that it would point if there were no local magnetic fields aboard the vessel.* Although actual statistics on the deviation of uncompensated compasses aboard vessels are not available, these deviations could be quite large, say 10 degrees to 15 degrees, and possibly even more on some vessels.

TABLE 2-1. CROSS TRACK ERROR AS A FUNCTION OR DISTANCE TRAVELED AND RESIDUAL DEVIATION OR OTHER ANGULAR HELM ERROR

DISTANCE TRAVELED MILES	ANGULAR ERROR (DEGREES)								
	1.00	1.50	2.00	2.50	3.00	4.00	5.00	7.50	10.00
1.00	0.02	0.03	0.03	0.04	0.05	0.07	0.09	0.13	0.18
2.00	0.03	0.05	0.07	0.09	0.10	0.14	0.17	0.26	0.35
3.00	0.05	0.08	0.10	0.13	0.16	0.21	0.26	0.39	0.53
4.00	0.07	0.10	0.14	0.17	0.21	0.28	0.35	0.53	0.71
5.00	0.09	0.13	0.17	0.22	0.26	0.35	0.44	0.66	0.88
6.00	0.10	0.16	0.21	0.26	0.31	0.42	0.52	0.79	1.06
7.00	0.12	0.18	0.24	0.31	0.37	0.49	0.61	0.92	1.23
8.00	0.14	0.21	0.28	0.35	0.42	0.56	0.70	1.05	1.41
9.00	0.16	0.24	0.31	0.39	0.47	0.63	0.79	1.18	1.59
10.00	0.17	0.26	0.35	0.44	0.52	0.70	0.87	1.32	1.76
12.50	0.22	0.33	0.44	0.55	0.66	0.87	1.09	1.65	2.20
15.00	0.26	0.39	0.52	0.65	0.79	1.05	1.31	1.97	2.64
17.50	0.31	0.46	0.61	0.76	0.92	1.22	1.53	2.30	3.09
20.00	0.35	0.52	0.70	0.87	1.05	1.40	1.75	2.63	3.53
22.50	0.39	0.59	0.79	0.98	1.18	1.57	1.97	2.96	3.97
25.00	0.44	0.65	0.87	1.09	1.31	1.75	2.19	3.29	4.41
27.50	0.48	0.72	0.96	1.20	1.44	1.92	2.41	3.62	4.85
30.00	0.52	0.79	1.05	1.31	1.57	2.10	2.62	3.95	5.29
35.00	0.61	0.92	1.22	1.53	1.83	2.45	3.06	4.61	6.17
40.00	0.70	1.05	1.40	1.75	2.10	2.80	3.50	5.27	7.05
45.00	0.79	1.18	1.57	1.96	2.36	3.15	3.94	5.92	7.93
50.00	0.87	1.31	1.75	2.18	2.62	3.50	4.37	6.58	8.82
60.00	1.05	1.57	2.10	2.62	3.14	4.20	5.25	7.90	10.58
70.00	1.22	1.83	2.44	3.06	3.67	4.89	6.12	9.22	12.34
80.00	1.40	2.09	2.79	3.49	4.19	5.59	7.00	10.53	14.11
90.00	1.57	2.36	3.14	3.93	4.72	6.29	7.87	11.85	15.87
100.00	1.75	2.62	3.49	4.37	5.24	6.99	8.75	13.17	17.63

It is precisely because of the deviation caused by the vessel's magnetic field that correcting magnets are found in all good compasses. A skilled compass adjuster can move the adjusting magnets so as to remove most of the deviation normally caused by the vessel's magnetic field. (A good compass adjuster can also serve as a consultant on compass placement and can advise the mariner how to stow other gear to minimize deviation in the first place.) However, it is seldom the case that all the effects of this magnetic field can be compensated for by the adjusting magnets, and *usually a small residual deviation* (say 2 degrees to 4 degrees, but sometimes more) *remains* after adjustment.

The mariner has two options for dealing with residual deviation. The first is simply to *ignore* any residual error and effectively compensate for its presence by fixing the vessel's position more often. As a rough rule of thumb, an unrecognized error of 1 degree means that a vessel would be approximately 1 mile off course (termed *cross track error*) if it traveled a distance of 60 miles. Table 2-1 shows the cross track error as a function of the distance traveled and the angular error or residual deviation. For short distances, small angular errors are practically insignificant and can sometimes be ignored. However, for longer distances, in conditions of poor visibility [which would prevent detection and identification of landmarks, fixed aids to navigation (ATONs) or buoys], or high seas, simply ignoring deviation cannot be recommended.

The second, and generally preferable, option is to measure the compass deviation, and use this measured value to correct the observed compass heading to a magnetic heading in the same manner as variation is used to "correct" the magnetic heading to a true heading. *However, unlike variation which depends solely on the vessel's position, deviation varies with the vessel's heading.* Therefore, it is necessary to use the deviation appropriate to the vessel's compass heading before it can be used to convert to the correct magnetic heading. Although theoretically this deviation could be different for each possible heading, in practice the deviation is determined for each 15 degree or 30 degree heading increment, then these values are interpolated to calculate the estimated deviation on intermediate headings. This process of determining the deviation on various headings is termed *swinging ship* or *swinging the compass* and is discussed below.

(Digressing briefly, it is important to emphasize that deviation varies with the vessel's *heading*. When converting a relative bearing to a true or magnetic bearing, novices often make the mistake of applying the deviation appropriate to the relative bearing rather than the vessel's heading. Be careful not to make this error!)

SWINGING SHIP

Normally, a professional compass adjuster will swing ship as part of his/her services to compensate the compass and provide a table of deviations to the mariner. In such cases, the mariner will probably wish only to spot check this table to verify its accuracy. However, the procedures--discussed below--are the same whether the entire deviation table is being prepared or individual values are being spot checked.

In brief, the procedure for swinging ship is to steady on a known compass course and then take bearings on a distant object or range. The vessel is positioned so that the magnetic bearing to the object to be observed is known. The compass bearing is read directly or converted from a relative bearing obtained using a pelorus and compared with the object's known magnetic bearing, and the deviation is calculated. Professional compass adjusters often use the sun for observation, but most mariners are unfamiliar with celestial navigation and elect to use something simpler, such as a prominent object or range. The object(s) selected for observation should be a good distance away (e.g., 6 miles) to minimize parallax error in the calibration. It is important that swinging ship is done when conditions are nearly ideal, in calm waters and in good visibility. The need for good visibility is obvious. The reason why calm waters are preferred is to simplify steadying the vessel on a compass heading and reading the compass. Experience shows it can take up to three hours to swing ship, so the exercise should be planned with sufficient time allowance to be completed within the daylight hours.

The procedure for swinging ship depends upon the compass to be examined and the ability to take bearings on objects not directly aligned with the fore and aft axis of the vessel. If the compass is graduated to the nearest degree, and designed and located so that an unobstructed view is possible throughout all 360 degrees, then only a compass is necessary. (This is likely to be the case for relatively few yachts.) If, as is more common, the compass is graduated only in 5 degree increments or bearings are not easily read throughout 360 degrees, then it is necessary to use a pelorus as well (discussed below).

Fig. 2-6. The Range Formed By The Spire in New Bedford
and the Butler Flats Light
Bears Approximately 310 Degrees.

DIRECT OBSERVATION USING A RANGE

The easiest method for swinging ship, if circumstances permit, is to use a range and read the compass directly. A range consists of two charted objects that can be viewed and aligned from a distance. For example, consider the spire in New Bedford and the Butler Flats light located south and east of New Bedford shown in the 1210-Tr chart and in Figure 2-6. Both of these objects are likely to be prominent, and relatively easy to identify. Approaching from the south, these two objects are exactly in line (one behind the other, or in range) on a bearing of 310 degrees true from the vessel to the objects. The bearing can be read from the chart as discussed in Chapter 3, but take the answer as given for this discussion. The variation in this area, read from the nearest compass rose, is approximately 015 degrees west, so the magnetic bearing of this range would be 310 + 015 = 325 magnetic. (See below for a handy rule to remember whether to add or subtract variation.)

Suppose that the vessel were steadied on a compass course of 000 degrees (compass north) while the vessel were somewhere south of the line drawn on the chart. (This would, of course, be evident from the vessel because the Butler Flats light would be to the *right* of the spire. At the precise instant that the light and the spire appeared to be in line, the magnetic bearing of the range would be 325 degrees from the vessel. At this same instant, suppose that the compass bearing of the range (read over the compass) were 323 degrees (while the compass heading were 000 degrees). The deviation on this heading is the difference between the magnetic bearing, 325 degrees, and the bearing read from the compass, 325 degrees, or 2 degrees. But, is it 2 degrees east, or 2 degrees west? It can, of course, be worked out from first principles (refer to Chapter I), but it is easy to remember the simple phrase, *"compass least, error east."* That is, if the compass bearing is less than the magnetic bearing (as it is in this case, 323 degrees is less than 325 degrees), then the deviation is "east." (If not, then the error would, of course, be "west.")

Thus, in this example, the estimated compass deviation on a heading of 000 degrees is 002 degree *east*. To confirm this result, the process might be repeated, and the average deviation noted.

It is convenient to use a worksheet, such as is shown in Table 2 - 2 to record the observations. This worksheet contains directions as well which makes it handy to use. The process is now repeated on a compass heading of 015 degrees, 030 degrees, etc., until all observations are recorded.

PLOTTING THE RESULTS

It is recommended that the results be plotted on a sheet of graph paper to see if there are any "anomalous" results that do not fit the pattern. Overall, the line drawn through the measured deviations should appear as a smooth curve (actually a mixture of trigonometric functions for those technically inclined) free of "bumps" or observations that appear discrepant. Such a curve is drawn in Figure 2-7 and appears generally to confirm the adequacy of the measurements, although the deviations on some headings, such as 240 degrees, should be rechecked. (In Figure 2-7 easterly deviations are shown with a plus sign, and westerly with a minus sign.) Additionally, the deviations on some headings are relatively large (5 or 6 degrees), so the compensation is far from perfect. (A more technical analysis, omitted here, suggests that improved compensation is possible. However, the example is continued for illustrative purposes.)

USE OF A PELORUS

As noted, most marine compass installations do not permit direct reading of compass bearings through a full 360 degrees. Additionally, many compasses are graduated only to 2 degrees or 5 degrees rather than in 1 degree increments. If either of the statements is true, it is necessary to modify the procedure given above for swinging ship. The most convenient solution is to use a pelorus, sometimes called a "dumb compass." A pelorus (see Figure 2-8) consists of a gradu-

TABLE 2-2. PORTION OF WORKSHEET FOR DETERMINATION OF DEVIATIONS FROM RANGE

DATE: 10-15-89 NAVIGATOR: LDM VESSEL: Altair

RANGE: Spire in New Bedford and Butler Flats Light

NOTES: Loran, Radar, VHF ON

Determined from Nautical Chart or Other Source
Determined from Nearby Compass Rose
True +/- Variation, + West, -East

TRUE BEARING OF RANGE: 310
VARIATION: 015 West
MAGNETIC BEARING OF RANGE: 325 Magnetic

Entry	Vessel's Head Per Compass	Magnetic Direction of Range	Direction of Range Per Compass	Estimated Deviation On This Heading	Notes
1 Where Obtained	2 Read From Lubber's Line Directly	3 Taken From Above Calculation	4 Bearing of Range as Read Over Compass	5 Difference Between Columns 3 and 4 If Column 4 < Column 3, Deviation is "East," Otherwise Deviation "West"	This worksheet is designed to be used for determination of deviation where a range is available and can be sighted over the compass. The true bearing of the range can be determined from a nautical chart, Light List, or other source. Compass deviation should be determined every 15 degrees of heading, generally starting at 000 degrees. The "notes" section should identify the electronics on-board, and operating at the time of the calibration. It is suggested that two tables be prepared, one with all electronics on, and the other with electronics off.
	000	325	323	2E	
	015	325	322	3E	
	030	325	320	5E	
	045	325	319	6E	
	060	325	320	5E	
	075	325	320	5E	

ated compass-like dial (1 degree increments) and sighting vanes that can be rotated around the dial to take bearings. Unlike the "north-seeking" compass dial, however, the position of the dial on the pelorus does not change with the vessel's heading. The pelorus is mounted and the dial fixed so that the 000 degree mark on the dial is pointed so as to be parallel to the vessel's bow, precisely aligned with the fore- and aft-axis of the vessel. (Consult the directions supplied with the pelorus for mounting instructions and pay particular attention to the alignment procedure.) The pelorus should be mounted so that the navigator can easily view objects throughout a full 360 degrees.

The bearings read from the pelorus are relative bearings (refer to Chapter 1), rather than compass bearings. For this reason it is necessary to calculate the compass bearing from the simple equation:

ship's heading +
object's relative bearing =
object's compass bearing.

This extra step requires a slight modification to the worksheet given in Table 2-2 to prepare a compass deviation table. This modified worksheet is shown in Table 2-3. To clarify by example, suppose that a compass deviation table is being prepared using the same range as given in Table 2-2. While on a compass heading of 015 degrees, the navigator sights over the vanes of the pelorus as the range is perfectly aligned. The navigator calls **"mark-mark-mark"** to allow the helmsman to make slight heading changes to bring the vessel back to the assigned 015 degree heading, and notes the relative bearing, say 307 degrees. Alternatively, the helmsman sings out the vessel's heading on hearing "mark-mark-mark," and the navigator notes this heading. The compass bearing to the range is, therefore, 015

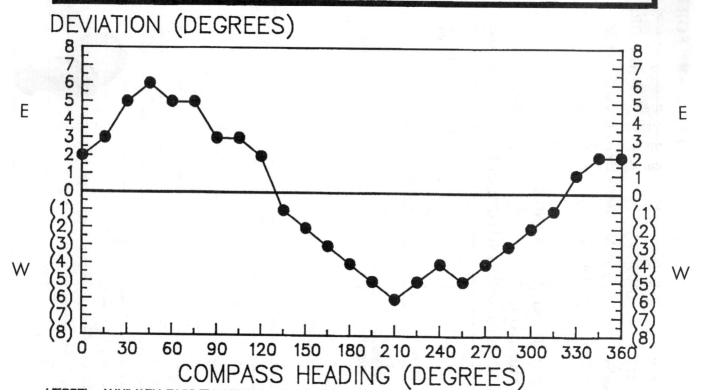

FIGURE 2-7. A PLOT OF COMPASS DEVIATIONS

DEVIATION (DEGREES)

COMPASS HEADING (DEGREES)

VESSEL: AUXILIARY FACILITY 273007, ALL RADIOS AND ELECTRONICS ON, DATA FROM 09-30-89 FOR COMPASS AT LOWER HELM STATION.

+ 307 = 322 degrees (360 degrees will have to be subtracted from this total if the total exceeds 360). The deviation on a compass heading of 015 degrees is, therefore, 3 degrees east as in the earlier example (remember, compass least, error east).

SPOT CHECKS

To spot check a previously prepared deviation table, all that is necessary is to take advantage of ranges that may appear near the vessel's course. In this case, the helm is put over briefly to align the vessel with the range, the compass heading noted, and the deviation on this heading calculated as before. During a typical voyage there are many opportunities for such spot checks, and these should be used to advantage. Throughout the navies of the world, it is common practice to check the compass at least once daily and to report the results to the captain. For the average boater, it is not necessary to make such frequent or formal checks, but it is appropriate to check deviation at least a few times during the boating season, and whenever a major voyage is planned. Deviation can change whenever new electronic gear is brought aboard (or moved), the vessel is laid up for the winter, or someone inadvertently leaves a flashlight or lightmeter-equipped camera near the compass. Compass deviation can even be affected if a member of the crew wears a sheath knife and strays too close! Lightning strikes near the vessel can also affect deviation, and the compass should be checked after electrical storms have passed through the area.

DEVIATION ON INTERMEDIATE HEADINGS

The deviation table consists of entries spaced every 15 degrees or every 30 degrees. Values for intermediate headings are obtained by interpolation. For example, if the deviation is 3 degrees east on a compass heading of 000 degrees and 0 degrees on a heading of 015 degrees, it would be approximately 2 degrees on a heading of 005 degrees. Fancy formulas are not warranted here, simply proportion the deviation directly and round the calculation to the nearest degree.

Fig. 2-8. A Precision Pelorus
(Photograph courtesy of C. Plath and Company)

USE OF THE DEVIATION TABLE

The deviation table is used for two important purposes. First, it is used to calculate the vessel's actual magnetic heading when steering a known compass heading. Second, it is used to calculate the correct compass heading to steer to make good a desired magnetic heading.

The first objective is solved by the deviation table directly. Refer to Table 2-4, for example,

TABLE 2 -- 4. SAMPLE DEVIATION TABLE

[ALL VALUES IN DEGREES (°)]

COMPASS TO MAGNETIC		MAGNETIC TO COMPASS	
(A) Compass Heading	(B) Deviation	(C) Magnetic Heading	(D) Deviation
000	2E	000	2E
015	3E	015	3E
030	5E	030	4E
045	6E	045	6E
060	5E	060	5E
075	5E	075	5E
090	3E	090	3E
105	3E	105	3E
120	2E	120	1E
135	1W	135	1W
150	2W	150	2W
165	3W	165	2W
180	4W	180	4W
195	5W	195	5W
210	6W	210	6W
225	5W	225	5W
240	4W	240	4W
255	5W	255	5W
270	4W	270	4W
285	3W	285	3W
300	2W	300	2W
315	1W	315	1W
330	1E	330	1E
345	2E	345	2E
360	2E	360	2E

prepared from the measurements discussed above. Suppose that the vessel's compass heading were 045 degrees. From the first two columns of this table (headed by the phrase "compass to magnetic"), the deviation corresponding to a compass heading of 045 degrees is 6 degrees east. The magnetic heading is the compass heading plus or minus the deviation. Converting from a compass heading to a magnetic heading is often termed "correcting," because this process removes (corrects for) the deviation error. A simple rule to remember is **correcting add east,** meaning that in converting from a compass heading to a magnetic heading, easterly deviation is added (westerly deviation is, therefore, subtracted). Using this rule, the corrected or magnetic heading would be 045 + 006 = 051 degrees magnetic. Similarly, a compass heading of 030 degrees corresponds to a magnetic heading (refer to Table 2-4) of 035 degrees.

TABLE 2-3. PORTION OF WORKSHEET FOR DETERMINING OF DEVIATIONS USING RELATIVE BEARINGS

DATE: 10-15-89 **NAVIGATOR:** LDM **VESSEL:** Altair

RANGE: Spire in New Bedford and Butler Flats Light

NOTES: Loran, Radar, and VHF Radio ON

TRUE BEARING OF RANGE: 310 — Determined from Nautical Chart or Other Source

VARIATION: 015 West — Determined from Nearby Compass Rose

MAGNETIC BEARING OF RANGE: 325 Magnetic — True +/- Variation, + West, -East

Entry	Vessel's Head Per Compass	Relative Bearing of Range	Direction of Range Per Compass	Magnetic Direction of Range	Estimated Deviation On This Heading
1 Where Obtained	2 Read From Lubber's Line Directly	3 Read From Pelorus	4 Vessel's Head (1) Plus Relative Bearing (4) (360° may have to be subtracted)	5 Taken From Above Calculation	6 Difference Between Columns 4 and 5 If Column 4 < Column 5, Deviation is "East," Otherwise Deviation "West"
	015	307	322	325	3E

Frequently, however, it is necessary to reverse the process. That is, to find the appropriate compass course to steer to make good a particular magnetic heading. For this task it is necessary to reverse the logic discussed above. For example, suppose that the mariner wants to make good a course of 045 magnetic. What compass course should be steered? From the above discussion note that on a magnetic heading of 035 degrees the deviation is 5 degrees east, whereas on a magnetic heading of 051 degrees, the deviation is 6 degrees east. A simple interpolation (rounded to the nearest degree) indicates that the deviation on a 045 degree heading is approximately 6 degrees ($5 + 10(6-5)/16$). Therefore, the approximate deviation on a magnetic heading of 045 degrees is 6 degrees east, as shown in Table 2-4.

Continuing the process leads to the results shown in Table 2-4, which completes the deviation table. Use the left half of the table when correcting from compass to magnetic, and the right half when "uncorrecting" from magnetic to compass. *(Unless the deviations are quite large, the two halves of the table are virtually identical and, in practice, these differences are often neglected.)*

COMPASS CALCULATIONS

Navigators need to become familiar with the calculations necessary for converting from true courses to compass courses, and vice versa. Although these calculations are quite simple, practice is necessary to ensure familiarity. For this reason, the following text and examples are given.

It is often necessary to convert from true to compass headings. As discussed in later chapters, courses are laid out on nautical charts, measured with respect to true north. But to undertake the voyage the navigator needs to determine how to convert this true course to a compass course to steer. The overall sequence for this conversion is to start with the *true course,* *add or subtract variation to calculate a magnetic course, and then again add or subtract deviation to calculate a compass course: true, variation, magnetic, deviation, compass, or as it is sometimes said, TVMDC.* In addition to learning the sequence of calculations, it is useful to have a handy rule to remember whether to add or subtract variation and deviation.

The time-honored memory aid is to learn the phrase: TIMID VIRGINS MAKE DULL COMPANY, ADD WHISKEY! Decoded, it reveals the sequence of calculations TVMDC, and the reminder to add "whiskey" (west) when converting from true to compass. For example, what is the compass heading to steer if the true course is 060, variation is 015 west, and the deviation table is as given in Table 2-4? First, start at the true course, 060, and convert to magnetic. Since the variation is west, it is added to the true course. The magnetic course is, therefore, $060 + 015 = 075$. The deviation corresponding to a magnetic heading of 075 degrees is 5 degrees east. From the simple rule to add west in this sequence, a 5 degree easterly deviation would be subtracted, and the required compass course would be $075 - 005 = 070$ degrees. The important points are to remember the sequence of calculations, and whether to add or subtract variation and deviation.

Sometimes it is necessary to reverse the process, and convert from compass to true. For example, a bearing on a distant object may be taken from the vessel's compass, and it is necessary to convert this bearing to true, before plotting on a nautical chart. The sequence of calculations is just the opposite to that discussed above, i.e., CDMVT. As well, the sign to apply to east or west variation or deviation is also reversed. That is, east is added, and west is subtracted. Although this is simple enough to remember, some prefer to use the additional memory aid: CAN DEAD MEN VOTE TWICE? AT ELECTIONS! The first letters are the memory aid to the sequence compass, deviation,

TABLE 2-5. ADDITIONAL COMPASS ERRORS WHICH ARISE IF VESSEL IS NOT STRAIGHT AND LEVEL, AND AT CONSTANT SPEED.

NAME	BRIEF DESCRIPTION	REMARKS
Northerly Turning Error	Applies principally when vessel is on northerly or southerly headings and the compass card is tilted with respect to the horizon. Effect is for compass to lag the turn, or momentarily show a turn in the opposite direction when turning from north. In turns from south, the compass leads the turn, i.e., shows the vessel turning more rapidly than it actually is. The effect is greatest in a rapid, steeply banked turn.	Of principal concern to aircraft, but of relevance to all fast boats. Arises from magnetic dip. Phenomenon described for northern hemisphere only.
Acceleration Error	Also due to dip, this error is greatest on headings of east or west and zero on north or south. If the vessel is accelerated on either of these headings, the compass will indicate an apparent turn to the north. When decelerating, the compass indicates a turn to the south. A memory aid to remember the word "ANDS," for acceleration - north, deceleration - south.	Effect greatest with vessels capable of large accelerations, e.g., speed boats. Also seen with aircraft. Often observed when boat butts into head sea, or planes down a swell while on an east or west heading.
Oscillation Error	Though listed as a separate error in some texts, this is actually a combination of the above errors. Results from erratic movements of the compass card caused by rough seas or abrupt helm changes. Helmsman has to "average" out oscillations mentally for precise steering.	
Heeling Error	Of particular relevance to sailing vessels, this error arises from change in the horizontal component of the induced or permanent magnetic fields at the compass due to rolling or pitching of the ship. To a lesser extent heeling errors may be affected by the angle of plane of a power boat.	Adjusted for by heeling magnets on some compasses. Adjustment is partially a function of the magnetic latitude of the vessel.

NOTE: See article by Kielhorn for details on some of these errors.

magnetic, variation, true, and add east. (Aircraft pilots are taught the phrase: CAN DUCKS MAKE VERTICAL TURNS?)

To illustrate, suppose that the compass heading of the vessel is 065 degrees, and an object is sighted bearing directly ahead per the vessel's compass in an area where the variation is 015 degrees west. What is the true bearing? Assuming that the deviation table is as given in Table 2-4, the deviation on a compass heading of 065 degrees is 5 degrees east and, therefore, the magnetic heading of the vessel is 065 + 005 = 070 degrees (add east). In turn, the true heading is the magnetic heading plus or minus variation. If east is to be added, then west is to be subtracted for this calculation, so the true heading is 070 - 015 = 055 degrees true. That's all there is to it. Practice with the Student Study Guide problems until you are proficient.

ADDITIONAL POINTERS ON THE COMPASS

It is important to remember that compass readings are most accurate only when the vessel is level (as opposed to heeling), traveling at a constant speed and maintaining a constant course. Otherwise, a series of additional compass errors is introduced, as shown in Table 2-5. It is not a good idea to use compass readings obtained while the vessel is heeling, turning, or accelerating/decelerating. The effects of these errors are to make the compass difficult to read, or to give erroneous indications. These errors are largest for vessels capable of substantial acceleration (e.g., speed boats), and substantial angles of heel or bank. (Consult the references at the end of this chapter for more details.) Directional gyros or gyrocompasses are less prone to these errors and sometimes favored by mariners for this reason (among others).

THE FLUXGATE COMPASS

Finally, any modern discussion of compasses would be incomplete without at least a passing mention of the fluxgate compass. The fluxgate compass senses the earth's magnetic field electronically, rather than with magnets. (Readers wishing a more complete discussion should refer to the bibliography.) The fluxgate compass consists of a sensor and a display unit. Figure 2-9 shows an illustrative display unit. The sensor can be located remotely, in an area of the vessel where magnetic disturbances are at a minimum. The display unit is small and can be mounted for optimum visibility. Most modern fluxgate systems are integrated with microprocessors, which can perform many useful functions. The model, pictured in Figure 2-9, automatically compensates for deviation (to within +/- 1 or 2 degrees) by simply making a 360 degree turn with the vessel! This, and other models, also can display headings in either true or magnetic (variation data are stored in the microchip) and can furnish electronic inputs to other navigation systems such as loran or radar.

Electronic compasses should be considered by serious mariners, *but do not eliminate the need for a magnetic compass, because electronics are dependent upon a reliable power supply.*

Fig. 2-9. Digital Display Unit of a Fluxgate Electronic Compass.
(Photograph courtesy of Cetrek Navstar, Inc.)

REFERENCES

Anon. *The Magnetic Compass, Principles, Selection Navigation,* E. S. Ritchie & Sons, Inc., Pembroke, MA, 1988.

Bowditch, N. *American Practical Navigator, An Epitome of Navigation,* Vol. 1, Defense Mapping Agency, Washington, DC

Cohan, L. S. "Compass Deviation Affected by Lightning," *Ocean Navigator,* No. 17, January/February 1988.

Collinder, P. *A History of Marine Navigation*, St. Martin's Press, Inc., New York, NY, 1955.

Dahl, N. *The Yacht Navigator's Handbook*, Hearst Books, New York, NY, 1983.

Defense Mapping Agency, Hydrographic/Topographic Center. *Handbook of Magnetic Compass Adjustment,* Fourth Edition, Pub. No. 226, Washington, DC, 1980.

Department of Transportation, Federal Aviation Administration. *Instrument Flying Handbook,* AC61-27C, Washington, DC, 1987.

Eyges, L. *The Practical Pilot, Coastal Navigation By Eye, Intuition and Common Sense,* International Marine Publishing Co., Camden, ME, 1989.

Fuson, R. H. (Translator). *The Log of Christopher Columbus,* International Marine Publishing Company, Camden, ME, 1987.

Ganssle, J. G. "Anatomy of a Fluxgate," *Ocean Navigator*, September/October, 1989.

Hempstead, R. L. "Magnetic Compasses in the Small Boat Environment," *Ocean Navigator,* No. 12, March/April 1987, pp. 21, et seq.

Jerchow, F. *From Sextant to Satellite Navigation, 1837--1987, 150 Years C. Plath,* Honeburg, FRG, 1987.

Kaufman, S. *Compass Adjusting For Small Craft,* Surfside Harbor Associates, Surfside, FL, 1978.

Kielhorn, W. V. *A Piloting Primer*, privately printed at Naples, FL, 1988.

Kielhorn, W. V. "The Northerly Turning Error," *The Rudder,* Vol. 73, No. 2, 1957, pp. 40-42.

Kielhorn, W. V., and H. W. Klimm. "A Preliminary Study of the Changes of Magnetic Structure in a New Steel Trawler," *Navigation, Journal of the Institute of Navigation*, Vol. 6, No. 6, pp. 365, et seq.

Queeney, T. E. "Beyond the Lodestone," *Ocean Navigator,* No. 3, September/October, 1985, pp. 33, et seq.

Queeney, T. E. "Future Heading Systems, Are Lasers The Next Step," *Ocean Navigator*, No. 12, March/April 1987, pp. 35, et seq.

Rousmaniere, J. *The Annapolis Book of Seamanship,* Simon and Schuster, New York, NY, 1989.

Saunders, A. E. *Small Craft Piloting and Coastal Navigation,* Alzarc Enterprises, Scarborough, Ontario, Canada, 1987.

Van Heyningen, M. A. K. "The Evolution of the Modern Electronic Compass," *NMEA News,* January/February, 1987.

Chapter 3

The Nautical Chart

This chapter provides an introduction to the nautical chart, how it is constructed, how to determine position, course, and distance on the chart, how to read the chart, and finally some practical ideas about chart interpretation and use. The material in this chapter is not difficult, but there is a lot to learn.

Read this chapter with a nautical chart, preferably the 1210-Tr, close at hand because it is impractical to include illustrations of all the features of the nautical chart in any one chapter of finite length. Refer to the chart often. Don't despair, it takes a great deal of experience to become fully familiar with the wealth of relevant information contained on nautical charts. This chapter is designed as an introduction. As you do the homework problems throughout the course you will gradually become more familiar with nautical charts, and how these are used.

At the outset, get in the habit of calling this a *chart*--not a *map*. A map contains information relevant to terrestrial navigation. What are the route numbers?, where do the roads lead?, which roads are improved?, which are limited access?, where can you find services?, where are the entrances to national parks?, etc., are all important questions to answer as you plan to take a family camping vacation or drive on a business trip. But, the height of a tower, for example, or descriptions of church spires, would probably not be shown on a map unless these were a point of particular interest to visitors.

However, the practice of marine navigation has unique information requirements. Water depths, aids to navigation (ATONs) and their relevant attributes (radio frequencies, light colors, sectors, and characteristics, etc.), landmarks, unmarked hazards to navigation, land outlines, bridge clearances, distance, direction, etc., are all pertinent to marine navigation. For this reason, the marine chart contains generally different information than its terrestrial counterpart, the map. Marine navigation, being both an ancient art and science, has evolved its own prejudices and jargon. To a marine navigator, a chart is a veritable treasure--something to be treated with reverence and care. To this group, a map is something that can be purchased at a gasoline station vending machine, located next to the advertisements for recaps, the cooler full of hot soda, and the dog with the infected ear. If you haven't guessed already, mariners are snobs. (For that matter, so are aircraft pilots, who refer to their maps as "aeronautical charts.") So don't risk being branded a "landlubber"; refer to a chart by its proper name.

A SOURCE OF VITAL INFORMATION

As noted above, a marine chart depicts information of use to marine navigation. This includes a host of data on navigable (and not-so-navigable) water and the contiguous land. The amount, complexity, and diversity of material presented on the typical nautical chart is literally astounding. Nautical chartmaking (cartography) is a highly developed art and science. Presenting the required information in easy-to-understand format requires bringing together a number of disciplines to select the "right" method of chart projection, appropriate choice of scale, chart symbols, abbreviations, lettering styles, colors, paper, and printing techniques to produce today's high-quality nautical chart.

REPRESENTATION OF A SPHERICAL SURFACE UPON A PLANE OR FLAT SURFACE

It only requires a little thought to realize that it is impossible to represent a spherical surface upon a flat surface without introducing some distortion--in distance, direction, shape, and/or area. Even the school reference globe made out of paper or plastic printed on flat or rotary pressses is made up of *gores* of essentially flat surfaces *cut* to *bend* and *fit* upon a spherical surface. If the globe were disassembled, and its separate pieces laid out, one would have a flat surface where areas would be "correct," but there would be huge gaps between the gores, and direction, shape and distances would have no meaning in the spaces between, nor continuity from one gore to another, except at the equator, where all gores are joined.

CHART PROJECTIONS

Throughout the history of navigation there have been numerous attempts to depict a round surface with a flat one. Some have been remarkably successful under certain conditions, but *all* such *projections* suffer some limitations. The goal of the various projections, a sampling of which are given in Figure 3-1, is to balance and minimize the distortions to produce a representation that preserves, to the extent possible, direction, distance, shape, area, and correct

GENERAL CHARTS	Azimuthal-Equidistant
	Gall-Peters
	Goode Homolosine
	Lambert Azimuthal Equal Area
	Lambert Conformal
	Miller Cylindrical
	Mollweide
	Orthographic
	Polar Stereographic
	Polar Gnomonic
	Robinson
	Simple Conic
	Sinusoidal
	Van der Grinten
CHARTS OF PARTICULAR INTEREST TO THE MARINER	Mercator
	Polyconic

Fig. 3-1. Although Numerous Chart Projections Have Been Devised, the Mercator and Polyconic are of Particular Interest to Mariners.

angular relationships. A projection which preserves correct angular relationships is termed *conformal*. This property, or a close approximation to it, is essential if the chart is to be used for navigation.

No chart projection is fully adequate over a large area, but several are sufficiently so to be useful to the small craft navigator. For navigation charts the spherical surface of the earth has been projected on a cylinder and also on a series of coaxial, tangent (touching the earth's surface at one point or along one line) cones to provide the *Mercator* and the *polyconic projections* respectively. These are shown in Figure 3-2 and are the two key projections as far as nautical charts are concerned. Each of these projections has its particular utility and each has limitations. A particular projection is chosen dependent upon the intended use. A Mercator projection, for example, distorts areas (particularly near the poles) substantially, and is unsuitable for depicting the relative size of countries. (Generations of students have grown up believing that Greenland, for example, is larger than the United States, because they have studied Mercator projections where this is apparently true. In actual fact, the United States is more than 4.3 times larger than Greenland.)

These projections, their development and use for small craft navigation will be discussed in some detail in this section.

THE MERCATOR PROJECTION

This projection has been one of the most useful for navigation for over 400 years. It was developed by a brilliant Flemish geographer by the name of Gerhard Kremer (latinized to Gerhardus Mercator) who published a world chart constructed by his method in 1569. The *Mercator projection* is a cylindrical projection,

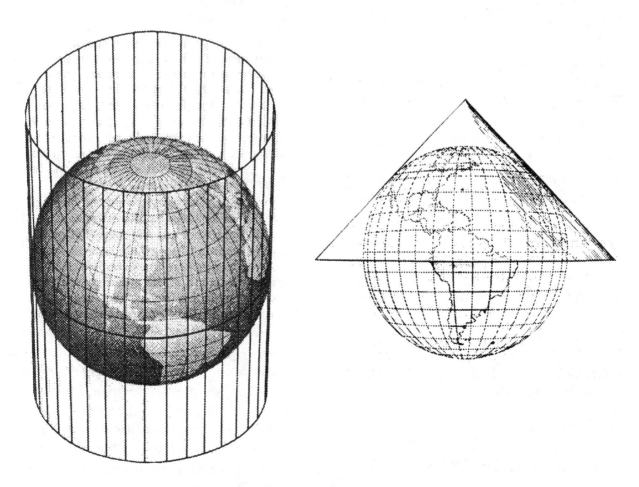

Fig. 3-2. Mercator and Conic Projections.

ingeniously modified, by expanding the scale at increasing latitudes, to preserve shape, direction, and angular relationships.

This projection is *conformal,* but distance and area relationships are distorted. Both the meridians and the parallels are expanded at the same ratio with increasing latitude. For the technically minded the expansion is equal to the secant of the latitude (secant H = 1/cos H), with a small correction to reflect the fact that the earth is not a perfect sphere. The projection does not include the poles and usually not even the uppermost 15° of latitude, because the value of the secant at these angles is too large, being infinity at Lat. 90° (N or S). Since the expansion is the same for all directions and angular relationships are correctly indicated, the projection is conformal and compass directions (rhumb lines or loxodromes) are shown as straight lines-- properties of value to the mariner.

Distances can be measured directly, *but not by a single distance scale for the whole chart (unless a large scale chart is used, see below) or for large areas.* Instead, the *latitude* scale is used *along* any meridian. (Remember, 1° Lat. = 60 M, 1' Lat. = 1 M.) Great circles appear as *curved* lines on the Mercator projection except for the meridians and the equator, which appear as straight lines. Note: The Mercator projection may also be made as an oblique projection (at an angle to the equator or meridian), using any great circle (rather than the equator) for the base line. Such a projection is termed an *oblique Mercator projection and is used for special navigation* applications which are beyond the scope of this course.

COORDINATES FOR THE MERCATOR PROJECTION

The format for the Mercator projection is rectangular. *Latitude* and *longitude* are the coordinates used for the Mercator projection. The parallels of latitude usually appear as horizontal, straight lines, running from the right to the left (in the western hemisphere), with the pro-

jections oriented such that north is at the top of the chart and south, at the bottom, east at the right margin, and west at the left. (There are some Mercator projections where, for various reasons, north does not appear at the top of the page. The Australians, for example, sell mercator projections in novelty shops with south at the top of the chart!)

The meridians appear as straight, parallel lines running from the bottom of the chart to its top. The scale for the meridians (longitude scale) is indicated on the top and bottom margins of the chart. The scale for the parallels (latitude scale) is provided on the right- and left-hand margins, and are also used for distance measurement. Compass roses, indicating *true* and *magnetic* directions are placed at convenient locations on the chart.

ESTABLISHING A POSITION ON THE MERCATOR PROJECTION

Since the Mercator projection results in a rectangular presentation, a rectangular coordinate system, using latitude and longitude, makes establishing a specific position on the globe an easy process on the chart:

1. Using the latitude scale at the right or left margins (these scales are *along* meridians), simply take the latitude value and draw a *light* pencil line from this point across the chart *parallel* to the top, bottom, and other parallels on the chart. (Use of a parallel rule or paraline plotter makes this easy.) Every point on this line has that same latitude.

2. To specify the position uniquely, now use the *longitude* scale at the top or the bottom of the chart (these scales are *along parallels*), to locate the desired longitude value and strike another *light* pencil line up or down, parallel to the meridians, and the sides of the chart. All points on this line (itself, a meridian) are at the same longitude. Where the two light pencil lines intersect, the position is uniquely specified.

USE OF PARALLEL RULERS AND DIVIDERS TO PLOT A POSITION ON THE MERCATOR PROJECTION

Experience soon shows the value of keeping the chart clean and free of unnecessary marks, lines, etc. Parallel rulers and the dividers help to minimize marks on the chart while plotting a position. (Interrupt your reading of this chapter to take a few minutes to read about parallel rules and dividers in Chapter 4.)

A common task in navigation is to plot a position on the chart. For example, a navigator may read the vessel's present position in latitude and longitude from a loran (see Chapter 9) and wish to plot this position on the chart. The technique is simple and is illustrated in Figure 3-3:

1. Place the parallel rulers--which are two straight edges constrained to remain parallel as they are "walked" or "opened and closed"--with one edge along a parallel of latitude shown on the chart. Holding the base ruler along the parallel, swing the other ruler to the desired latitude value on the left or right scale. A light pencil line is drawn only in the vicinity of the approximate longitude, which is "eyeballed" or estimated from the longitude scale at the top or bottom of the chart.

2. After the latitude line has been drawn, take the dividers and set their points so that one point falls on the nearest meridian of longitude, and the other at the value of longitude desired. Now, bring the dividers, carefully so as not to disturb the setting, down along the meridian until the desired latitude line (parallel) is encountered. If the line crosses the meridian, simply measure along the latitude line (parallel) with the dividers from the meridian. Where the other point of the dividers falls is the desired longitude. The two coordinates now specify the vessel's position, uniquely. If the latitude line (parallel) does not cross the meridian, simply swing the parallel rulers (keeping the base ruler along the parallel) so that the other ruler falls along the desired parallel and crosses the meridian, as well. Then, as above, measure the increment of longitude from the meridian along the parallel ruler, to the position.

3. The process can also be used with the meridian first, and the dividers set off of the parallel and the latitude scale. In addition, the dividers may be used directly, without the parallel rulers, to locate the position. In this case, the dividers are maintained "parallel" to the meridian or parallel by eye--relatively easy to the practiced navigator--as the position is struck.

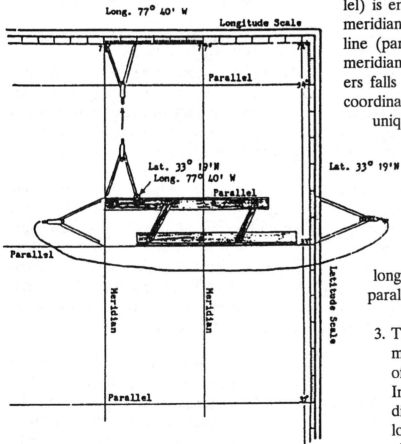

Fig. 3-3. Plotting a Position on the Mercator Projection Using Latitude and Longitude Coordinates.

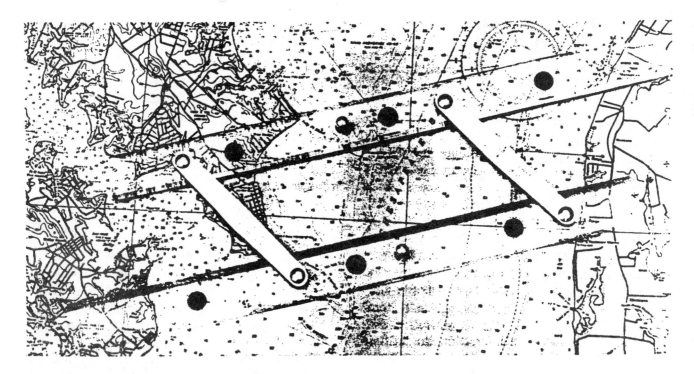

Fig. 3-4. Determining Direction Using a Compass Rose and a Set of Parallel Rulers.

READING A POSITION FROM THE MERCATOR CHART

Often it is of interest to reverse the above process. That is to find the latitude and longitude of some object on the chart. Taking (reading) such a position from the Mercator chart is a very simple process, similar to plotting one:

1. At the desired position, walk the parallel rulers from a parallel of latitude. Measure the latitude increment *along* a nearby meridian with the dividers.

2. Taking the dividers over to the latitude scale at the right or left margin of the chart, determine the value of latitude by measuring the length set on the dividers from the parallel up or down along the scale.

3. Now, take the dividers and measure along the parallel rulers from the position to the nearest meridian. Take the set dividers to the top or the bottom of the chart and measure from the meridian along the longitude scale to determine the value of the longitude increment. Read the longitude directly under the point of the dividers.

4. The dividers can be used alone, without the rulers, keeping them parallel by eye, as above. Practice with the rulers/dividers will develop sufficient confidence and familiarity with the process, to the point that the rulers will no longer be required, and the dividers can then be used alone.

DIRECTION ON THE MERCATOR PROJECTION

A marine chart developed on the Mercator projection usually has several compass roses (true and magnetic) placed at convenient locations about the chart. Directions are measured from these roses using the parallel rulers, a paraline plotter, or other suitable method. The process is very simple and is illustrated in Figure 3-4:

1. Place the parallel rulers along the course or bearing line to be measured.

2. Holding the base ruler along the line, walk the rulers, keeping them parallel to the line, to the center of the rose, which is indicated by a small cross.

3. With the ruler through the center cross, simply read the direction off of the true (or magnetic) rose in the desired direction. The reciprocal (180°) is read in the opposite direction.

Alternatively, if a paraline plotter is used, the plotter is aligned with the course and rolled to the nearest compass rose to measure direction, taking care not to disturb the alignment. The paraline plotter is generally easier to use if a large flat surface is available. Maintaining alignment is quite easy under these ideal conditions. If, however, the navigator's workstation is cramped and uneven, maintaining alignment is more of a trick. In any event, practice is necessary.

It is useful at this point to make some comments on the appropriate choice of direction on nautical charts. In principle, directions can be measured or specified relative to *true* north, or relative to *magnetic* north. (Compass north, as discussed in Chapter 2, has *no* place on the chart because compass deviation differs from vessel to vessel.) Traditionally, true north has been used for directional reference by the merchant marine and all navies of the world. More recently, some small boat navigators have (sometimes passionately) advocated the use of magnetic north as a reference.

Traditionalists point out that most celestial computations are carried out in terms of true north, marine gyrocompasses "point" to true north, the meridians on either Mercator or polyconic projections are oriented with respect to true north, tidal current data (see Chapter 8) are given with respect to true north, and, finally, that most ATON information (e.g., the bearings of ranges) is provided with respect to true north. Advocates of the use of magnetic north argue that true directions must generally be converted to magnetic (and, indeed, to compass north) before use, introducing the possibility of error in the TVMDC computations (see Chapters 2 and 12). Moreover, they add, nearly all commercial continental aircraft navigation is carried out

without so much as a mention of true north. They concede that true north is appropriate for celestial, bluewater, or polar navigation, but argue that it has little relevance for the coastal small boat skipper.

Each side of this "controversy" has points in its favor. In truth, either system can be made to work for coastal navigation (at least in the lower latitudes) provided that it is used with intelligence. However, one system should be chosen, to avoid the confusion associated with a mixed system of units. Therefore, for purposes of this course, true north will be taken as the appropriate reference point. The choice is made largely because plotters that read off parallels or meridians measure relative to true north, and also because the ATON and tidal current information (see Chapter 8) is generally keyed to true north.

MEASURING DISTANCE ON THE MERCATOR CHART

The *latitude* scale, shown on either side of the Mercator chart, is used for distance measurement. Since one degree of latitude is equal in distance on the earth's surface to 60 nautical miles, and one minute of latitude is, therefore, equal to one nautical mile, the degrees and minutes and tenths of minutes or seconds markers indicating the latitude along the meridians on the sides of the chart provide excellent scales to measure distance on the Mercator chart.

Remember, however, that Mercator's Projection *expands* the scale as latitude increases. So, it may be important *where* on the scale the distance is measured. (Unless a very small scale chart is used, however, this scale expansion is of theoretical interest only.) Distance is taken using the navigator's dividers. If the length of the course is shorter than the maximum extension of the dividers, the dividers are extended to the length of the course. The dividers are then moved (without changing their setting) so that these are aligned with one of the meridians at the right or left edge of the chart, and the length read out in

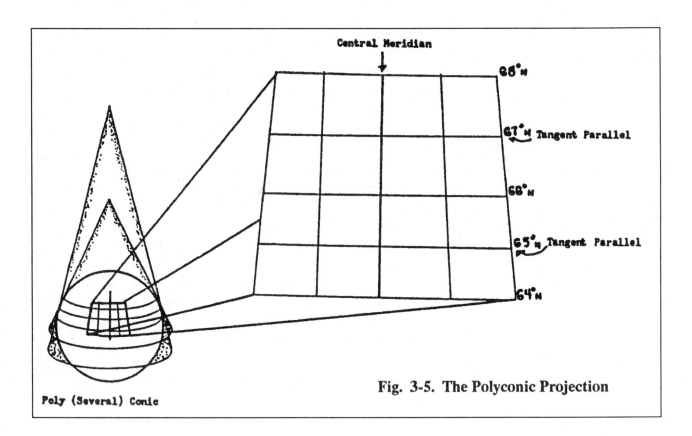

Central Meridian

66°N

67°N Tangent Parallel

66°N

65°N Tangent Parallel

64°N

Poly (Several) Conic

Fig. 3-5. The Polyconic Projection

minutes and tenths of minutes or minutes and seconds. Distance is determined by remembering that one minute is equal to one nautical mile. A distance of 10.7 minutes, for example, translates to 10.7 nautical miles. If a very small scale chart is being used (see below) it is important to measure this distance at or near the midpoint of the course line. For coastal charts (see below) this refinement is unnecessary.

If the length of the course is longer than the maximum extension of the dividers, it is measured by setting the dividers to a convenient distance on the meridian (e.g., 2, 5, 10 nautical mile, depending upon the scale of the chart) and walked along the course in a series of "steps," mentally counting in multiples of the convenient distance. The final "step" will be shorter, and the dividers are reset to this length and the increment read on the meridian.

Alternatively, several of the plotters on the market are equipped with one or more distance scales. For example, the Weems and Plath Parallel Plotter is equipped with three distance scales,

corresponding to chart scales (see below) of 1:80,000, 1:40,000, and 1:20,000 respectively. Using this type of plotter, the distance can be read directly from the appropriate distance scale. Be very careful, however, to note the exact scale of the chart to use the correct scale on the plotter. Otherwise, you have convenience at the expense of error! Trivial errors like this can easily arise if charts of more than one scale are used on the voyage, as for example, using both a coastal chart (see below) for the en route portion of the voyage, and a harbor chart (see below) for the final approach. It is easy to make the mental error of continuing to use the coastal scale on the plotter for the harbor chart. (See Chapter 12 for a discussion of other "trivial errors" that have led navigators to grief!)

THE POLYCONIC PROJECTION

Nearly all marine navigation charts for the Great Lakes are based on a *polyconic* projection--a series of cones concentric with the earth's axis, and tangent to the sphere at different parallels of latitude. The earth's surface features are projected on the resulting surface, outward

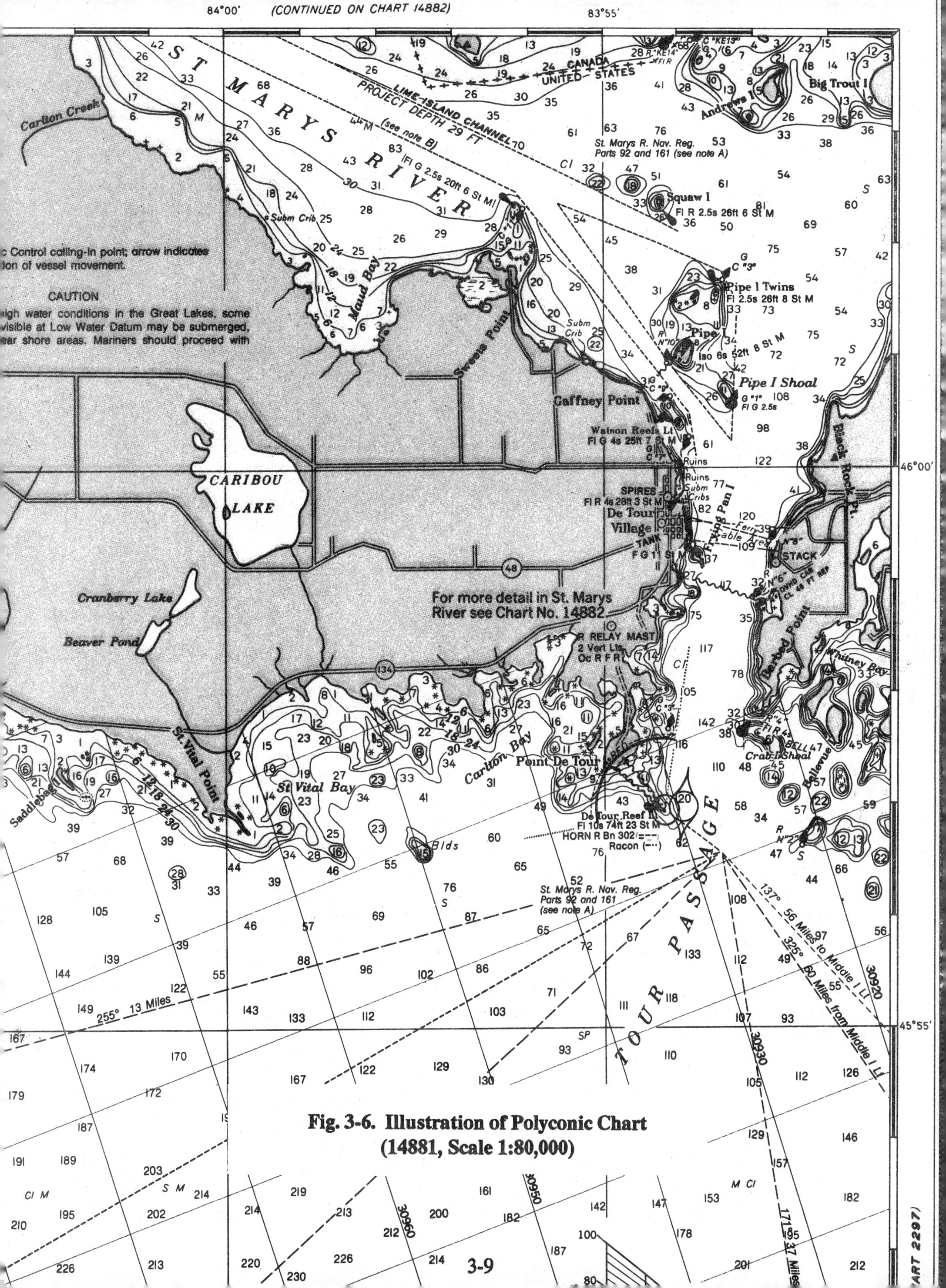

ST MARYS RIVER

Carlton Creek

Maud Bay

Streets Point

LIME ISLAND CHANNEL
PROJECT DEPTH 29 FT
(see note B)

CANADA
UNITED STATES

St. Marys R. Nav. Reg.
Parts 92 and 161 (see note A)

Big Trout I

Andrews I

Squaw I
Fl R 2.5s 26ft 6 St M

Pipe I Twins
Fl 2.5s 26ft 8 St M

Pipe I
Iso 6s 52ft 8 St M

Pipe I Shoal
G "I"
Fl G 2.5s

c Control calling-in point; arrow indicates
ion of vessel movement.

CAUTION
igh water conditions in the Great Lakes, some
visible at Low Water Datum may be submerged,
ear shore areas. Mariners should proceed with

Gaffney Point

Watson Reefs Lt
Fl G 4s 25ft 7 St M

CARIBOU
LAKE

Ruins
Ruins
Subm
Cribs

Frying Pan I

SPIRES
Fl R 4s 28ft 3 St M

De Tour
Village

TANK
F G 11 St M

Black Rock Pt.

Barbed Point

STACK

Cranberry Lake

Beaver Pond

For more detail in St. Marys
River see Chart No. 14882

Whitney Bay

R RELAY MAST
2 Vert Lts
Oc R F R

St Vital Point

Saddlebag

Carlton Bay

Point De Tour

St Vital Bay

Crab I Shoal

Bellevue

De Tour Reef Lt
Fl 10s 74ft 23 St M
HORN R Bn 302
Racon (—·—)

St. Marys R. Nav. Reg.
Parts 92 and 161
(see note A)

TOUR PASSAGE

137° 56 Miles to Middle I Lt

325° 80 Miles from Middle I Lt

255° 13 Miles

Fig. 3-6. Illustration of Polyconic Chart
(14881, Scale 1:80,000)

171° 37 Miles

ART 2297)

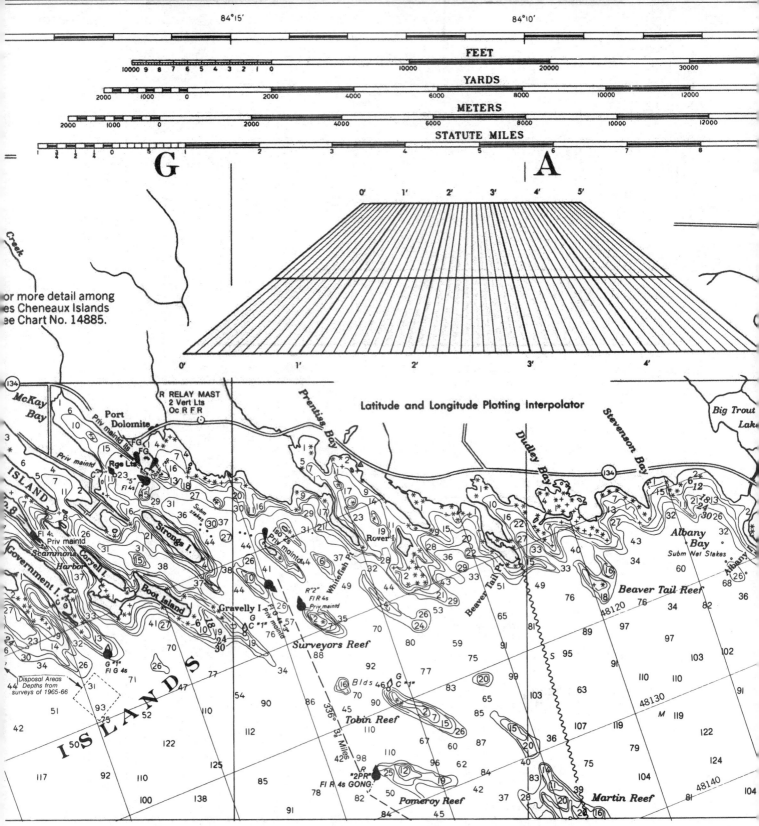

Fig. 3-7. Plotting Interpolator Included in Polyconic Chart.

from the center of the earth. When a plane portion is taken from the polyconic surface, as shown in Figure 3-5, the meridians appear almost as straight lines, very slightly curved *converging* northward beyond the top of the chart, toward the apexes of the cones.

Great circles appear as essentially straight lines and parallels of latitude appear as slightly curved, almost parallel lines intersecting the meridians at 90° angles and diverging as they approach the edges of the chart. Distortion is least along the *central meridian* and increases toward the sides of the chart, as the distance between parallels of latitude increases. Although the polyconic chart is *not* conformal, great circles do appear as essentially straight lines, and radio signals (following great circles) can be plotted as straight lines on this projection.

LATITUDE AND LONGITUDE SCALES ON THE POLYCONIC CHART

On the polyconic chart the parallels of latitude appear as slightly curved lines diverging toward the sides of the chart, and the meridians converge to an imaginary spot off the top of the chart. These "distortions" are readily apparent on a chart of a large area, but are virtually undetectable on the charts generally used by operators of small vessels. Figure 3-6, for example, reproduces a portion of the 14881 polyconic chart (produced in the original at a scale of 1:80,000). As a practical matter, latitude and longitude can be determined in the same manner as on a Mercator chart. For extremely accurate plotting, an interpolator is generally reproduced somewhere on the polyconic chart, as illustrated in Figure 3-7. (Because its use is so specialized, the interpolator is not discussed in this text.) Incidentally, bar charts for measurement of distance (in feet, yards, meters, and statute miles) are also shown in Figure 3-7.

DISTANCE ON THE POLYCONIC CHART FOR GREAT LAKES REGION

Distance on Great Lakes charts are indicated in *statute* miles (mi.) and *not* in nautical miles (M). Large scale Great Lakes charts may also indicate distances in meters (m), yards (yd.), and feet (ft.). Bar graphs are provided for measuring distances.

DIRECTION ON THE POLYCONIC CHART FOR GREAT LAKES REGION

Although the polyconic projection is *not* conformal, for the chart scales used by the small craft operator, any lack of conformality is practically unmeasurable. Compass roses are provided on Great Lakes charts, and the nearest rose should be used when measuring true and magnetic directions. Also, variation changes about one degree for every change of about a degree in longitude. Thus, for long east-west trips, corrections of magnetic and compass courses must be made about every 40 statute miles. When the distance over which the direction is to be measured is very long, and is in a predominately east-west direction, measure the course line angle at the charted meridian nearest the halfway point of the line between the two points of interest. Figure 3-8 summarizes the key contrasts between the Mercator and polyconic projections.

CHART SCALES

Since a chart is a representation of the physical and geographical nautical features of the earth's surface on a plain piece of paper, it is important to be able to relate distance on the earth's surface to distance shown on the chart. The term for this earth-to-chart distance relationship is scale. *Scale* is nothing more than the number of distance units on the earth's surface represented by the same distance unit on the chart. The unit may be inches, using the English (or American) system of units, or meters, if using the metric system, or any other units for that matter.

The scale on the nautical chart is expressed as a ratio of the units, such as one inch on the chart is equivalent to 2,500 inches on the earth's surface, written 1:2,500. There are several scales in use, depending on the area being charted and the detail to be included.

The relative size of the scale (large- or small-scale) is determined by the relative size of the ratio expressed as a fraction. The larger the *value* of the fraction, the larger the scale. A scale of 1:2,500 (expressed as a fraction, 1/2,500) has a much *larger* value than the scale of 1:5,000,000 where the fraction has a value of 1/5,000,000. Thus, a chart with a scale of 1:2,500 would be considered a *large-scale* chart, and a chart with a scale of 1:5,000,000 would be considered a *small-scale* chart. A *large*-scale chart covers a small area. A *small*-scale chart covers a large area. *Put*

ATTRIBUTE	MERCATOR	POLYCONIC (Great Lakes)
Conformal	Yes	No
Distance Scale	Variable, given in nautical miles (measure at mid-latitude)	Nearly constant, given in statute miles
Angle between parallels and meridians	90°	90°
Appearance of parallels	Parallel straight lines, unequally spaced	Arcs of nearly concentric circles nearly equally spaced*
Appearance of meridians	Parallel straight lines, equally spaced	Straight lines converging at pole
Straight line crosses meridians	Constant angle (rhumb line)	Variable angle (approximate straight line)
Great circle	Curved line (except at equator and meridians)	Approximated by straight line
Rhumb line	Straight line	Curved line
Distortion of shapes and areas	Increases away from equator	Very little
Illustrative uses	Large-scale, coastal, and pilot charts	Great Lakes
How direction measured	Reference to any meridian, parallel, or compass rose	Direction at any point should be measured by reference to the meridian passing through that point or compass rose.

* Parallels are equally spaced only along the central meridian of the chart and are not concentric, but become farther apart toward the edges of the chart. However, these differences are not noticeable on large-scale charts.

Fig. 3-8. Mercator and Polyconic Charts Contrasted.

another way a large-scale chart shows a large amount of detail, a small-scale chart contains a small amount of detail. Always use the largest scale chart available for navigation to show the maximum detail.

TYPES OF MARINE CHARTS

There are several types of marine charts. In general, these are differentiated by their scale and their intended use. These types, and their principal uses, are:

SAILING CHARTS. Scales of 1:600,000 and smaller. Used in navigation offshore, outside of coastal areas, or for sailing between distant coastal ports. The shoreline and topography are generalized. Offshore soundings, principal lights, outer buoys, and landmarks visible at considerable distances are shown. Detail needed for close-in navigation is lacking. Charts of this series are useful for plotting the track of major tropical storms, and/or long voyages.

GENERAL CHARTS. Scales between 1:150,000 and 1:600,000. Used for offshore, but within coastal zones of navigation outside of outlying reefs and shoals when the vessel is generally within sight of land or aids to navigation and its course can be directed by coastal piloting techniques.

COAST CHARTS. Scales between 1:40,000 and 1:150,000. Used for inshore navigation of bays and harbors of considerable width and for large inland waterways and coastal passages. The 1210-Tr chart, for example, is a coast chart.

HARBOR CHARTS. Scales larger than 1:40,000. Used in navigating harbors, anchorage areas and small waterways. These charts show considerable detail, even to individual piers and slips.

SMALL CRAFT CHARTS. Scales of 1:40,000 and larger (although some are at smaller scales). These are special, composite type charts of inland waters, including the intracoastal waterways. The Mercator projection is used on these charts, but it may be skewed-- north does not necessarily appear at the top--to fit the expanse of water on to the chart. A river, for example, would run *lengthwise* on the chart, and north could be toward the side. Small Craft Charts are printed on lighter weight paper and folded rather than rolled. These charts contain additional information of interest to small craft operators, such as data on marinas, tide predictions, and weather broadcast information. They

SCALE OR REPRESENTATIVE FRACTION	1 INCH EQUALS APPROXIMATELY		CHART CLASSIFICATION	
	NAUTICAL MILES	STATUTE MILES		
1:2,500 1:10,000 1:20,000	0.03 0.14 0.27	0.04 0.16 0.32	Harbor	Small Craft
1:40,000	0.55	0.63	Coast	
1:80,000	1.10	1.26		
1:150,000 1:300,000	2.06 4.11	2.37 4.73	General	
1:600,000 1:1,500,000 1:14,000,000	8.23 20.57 192.01	9.47 23.67 220.96	Sailing	

Fig. 3-9. Chart Scales and Classification.

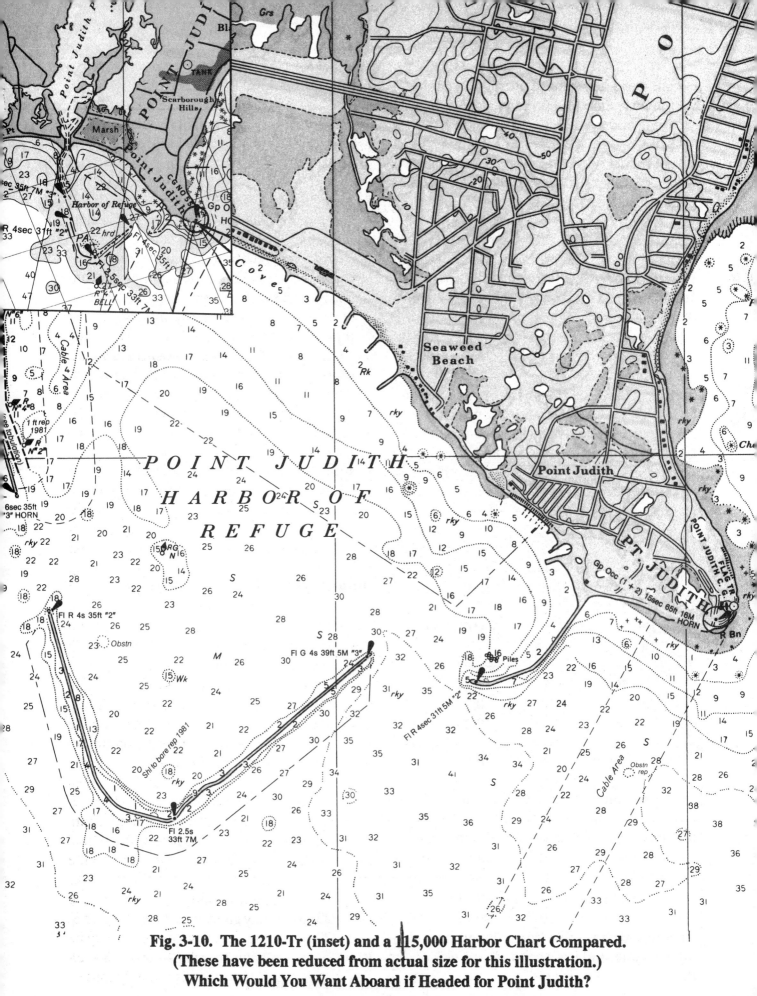

Fig. 3-10. The 1210-Tr (inset) and a 1:15,000 Harbor Chart Compared.
(These have been reduced from actual size for this illustration.)
Which Would You Want Aboard if Headed for Point Judith?

are designed for use in open boats and runabouts. Figure 3-9 summarizes the attributes of these various charts.

It was noted above that you should use the largest scale chart available for navigation. Figure 3-10 illustrates this point by comparing Point Judith harbor of refuge as shown on the 1210-Tr chart (scale 1:40,000) with a harbor chart (scale 1:15,000) of the same area. Which of these would you wish to have aboard if headed for Point Judith? The harbor chart shows much more detail in the harbor of refuge area, and in Point Judith Pond as well.

Soundings, discussed below, land details, and even individual houses can be seen on the harbor chart. In contrast, the coast chart provides only limited detail. Even the entrances to the harbor of refuge are difficult to see clearly on the coast chart.

WHAT CHARTS ARE AVAILABLE?

Nautical charts are available from authorized National Ocean Service or Defense Mapping Agency sales agents. The names and addresses of these agents are given in a *Nautical Chart Catalog,* issued in five short volumes (charts themselves, really) that cover the entire United States. Volume 1, for example, is titled *"Atlantic and Gulf Coasts, including Puerto Rico and the Virgin Islands."* These are available free of charge from the National Ocean Service.

These same chart catalogs list all the available charts and provide information on the chart scale, chart number, and price. For example, the area covered by the 1210-Tr chart (a special-purpose training chart) is actually covered by a coastal chart number 13218, at a scale of 1:80,000. (Portions of this area are also covered by sailing and general charts, as well as harbor charts.)

Many marinas have copies of the chart catalog available, and it is a good idea to pick one of these up on your next visit.

SOUNDINGS AND BOTTOM CHARACTERISTICS

Two of the most important types of information presented on a nautical chart are the depth of water and the bottom characteristics. This information is depicted by the use of a combination of numbers, underwater contour lines, color codes, and a system of standardized symbols and abbreviations.

The soundings (depth of water) on the chart represent the water depth as measured or estimated from a specified *datum. Datum as used in this sense refers to the base line or plane from which a chart's depth measurements are made.* Historically, different datum levels were used for charts of the east and west coast. On the east coast, the tidal datum was *mean low water* (the average low tide over a long period). The tidal cycle on the east coast generally produces approximately two low tides daily. But, these two low tides are of approximately equal height--and the chart datum, therefore, was mean low water (MLW the average of all low water observations). On the west coast, and at some other locations, the two low tides are generally of unequal depth, and the average of the lower of the two, designated *mean lower low water* (MLLW), was used for datum. However, this convention is being changed so that datum in either case will be mean lower low water in future editions of US charts. (This datum change is only a matter of definition and will not, in and of itself, affect any of the charted depths on the east coast. In any event, the specific datum selected will be noted on the nautical chart.)

The purpose of using a "low water datum" is to produce reasonable, yet "conservative," depth information for the chart. That is, the actual depth of water will generally be *greater* than the charted depth. But it is important to remember that *average* values are used in determining the chart datum. At any given time (see Chapter 8) in any location, the actual water depth may be lower or higher than the chart datum. So, although this depth convention is arguably conser-

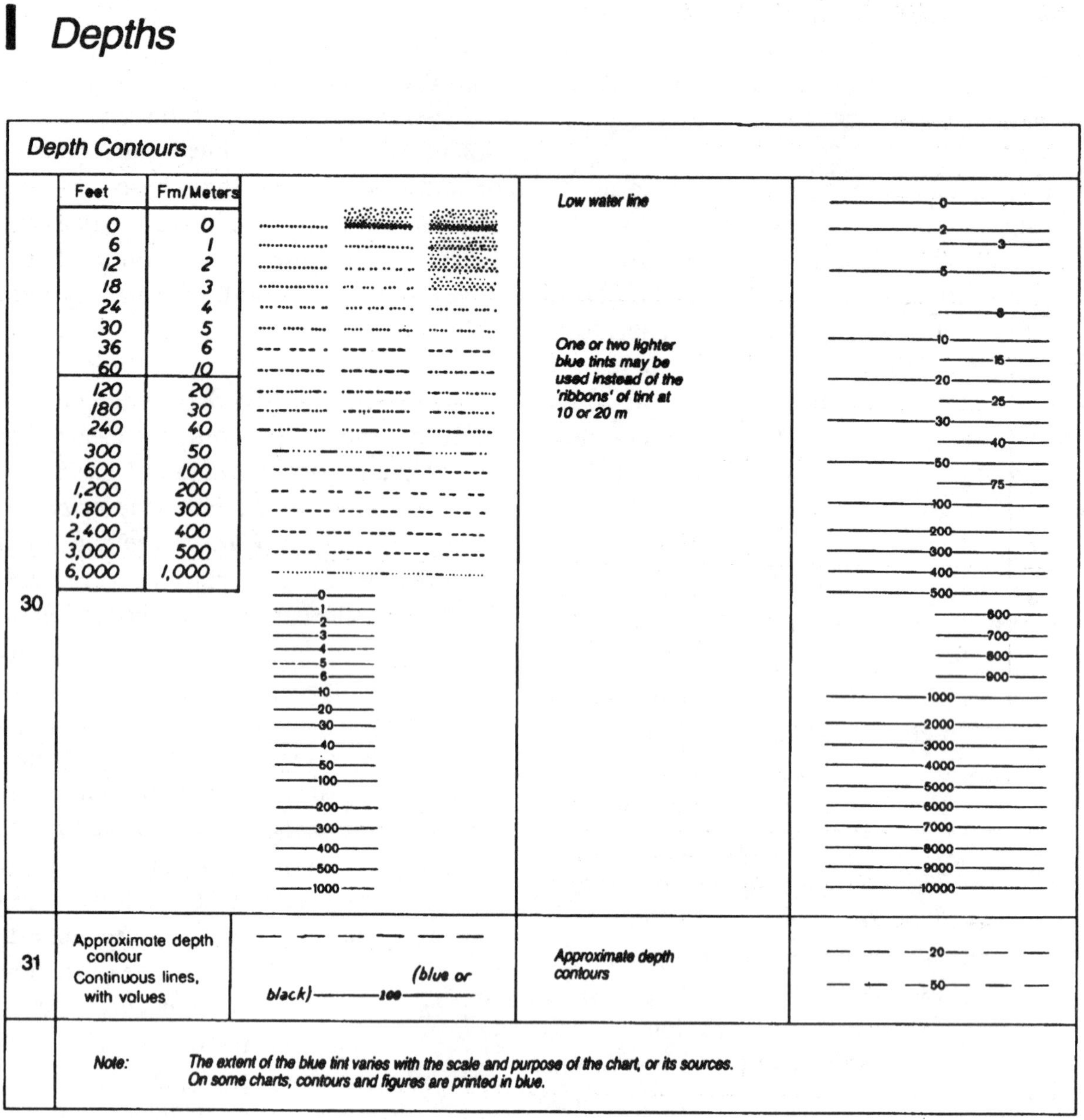

Depth Contours

	Feet	Fm/Meters			Low water line
	0	0			
	6	1			
	12	2			
	18	3			
	24	4			
	30	5			
	36	6			One or two lighter blue tints may be used instead of the 'ribbons' of tint at 10 or 20 m
	60	10			
	120	20			
	180	30			
	240	40			
	300	50			
	600	100			
	1,200	200			
	1,800	300			
	2,400	400			
	3,000	500			
30	6,000	1,000			

| 31 | Approximate depth contour / Continuous lines, with values | (black) ——100—— (blue or black) | Approximate depth contours | —— — —20— — — / — — —50— — — |

> Note: The extent of the blue tint varies with the scale and purpose of the chart, or its sources. On some charts, contours and figures are printed in blue.

Fig. 3-11. Soundings and Bottom Characteristics

vative, the mariner is not relieved of the responsibility of considering the actual height of tide at the time of interest.

Contour lines connect points of equal depth and profile the bottom shape. These lines are either numbered or coded according to depth, using particular combinations of dots and dashes. Figure 3-11, for example, reproduces an illustration from *Chart Number 1 (Nautical Chart Symbols and Abbreviations, Ninth Edition,* January 1990, see the attached references), that shows some of the standardized symbols and conven-

tions for soundings and depth information. Every mariner should have a copy of *Chart Number 1* for ready reference. The panels of this chart are also reproduced on the back of the 1210-Tr chart for instructional purposes. However, *Chart Number 1* is more convenient to have aboard ship.

Charted depths of water may be given in feet, fathoms (1 fathom equals 6 feet), or in meters (1 meter equals approximately 3.3 feet). New charts will typically contain metric units. The chart legend, discussed below, informs the user of the

Types of Seabed			
Rocks → K			Supplementary national abbreviations: a–ag
1	S	Sand	S
2	M	Mud	M
3	Cy; Cl	Clay	Cy
4	Si	Silt	Si
5	St	Stones	St
6	G	Gravel	G
7	P	Pebbles	P
8	Cb	Cobbles	Cb
9	Rk; rky	Rock; Rocky	R
10	Co	Coral and Coralline algae	Co
11	Sh	Shells	Sh
12	S/M	Two layers, eg. Sand over mud	S/M
13.1	Wd	Weed (including Kelp)	Wd
13.2	Kelp	Kelp, Seaweed	
14	Sandwaves	Mobile bottom (sand waves)	
15	Spring	Freshwater springs in seabed	T

Fig. 3-11. (cont'd.) Soundings and Bottom Characteristics

depth units. *In some cases, more than one set of units may be found on the same chart, so close inspection is necessary to interpret correctly the depth information given.* Different colors or tints are used to convey depth information; refer to *Chart Number 1* for details.

Dredged channels are shown on the nautical chart by two dashed lines to represent the *approximate* horizontal limits of dredging. The controlling depth of the channel and date of measurement are shown on the chart near the lines enclosing the channel or in a separate data block on the chart. Figure 3-12, for example, shows a portion of the 1210-Tr chart depicting the Cape Cod channel and the accompanying data block that provides information on channel depths.

The nautical chart also provides information on the nature and "quality" of the bottom. Figure 3-11 also shows a selection of some of the many abbreviations (e.g., "rky," "S," "S/M," "M") that are used to describe the quality of the bot-

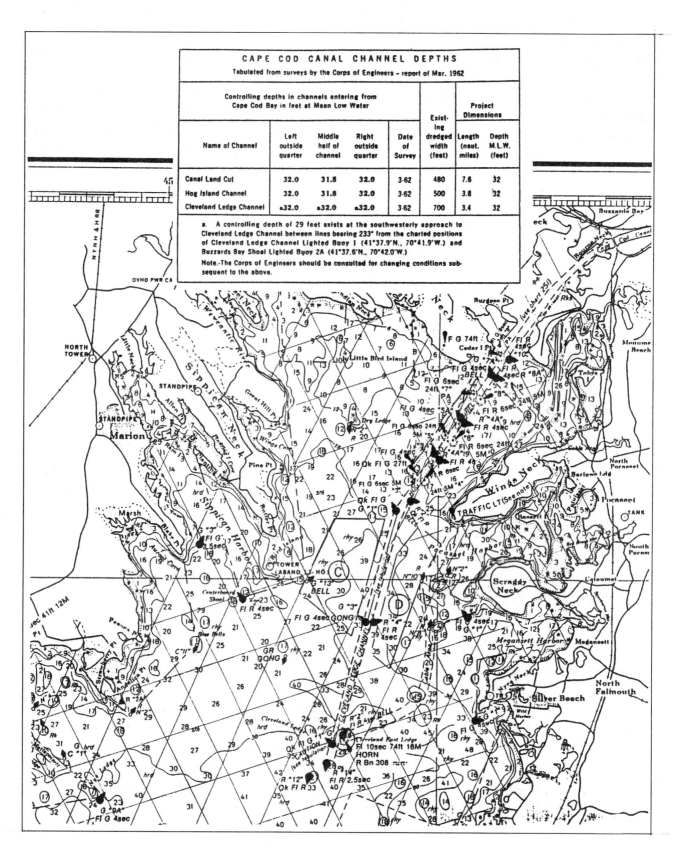

CAPE COD CANAL CHANNEL DEPTHS

Tabulated from surveys by the Corps of Engineers – report of Mar. 1962

Name of Channel	Controlling depths in channels entering from Cape Cod Bay in feet at Mean Low Water				Existing dredged width (feet)	Project Dimensions	
	Left outside quarter	Middle half of channel	Right outside quarter	Date of Survey		Length (naut. miles)	Depth M.L.W. (feet)
Canal Land Cut	32.0	31.5	32.0	3-62	480	7.6	32
Hog Island Channel	32.0	31.8	32.0	3-62	500	3.8	32
Cleveland Ledge Channel	a32.0	a32.0	a32.0	3-62	700	3.4	32

a. A controlling depth of 29 feet exists at the southwesterly approach to Cleveland Ledge Channel between lines bearing 233° from the charted positions of Cleveland Ledge Channel Lighted Buoy 1 (41°37.9'N., 70°41.9'W.) and Buzzards Bay Shoal Lighted Buoy 2A (41°37.6'N., 70°42.0'W.).

Note.-The Corps of Engineers should be consulted for changing conditions subsequent to the above.

Fig. 3-12. The Cape Cod Channel as Shown on the 1210-Tr Chart.

tom. This information is useful in deciding where to anchor and which anchor to use in an unfamiliar harbor. For example, a "rky" (rocky) bottom generally presents difficulties in anchoring or removing the anchor, and a sandy bottom may present poor holding conditions, whereas clay ("Cy" or "Cl") is typically the best holding bottom.

Finally, the *style* of the lettering provides some additional depth-related information. **Vertical** lettering is used to represent features that are dry at mean high water, whereas *leaning* or *slanting* letters are used for water and underwater features that cover and uncover with tidal action.

HEIGHTS

Clearances of bridges and heights of landmarks are given in height above *mean high water*

(MHW). This convention is analogous to using mean lower low water for soundings--the intent is to produce a "conservative" number in that the actual clearance is likely to be *greater* than the charted clearance. For example, a bridge height might be shown as 30 ft., but the mean tidal range might be 8 ft. (see Chapter 8), so the bridge height could range (on average) from 30 ft. to 38 ft. This could be of substantial interest to the skipper of a sailboat with a 34 ft. mast. Once again, however, averages are used. On occasion the tidal height may be higher than mean high water, so this convention does not excuse the mariner from consulting the appropriate references (see Chapter 8) to determine the actual clearance.

BASIC CHART INFORMATION

ESSENTIAL INFORMATION

Essential chart information is contained in a number of places on a nautical chart. These are described below.

General Information Block (illustrated in Figure 3-13) contains the following items:

1. The chart title, which is usually the name of the prominent navigable body of water within the area covered in the chart.
2. A statement of the type of projection and the scale.
3. The unit of depth measurement (feet, fathoms, or meters) and datum plane.

Notes: All notes should be read carefully because they contain information that cannot be presented graphically such as:

1. The meaning of special abbreviations used on the chart.
2. Special notes of caution regarding danger, prohibited areas, dumping areas, safety areas, firing areas, vessel traffic zones, etc.
3. Tidal information.
4. Reference to anchorage areas.

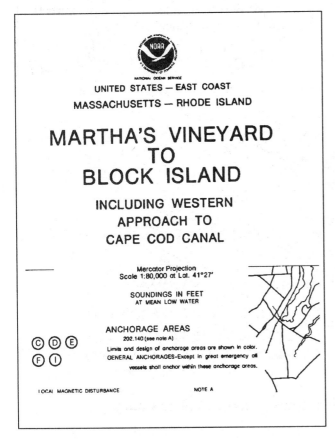

Fig. 3-13. General Information Block of 1210-Tr Chart

Building or House--One of these terms, as appropriate, is used when the entire structure is a landmark, rather than an individual feature of it.

Spire--A slender pointed structure extending above a building. It is seldom less than two-thirds of the entire height of the structure, and its lines are rarely broken by stages or other features. The term is not applied to a short pyramid-shaped structure rising from a tower or belfry.

Cupola--A small dome-shaped tower or turret rising from a building.

Dome--A large, rounded, hemispherical structure rising above a building or a roof of the same shape.

Chimney--A relatively small, upright structure projecting above a building for the conveyance of smoke.

Stack--A tall smokestack or chimney. The term is used when the stack is more prominent as a landmark than accompanying buildings.

Flagpole--A single staff from which flags are displayed. The term is used when the pole is not attached to a building.

Flagstaff--A flagpole rising from a building.

Flag tower--A scaffold-like tower from which flags are displayed.

Radio tower--A tall pole or structure for elevating radio antennas.

Radio mast--A relatively short pole or slender structure for elevating radio antennas, usually found in groups.

Tower--A structure with its base on the ground and high in proportion to its base, or that part of a structure higher than the rest, but having essentially vertical sides for the greater part of its height.

Lookout station (watchtower)--A tower surmounted by a small house from which water is kept regularly.

Water tower--A structure enclosing a tank or standpipe so that the presence of the tank or standpipe may not be apparent.

Standpipe--A tall cylindrical structure, in a waterworks system, the height of which is several times the diameter.

Tank--A water tank elevated high above the ground by a tall skeletal framework. The expression gas tank or oil tank is used for the distinctive structures described by these words.

SOURCE: Bowditch, N. *American Practical Navigator, An Epitome of Navigation,* Vol. 1, Defense Mapping Agency, Washington, DC 1984.

Fig. 3-14. Illustrated Definitions for Charted Landmarks.

Edition Number. The edition and/or revision numbers of the chart indicate the recency of the chart.

1. The edition number and date of the chart are located in the margin of the lower left-hand corner.

2. In addition, hand-written notations may be placed on a chart incorporating corrections occurring after the date of issue which were published in the *Notice to Mariners* or *Local Notices to Mariners.* Corrections occurring after the date of issue and published in this manner must be entered by hand on the chart. This is the chart owner's responsibility. Note: no matter how recent a chart is,

between the time of the survey and the time of printing and distribution, it is likely that some changes or updating needs to be made to ensure its accuracy.

CHART TERMS HAVE VERY PRECISE MEANINGS

Just a glance over a nautical chart will show that a very specialized vocabulary is used in connection with the chart symbols. For example, several terms are used to describe various landmarks, such as towers or similar structures on the island of Martha's Vineyard (refer to the 1210-Tr chart). There are radar towers, lookout towers, and spires. Just north, on the Elizabeth Islands and nearby mainland Massachusetts, can be found monuments, water towers, houses, cupolas, standpipes, stacks, tanks, and more lookout towers. Each has a unique and specialized meaning. Although the distinctions among many of these terms is obvious, there are subtleties and specialized "terms of art" that are used. Figure 3-14, for example, shows a sampling of terms and associated definitions for man-made landmarks as used in the construction of nautical charts. (A more complete list can be found in Bowditch and other references given at the end of this chapter.) Compare, for example, the differences among the terms spire, cupola, and dome. All are found atop buildings, but each is recognizably different. It is worth the time required to study the meaning of such specialized terms and to compare what is shown on the chart to what can be seen from a vessel. Experienced mariners have a mental picture of each of the items defined in Figure 3-14, which enables them to locate landmarks quickly from the chart descriptions.

There are numerous specialized conventions employed in the construction of charts to convey precise meanings. Continuing with landmarks as an example, a large circle with a dot at its center is the symbol used to denote selected landmarks that have been *accurately* located. Capital letters are used to identify the landmark, e.g., MONUMENT, CUP (or CUPOLA), DOME in this case. However, a small circle, without a dot, is used for landmarks not accurately located. These are denoted by capital and lower case letters, e.g., Mon, Cup, Dome. (In some cases the letters PA, denoting position approximate, is also used to minimize ambiguity.) In other cases only one object of a group is charted. This is denoted by a descriptive legend in parentheses, including the number of objects in the group, e.g., (TALLEST OF FOUR). The prudent mariner soon learns to use only accurately located landmarks to determine lines of position (LOPs) or fixes (see Chapter 6). Landmarks that are not accurately located can be used for recognition purposes and to form the visual context for identifying other accurately known landmarks for LOPs. For example, a MONUMENT might be located between a Cupola and a Dome. Observation of these latter objects could serve to identify the MONUMENT which would be used for determination of an LOP.

These specialized definitions and conventions are used to save space and convey a wealth of information on the nautical chart. But, all this efficiency is to little avail if the mariner doesn't take the time to learn these subtleties.

PRACTICAL POINTERS ON FINDING YOUR POSITION BY REFERENCE TO THE NAUTICAL CHART

The wealth of detail on the modern nautical chart is designed to facilitate piloting by reference to charted objects. Examination of the 1210-Tr chart shows a sample of the myriad of charted objects. But it requires substantial practice before a mariner can rapidly and reliably orient himself/herself from a comparison of visual observations with what is presented on the nautical chart. In principle, the process is easy. The mariner often has at least an approximate idea of the vessel's position. Plotting a fix (discussed in Chapter 6) is simply a matter of selecting two or more prominent objects shown on the chart, locating these visually, determining their bearings using a hand held compass (see Chapter 4), and plotting the bearings on the chart.

The vessel's position is fixed at the point (or in the area) where these two (or more) bearings intersect. However, things are not always as simple as they seem. Visual detection and identification of charted objects often presents a challenge to the mariner. Some practical tips on this topic are offered here. Additional material can be found scattered throughout this text. The reader is also referred to the interesting book by Eyges listed among the references for additional insights.

OBJECT DETECTION

To use charted landmarks for position determination it is generally necessary to detect (see) and identify (recognize) these objects. Object detectibility is a complex function of size, shape, color, lighting, obstructions (masking), and other factors. A complete discussion of this topic is well beyond the scope of this course. However, some practical aspects are noteworthy.

An object generally needs to be visible to be detected (see below for some important exceptions.) Although this point may seem obvious, the implications are more subtle. *The mere fact that an object is charted does not imply that it is visible from all distances, at all aspects, and at all times.* For example, objects can be masked (blocked) by other objects, terrain, foliage, or simply the curvature of the earth. If the height of the object is given (as it is for most lights and selected other objects), calculation of the maximum distance at which it can be seen is relatively straightforward, as discussed in Chapter 6 (in general) and Chapter 10 (for lights in particular). If the observer is beyond this distance, the object cannot be seen. Terrain, foliage, meteorological visibility, and other factors also affect target detectibility. Not all of these factors can be determined by inspection of the chart. In some cases, elevation contours are shown for terrain, and the mariner can make an approximate determination whether or not an object is likely to be visible. But, often these contours are not shown and/or the height of the object is not given. In these cases, the mariner cannot determine whether or not an object is visible. The fact that an object is charted generally means that it can be seen from some useful distance, and/or from some aspects, but it does not mean that the object can be seen from all aspects and from all distances. Refer to the 1210-Tr chart, for example, and look at Nashawena Island. Two objects are charted on this island, a monument and a house. No height is given for either object and no elevation contours are given for the island, so it is not possible to determine from the chart alone

The monument on Nashawena Island 70mm lens, vessel 100 yards off beach. It is charted, but would you wish to rely on being able to see it?

whether or not (and from angle) either of these objects would be visible. As a matter of fact, the house on the island cannot be seen from a position to the southwest, and the monument is quite difficult to see at all, except at close range.

Objects may be masked (hidden from view) by trees or foliage as well as terrain or the earth's curvature. Here again the unwary navigator may have difficulty reconciling the observed scene with the chart. In the case of tree masking, many trees lose their leaves in the winter, and an object may be readily visible, but not so in the summer when the leaves shield the object. The color of the object and the lighting conditions also affects visibility. Objects that are backlighted or in shadow have a different visual appearance than under different lighting conditions. This effect can be quite dramatic in some cases.

The size of the object is important for two reasons. First, objects can be masked by the earth's curvature (see Chapter 6). The maximum range that a 5 ft. buoy could be seen if the observer's height of eye were 10 ft. (based upon horizon distance calculations shown in Table 6-2) is 6.3 nautical miles. Beyond this distance the buoy will be masked by the horizon. And, indeed, at night (depending upon the visibility and

intensity of the light) the light on the buoy might be seen at this distance. During the daylight hours, however, the maximum distance that the buoy could be seen (at least with the unaided eye) is probably much less, say 1/2 to 1 nautical mile, give or take. So the second reason why object height is important relates to the resolving power of the eye.

Object height, incidentally, is the chief reason why a harbor breakwater is often a poor reference mark in coastal navigation despite its relatively massive appearance on the nautical chart. Particularly at high tide, a breakwater may only be seen when quite close to the harbor entrance. Beginning boat crew operators in the Coast Guard Auxiliary training program often waste time trying to spot harbor entrances by looking for breakwaters, and overlook otherwise conspicuous targets that could be used for position fixing.

Another important reason why a charted object may not be able to be observed is that it is no longer there! Charted structures may be demolished and/or removed. In due course, these changes are reported and chart corrections listed in the *Notices to Mariners* (see Chapter 10) and made in subsequent editions of the chart. How-

The same monument on Nashawena Island photographed through a 200mm lens, vessel 100 yds. off beach.
(Both photographs courtesy of Mr. Charles Leavitt, United States Coast Guard Auxiliary.)

ever, either process is not instantaneous and there will be some time period when the chart does not exactly match reality. For example, look at Cuttyhunk Island on the 1210-Tr chart. A lookout tower is charted very near the "K" in "Cuttyhunk." This structure was there when (1985) the 1210-Tr chart was reissued. However, on the "real" chart of the 1210-Tr waters (Chart 13218) this structure is no longer shown. Instead, a tank is shown at approximately the same location.

Students often ask why roads are shown on the nautical chart. They reason that a road is most unlikely to be seen and, therefore, is a useless addition to the chart. In fact, roads can be useful because, although the road itself may well be invisible, cars, trucks, and busses can often be seen. This is particularly true at night, when headlights or tail lights are conspicuous.

IDENTIFICATION/RECOGNITION

As noted, an object needs to be identified (recognized) as well as detected. Identification is almost as complex a subject as detection, but it is possible to provide some practical pointers.

First, take the time to study the various object definitions and abbreviations to be found in *Chart No. 1* and related publications. As noted elsewhere in this chapter, the terms used often have precise meanings which are useful for recognition purposes. One day it may be very important for you to know the difference between a standpipe and a gas tank. None the less, as precise as the chartmakers attempt to be, some of the terms admit to various interpretations, and even diligent study of the definitions may be insufficient to solve all recognition problems. For example, consider the term "abandoned light house." This term is used in the technical sense to denote a light house that is no longer functioning in that capacity. But, what does it look like? Aside from the fact that working lighthouses themselves differ considerably in appearance, abandoned lighthouses differ even more depending upon condition. In the Delaware Bay, for example, there is an abandoned

lighthouse that is little more than a foundation. (The word "ruins" shown on the Delaware Bay chart might alert us to this, but also admits to various interpretations. The "ruins" of the temples of the sun and moon near Mexico City are massive structures that can be seen for miles!) Not all light structures are in the same state of collapse. The abandoned lighthouse off Sakonnet Point, shown as "Tower, Abandoned Lighthouse" on the 1210-Tr chart is fully restored and (during daylight hours) looks for all the world just like an operating lighthouse. It takes time, experience, and local knowledge to become expert in identifying charted features.

Second, it is useful to note that object identification is generally easier if the object is considered as part of an entire scene, rather than in isolation. For example, a tank located next to other prominent objects is often more easily recognized and identified than a lone tank. None the less, the alert observer should anticipate the possibility that some of the surrounding objects shown on the chart may be hidden or difficult to recognize. The observer's "mental image template" may not match exactly the chart appearance. Incidentally, visibility plays a part in object identification as well as detection. If the visibility is poor, perhaps only one or two prominent objects may be visible and it may be difficult to locate oneself. Alternatively, if the visibility is greater, many objects may be visible and orientation much simpler.

Third, notwithstanding the fact that objects generally need to be visible in order to be detected and identified, there are a few noteworthy counterexamples to this "obvious" truth. For example, in many locations of the world, large powerplants (typically shown on nautical charts if located near the shore) can be found. The steam exhaust from the cooling towers of these plants is often visible at a much greater range than the cooling tower itself. Although the steam cloud may not enable precise position fixing, it can assist in orientation. Airports serve as another example of an object generally shown on

15	+ 35 *Rk*	35 *Rk*	Non-dangerous rock, depth known	21 R	$^{35}_{R}$. $^{35}_{R}$ +(35)
16	+ Co 3₁ + + *Reef Line* + + +	Coral reef which covers	+Co+ Co	
17	*Breakers* Br	Breakers		5₈ ^{19} Br 18

Wrecks			

Plane of Reference for Depths → H

20	⊂ ⊃ ⊃ ◯ ⊃Hk	◯⊃Hk	Wreck, hull always dry, on large-scale charts	Wk	
21		⊂ ⊃ ⊃ Hk	Wreck, covers and uncovers, on large-scale charts	Wk	Wk Wk Wk Wk
22		⊂ ⊃ Hk	Submerged wreck, depth known, on large-scale charts	5₂ Wk	⊂ 9 ⊃ Wk
23		⊂ ⊏ ⊐ ⊐ Hk	Submerged wreck, depth unknown, on large-scale charts	Wk	Wk Wk
24	↓ ↓ PA	Wreck showing any portion of hull or superstructure at level of chart datum	↓	⊂⊞⊃ ◯ Wk ◯ ◯ Wk
25	⟨⊞⟩ Masts Mast (10 ft) Funnel	Wreck showing mast or masts above chart datum only	⊞ Mast	
26	5₄ Wk	Wreck, least depth known by sounding only	4₆ Wk 25 Wk	⊞ (9)
27	2⏌ Wk 5 Wk	2⏌ Wk 5₄ 5 Wk	Wreck, least depth known, swept by wire drag or diver	4₆ Wk 25 Wk	⊞ 2⏌ Rk
28	⊞		Dangerous wreck, depth unknown	⊞	
29	+++		Sunken wreck, not dangerous to surface navigation	+++	
30	8 Wk		Wreck, least depth unknown, but considered to have a safe clearance to the depth shown	25 Wk	5

Fig. 3-15. A Sampling of Symbols Used to Denote Dangers on the Nautical Chart.

E *Landmarks*

Plane of reference for Heights → H   Lighthouses → P   Beacons → Q

General

1	⊙TANK ○ Tk ⊕ ⊘		Examples of landmarks	◆Building ⊙Hotel ☒	
2	⊙ CAPITOL DOME ⊙ WORLD TRADE CENTER		Examples of conspicuous landmarks	◆BUILDING ⊙ HOTEL ☒ WATER TOWER	
3.1			Pictorial symbols (in true position) 		
3.2			Sketches, Views (out of position) 		
4			Height of top of a structure above plane of reference for heights	☒ (30)	
5		(30)	Height of structure above ground level	☒ (30)	

Landmarks

10.1	✚ Ch	Church	✚ ⊟	Ch.	✚ ■
10.2		Church tower	✚ Tr. ⊟ Tr.		
10.3	⊙SPIRE ○ Spire	Church spire	✚ Sp. ⊟ Sp.		☒ ☒ ☒
10.4	⊙CUPOLA ○Cup	Church cupola	✚ Cup. ⊟ Cup.		♀
11	✚ Ch	Chapel			☒
12	☒	Cross, Calvary			+ ±
13	⊠	Temple	⊠		⊕
14	⊠	Pagoda	⊠		
15	⊠	Shinto shrine, Josshouse	⊠		卍

Fig. 3-16. Building and Structure Symbols Shown on Chart No. 1.

nautical charts that may not be directly visible. Although the control tower or the hangers may not be able to be seen from the bridge of a sport fisherman, aircraft descending to land are able to be observed. Just remember that the prevailing approach paths of aircraft may depend upon the wind direction, so some caution needs to be exercised.

Fourth, it is often easier to recognize objects and determine your position if you are reasonably sure of it to begin with. This may sound foolish or, at best, obvious, but this is not a trivial statement. If you keep a good dead reckoning plot (Chapter 5) and take frequent position fixes (Chapter 6) you have a good (though approximate) idea of your position at all times. When you decide to fix the vessel's position again, it is not necessary to go hunting all over the chart to find the charted location of the two towers visible off the port beam! Sometimes knowledge of your approximate position enables you to make a plausible identification of an object that cannot be identified directly. For example, many shoreside communities have conspicuous water towers. Unless the tower has the town name written on it, or presents some unique "scene," the identification of these towers may be difficult. If you have kept track of your position well, the tower might be plausibly identified because it is the only tower that is consistent with the vessel's approximate position. Conversely, if you are much less certain of your position, it's a much tougher job to match the chart with what can be seen. The same tower might conceivably be that belonging to any of several towns along the coastline.

Fifth, beginning navigators often focus on man-made features shown on the chart for orientation and position determination. Land masses can often assist in the identification of charted objects and/or be useful directly. Gibraltar ("The Rock" to many of WW II vintage) serves as a dramatic example of a land feature that is easily visible (in good weather) and readily identifiable. Closer to the 1210-Tr waters, it should be

clear that Gay Head and the associated light should also be easily recognizable. Small hash marks shown on the chart near Gay Head suggest some sort of bluffs, and the elevation of the light (170 ft.) is unlikely to be the result of a very tall tower. This conjecture is correct, these 150 ft. palisades are very characteristic and easy to identify. Make sure that you familiarize yourself with the land features shown on the nautical chart.

So it is that object recognition is as much a mental as a physical activity, rather like putting together the pieces of a navigational puzzle. This point is made at several places in the chapters ahead.

AIDS TO NAVIGATION (ATONS)

The nautical chart contains much information on ATONs, such as lights, buoys, daybeacons, beacons, radio/radar stations, and fog signals. In the case of lighted ATONs, for example, the nautical chart provides information on the location, markings or numbers, color (including sectors of various colors), light characteristics, nominal range, height of light, whether or not sound signals or a radio beacon are part of the same facility, and other pertinent information. Refer to *Chart Number 1* for details.

DANGERS TO NAVIGATION

The nautical chart contains a great deal of information on dangers to navigation, such as submerged rocks, reefs, pilings, snags, wrecks, and obstructions. Figure 3-15 contains a sample of the many separate symbols used to depict these dangers to navigation on the modern nautical chart.

OTHER CHART FEATURES

The nautical chart also contains a wealth of additional data on such items as the characteristics of the coastline, land, ports and harbors, topography, buildings and structures (as noted above and shown in Figure 3-16), and even tides and currents. Again, reference should be made to *Chart Number 1* for details.

ACCURACY OF CHARTS

A chart is only as accurate as the survey on which it is based. The prudent navigator must consider:

1. The source and date of the chart are generally given in the title along with the changes that have taken place since the date of the survey. Earlier surveys often were made under circumstances that precluded great accuracy of detail. A chart based on such a survey should be regarded with caution. Except in well-frequented waters, few surveys have been so thorough as to make certain that all dangers to navigation have been *found and charted.*

2. The scope of sounding data is another clue to estimating the completeness of a survey. Most charts seldom show all soundings that were obtained. However, if soundings are sparse or unevenly distributed in charted coastal waters, the prudent navigator exercises care.

3. Large or irregular blank spaces among soundings may mean that no soundings were obtained in those areas. Where the nearby soundings are "deep," it may logically be assumed that in the blanks the water is also deep. However, when surrounding water is "shallow," or if it can be seen from the rest of the chart that reefs are present in the area, such blanks should be regarded with *great caution.* This is especially true in areas with coral reefs and off rocky coasts. Give such areas a wide berth.

4. Everyone responsible for the safe navigation of a vessel must have a thorough working knowledge of the nautical chart. Select a chart you commonly use in navigating, and with this in hand, reread this chapter.

PRUDENT ADVICE REGARDING CHARTS

This is a good point in the narrative to inject some prudent advice on the use and storage of nautical charts from the point of view of the navigator.

First, ensure that you always have on-board the *latest* charts of the area to be sailed. The point is made at several places in the text that changes in landmarks, ATONs, and other charted features occur almost constantly. Charts are revised periodically to reflect these changes, so the latest charts need to be used. Additionally, changes are recorded in a publication, *Notices to Mariners,* available in both hard copy and via computer or teletype (see Chapter 10). The prudent navigator notes these changes on the latest charts available.

Second, ensure that you have charts at the *proper level of detail* or *scale* for the intended voyage. As a practical matter, this means that you should generally use the largest scale chart available for the waters cruised. Aircraft pilots (at least those that are instrument rated) observe a useful distinction between what are termed *en route* charts, used for point-to-point navigation, and *approach* charts, used for the final approach to an airport. A similar categorization is appropriate to marine navigation. From the point of view of the coastal mariner, the nautical equivalent of an en route chart would be the coastal charts, and the equivalent to the approach charts would be the harbor and/or small craft charts. However, no competent instrument pilot would be content to fly with only enroute charts and the approach chart for the intended destination. They recognize that unanticipated difficulties (e.g., weather beneath landing minimums at destination, mechanical malfunction, unforecast headwinds, etc.) may require them to divert to alternate destinations. Indeed, under certain flight conditions, the specification of an alternate is legally required when an instrument flight plan is filed. The situation facing mariners is almost exactly analogous to that of aircraft pilots. Weather at the intended destination may be unacceptable; larger than anticipated currents (see Chapter 11) or other factors (e.g., standing by to assist a disabled vessel, towing a

3-28

disabled vessel) may cause fuel to be expended at a greater rate than anticipated, mechanical difficulties (e.g., a rough running engine, etc.) and other factors may make a diversion to an alternate harbor attractive and prudent. However, the safety margin afforded by alternates could be seriously eroded if the right approach charts are not available. Suppose, for example, that you are voyaging in a twin engine sport fisherman on the waters covered by the 1210-Tr chart. You depart from some port on the Sakonnet River intending to head into the harbor at Point Judith (please refer to the 1210-Tr chart). Just off Brenton Reef (near Newport Neck), the port engine starts to run rough, and you begin to consider options available. The harbor at Newport is close by and likely to have marinas with repair facilities. But, a glance at the 1210-Tr chart shows this area in a uniform shade of blue, with no sounding detail whatsoever. (In ancient days this area would have been labeled *Terra Incognita* and festooned with images of sea serpents and other unsavory characters!) The inset in the 1210-Tr chart indicates that these waters are covered in chart number 13221 (Narragansett Bay). As a prudent navigator, you should have foreseen this contingency and taken along the 13221 (and other) chart(s). If this chart were not on-board, an otherwise routine diversion could have the makings of a real problem. All may end well, but the level of cockpit tension is sure to go up a few notches. This brief scenario also illustrates another point: charts should be stowed in a known location and be easily accessible (see below). You should be able to find the 13221 chart in a hurry if necessary--now is not the time to have to rummage around the mayonnaise jars and cleanser (just behind the pickle relish) to find it.

Third, take the time to study the charts (and related publications) when you *plan* a voyage--in the safety and comfort of your den or living room rather than in a possibly cramped and wet cockpit. Although not every aspect of a voyage can be planned in advance, most can. Overall voyage legs, time-speed-distance calculations (at least

for power vessels), fuel consumption, tides and currents, destination alternates, and even the landmarks and ATONs to be used for fixes can be evaluated before the vessel slips a mooring line. To simplify the logistics of planning, some mariners actually have two copies of the relevant charts and other publications, one set for their home or office, and another set for the vessel.

Fourth, any chart discrepancies noted during the voyage should be reported to the appropriate agency. Mariners' reports are an important source of chart corrections and these are strongly encouraged.

In short, simply remember the four R's: charts should be *recent*, at the *right scale, readily accessible*, and *reviewed* beforehand.

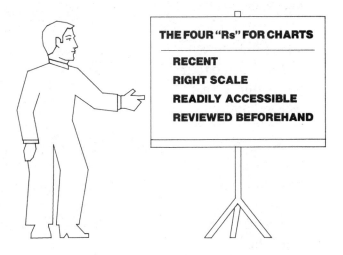

THE FOUR "Rs" FOR CHARTS

RECENT
RIGHT SCALE
READILY ACCESSIBLE
REVIEWED BEFOREHAND

CHART STORAGE

Most textbooks on large ship navigation include at least some passing remarks on chart storage. The advice usually reads that charts should be stored flat, to avoid creases or "rollup." This idea is just fine if you own the Queen Elizabeth (either edition) or other large vessel. However, most of us do not have the luxury of a draftsman's storage cabinet and have to make do with much less space. It is virtually impossible to store charts flat on the typical recreational vessel. Therefore, it boils down to a choice of whether to roll or fold your charts. Either scheme has passionate advocates; odd for such a mundane issue. In truth, either scheme can work and the choice depends in part on the available storage and working space in the vessel. If the navigator's work station will permit a chart to be laid out without folding, rolling might be a better idea. Plastic tubes can be purchased to store charts, often easily attached to the overheads of the cabin. If, however, the chart table is better suited to serving tea than navigation (as is true for many vessels produced today), charts will have to be folded in any event. Folding is a better option for storage in this case. (If charts are folded, try to avoid putting sharp creases in the chart, this increases the difficulty of plotting and introduces weak points where tears can originate.)

More important than the "fold or roll" controversy, charts should be stored in a dry (well relatively dry) location and arranged for easy access. Use gummed labels or some other method to identify the chart as filed, otherwise it can be a chore to find the right chart. Also, take the time to lay out the charts necessary for each voyage beforehand.

Always check to ensure that you have the correct charts for the planned voyage (including alternate destinations) as part of the pre-voyage check list. It is much easier to replace a chart at the marina than to discover it missing when enroute.

EPILOGUE: IF CHARTS COULD SPEAK, OH WHAT TALES THEY COULD TELL

As the foregoing material shows, the modern nautical chart is a marvel. The compact symbols and format enable a chart to convey on one sheet of paper what would require volumes of written material to cover.

Yet, the chart leaves fascinating stories untold, concealed by such compact symbols and text as: wreck, PA, or "Danger, unexploded depth charges." Part of the fascination of these charts is the fun of imagining or researching the stories behind these cryptic notations. Such chart

research can be done during the long winter's nights, poring over dusty volumes from the library or used book store. To introduce you to this sport, the following historical anecdote, taken from the *Navigator,* is offered with respect to the waters covered by the 1210-Tr chart.

On 4 May 1945, Grossadmiral Donitz, commander of the German submarine fleet, gave the order to cease hostilities. At this same time, the U-853, under the command of Oberleutenant Helmut Froemsdorf, was making a deep penetration of the Eastern Sea Command. So deep, in fact, that the boat was in Rhode Island Sound. The U-853 was a Type IX-C, 750 tons, and snorkel-equipped, which meant that the submarine could remain submerged for extended periods. Unfortunately, it also meant that Oberleutenant Froemsdorf did not learn that the war was over.

In any event, on 5 May at 5:40 PM, the U-853 torpedoed the *Black Point*, a British steamer of some 5,300 tons, breaking it in half. This was off Point Judith on a True Bearing of 129 degrees and a distance of 5,910 yards. On the 1210-Tr chart a Wreck symbol is located at coordinates 41° 19.7'N and 71° 25.8'W. This marks the resting place of the *Black Point*.

The passing Yugoslav freighter *Kamen* sent out an SOS and the first vessel to arrive on the scene was the Coast Guard Frigate *Moberly*, commanded by LCDR L. B. Tollaksen, USCG. He was later joined by the Destroyer *Ericson* and the Destroyer Escorts *Amick* and *Atherton*.

By 7:20 PM the U-853 had been located and was depth-charged. The boat slipped away but was again detected at 11:37 PM. A hedge-hog attack by the *Atherton* settled the matter and the U-853 was sunk. Despite this, the attack continued until 1:10 AM on 6 May. Numerous vessels participated in this action. Later in the morning of 6 May, the surface vessels were joined by two blimps and the attack resumed.

Finally one of the blimps reported a large oil slick and the action was broken off. One of the surface vessels recovered Oberleutenant Froemsdorf's cap and the chart table in the floating debris.

Over 200 depth-charges were dropped in the area during this engagement. On the chart you will notice a two-mile diameter circle centered on coordinates 41° 14'N and 71° 25'W; marked "DANGER"--unexploded depth charge--May 1945." This was the general area of the attack.

Approximately three miles to the SE of this area is a wreck marked "PA." This is the final resting place of the U-853; the last German submarine to be sunk in WWII. As an exercise, take the time to plot the various positions and locate these on the 1210-Tr chart.

The battle of the Atlantic had come to an end.

REFERENCES

Anon. "The Secret of the Chart," *The Navigator,* USCG Auxiliary National Board Inc., Spring 1986.

Bowditch, N. *American Practical Navigator, An Epitome of Navigation,* Vol. 1, Defense Mapping Agency, Washington, DC, 1984.

Committee on Map Projections of the American Cartographic Association. *Which Map is Best?,* American Congress on Surveying and Mapping, Falls Church, VA, 1986.

Department of Commerce, National Oceanic and Atmospheric Administration, National Ocean Service, and Department of Defense, Defense Mapping Agency, Hydrographic/ Topographic Center, *Chart No. 1, United States of America Nautical Chart Symbols and Abbreviations,* Ninth Edition, January 1990.

Departments of the Air Force and Navy. *Air Navigation,* AFM 51-40, NAVAIR 000-80V-49, 15 March 1983, U. S. Government Printing Office, Washington, DC, 1983.

Eyges, L., *The Practical Pilot,* International Marine Publishing Co., Camden, ME, 1989.

Hinz, E. *The Complete Book of Anchoring and Mooring,* Cornell Maritime Press, Centreville, MD, 1986.

Maloney, E. S. *Chapman, Piloting, Seamanship and Small Boat Handling,* Hearst Marine Books, New York, NY, 1983.

Ministry of Defense (Navy) BR 45(1). *Admiralty Manual of Navigation,* Volume 1, Her Majesty's Stationary Office (HMSO), London, UK, 1987.

Mixter, G. W. (edited by D. McClench) *Primer of Navigation,* Fifth edition, Van Nostrand Reinhold Company, New York, NY, 1967.

Naval Training Command. *A Navigation Compendium, NAVTRA 10494-A, US Government Printing Office, Washington, DC, 1972.*

Wilford, J. N. "The Impossible Quest for the Perfect Map," *The New York Times*, Tuesday, 25 October 1988.

Chapter 4

The Navigator's Tools & Instruments

In addition to the magnetic compass, charts, parallel rules, dividers, aircraft navigational plotter, and pelorus described in the foregoing chapters, navigators of small craft may use several other tools or instruments. Many of these are relatively inexpensive, particularly in comparison to the obvious benefits of their use. Accuracy depends on good *quality*, but also upon good *technique* in the tool's use. A navigator is encouraged to obtain the best tools for the money and projected use. The most expensive tools, however, are not necessarily the best, nor are the least expensive a bargain.

Just as any artisan knows, good tools cost money--but quickly prove their worth. For example, novices rapidly find, to their dismay, that the inexpensive student drafting compass and dividers (made of plated, stamped steel) quickly fall apart, or rust in the marine environment. But, the same tools made of marine brass prove their worth by their long and dependable service.

Remember, the marine environment (salt or fresh water) is harsh, and only well-designed and constructed tools and instruments survive its test. A selection of tools, which the navigator may find useful, is described below. Not all are appropriate for each and every small vessel. Loran-C, for example, would not be appropriate for use in an area with no loran coverage, and radar possibly too elaborate and costly for use on very small vessels operating in fog-free areas. None the less, these are included in this chapter for the sake of completeness and also because prices of more sophisticated marine electronics have fallen substantially in recent years, becoming affordable to a much wider spectrum of boaters.

PLOTTERS

A plotter is one of the most common and important of the tools used by the navigator. The basic purpose of a plotter is to be able to draw straight lines on the nautical chart and to measure the angle of these lines with respect to either the parallels of latitude or the meridians of longitude. For example, a common task is to draw a course line (or intended track line) on the chart and to measure the true or magnetic bearing of this course. Plotters are also used to draw in lines of position (LOPs) to represent visual or electronic bearings. Finally, plotters are used, in lieu of the mileage scales on the nautical chart, to estimate the distances involved over the course legs drawn. (These uses are discussed in Chapters 5 and 6 following.)

The device traditionally used by navigators for this purpose is a set of parallel rules (also written parallel rulers), and many mariners still prefer this tool. But, there are several plotting devices other than parallel rulers in common use by small craft operators. One such tool that is particularly easy to use is the "paraglide" or "paraline"-type plotter. This is a graduated rule, with protractors and parallel lines, attached to a roller, constrained to roll such that the rules always (well, nearly always) remain parallel. With this tool, the user has the option of either rolling the gliding rule from the course line over to a convenient compass rose and taking the reading from the rose directly along the edge of the rule, or simply gliding the rule from the course line over to a meridian or parallel and reading the direction using one of the protractors inscribed on the face of the rule. Both methods are suitable and easy to use on small craft, provided that there is a large enough flat surface available to spread the chart. There are other plotting devices, termed "coursers," which are essentially like the "paraline"-type plotter, without the roller, but with many parallel lines scored lengthwise. These are used in the same manner as the rolling type only rather than roll, the parallelism is maintained by "eyeball" relative to the many parallel lines printed on the plotter.

Another "tool" consists of two identical drafting triangles (30°-60°-90°) used, hypotenuse

to hypotenuse to form two parallel lines, which can be expanded by sliding the triangles together until the compass rose center is touched (see Figure 4-1). Although drafting triangles have their supporters, most navigators find these inconvenient to use on small vessels, particularly if any sea is running.

Additionally, there are many other novel devices for plotting. (Descriptions and advertisements for these can be found in many of the popular boating magazines.) Some have the capability of solving current sailing problems (see Chapter 7), relative bearing problems, or other navigational tasks. As these are generally inexpensive, it is a good idea to try several before settling on the plotter of choice.

DRAFTING COMPASS

The drafting compass is an instrument similar to a pair of dividers, except that one leg has a pencil lead attached. This tool is used for swinging arcs and drawing circles on charts or maneuvering boards. The uses of the drafting compass are detailed in Chapters 6, 7, 9, and 10 and include drawing circular lines of position, solving current triangles, and drawing arcs of visibility of lights.

WRIST WATCH (or other accurate time piece)

Time is one of the basic dimensions of piloting. A reliable time piece is essential. Without a means of telling time, dead reckoning navigation, running a search pattern, or identifying the proper characteristic of an aid to navigation are all impossible. Every crew member should get in the habit of wearing a wrist watch when under way. The wrist watch should be waterproof and have means of indicating hours, minutes, and seconds. Experience has shown that digital electronic watches with chronograph (stop watch) features are usually accurate enough for piloting and navigation work. It is also convenient to use a watch that has the option of displaying time in the 24-hour format, as this eliminates the need to convert from one time system to another.

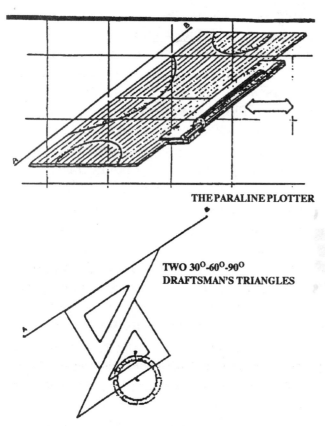

THE PARALINE PLOTTER

TWO 30°-60°-90°
DRAFTSMAN'S TRIANGLES

Fig. 4-1. The "Paraglide" or "Paraline" Type Plotters and the Draftsman's Triangles Used to Determine Direction.

PENCILS

An ample supply of pencils (and sharpener) is required for chart work. Pencils are used to draw courses, LOPs, fixes, and for chart labels. It is important to use a correct type of pencil for plotting. The pencil should leave a line which is easy to see, does not smudge, and is easy to erase completely without leaving a permanent mark on the chart. (Erasures, incidentally, do not arise solely because of errors in plotting. Many mariners reuse charts and erase the previous voyage plots.) A medium (No. 2) pencil is best. Keep your pencils sharp; a dull pencil can cause considerable error in plotting a course and will also smudge up the chart. A 0.5 mm mechanical pencil is excellent for chart work.

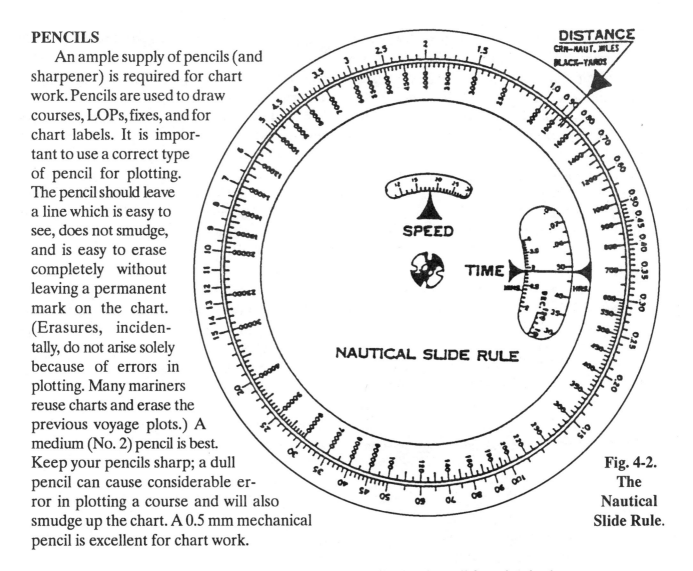

Fig. 4-2. The Nautical Slide Rule.

As an historical aside, the modern practice of drawing course lines and lines of position on charts is of relatively recent origin and reflects the widespread availability and relatively low cost of the modern nautical chart. Charts used by early mariners were extremely valuable and difficult to acquire, and most of what is now termed "chartwork"--such as the simple task of maintaining a DR plot discussed in Chapter 5-- was done by laborious calculation rather than simple drafting. Cutting up charts to produce the many illustrations in this text is a procedure that would have left Columbus and his peers aghast!

NAUTICAL SLIDE RULE

The purpose of the nautical slide rule is to quickly solve problems in time-speed-distance (TSD), with minimal chance of error. Although there are many varieties of nautical slide rules

available, they all function in the same manner. For any two values of a TSD problem, the third value can be readily determined. Figure 4-2 depicts a commonly used nautical slide rule. The nautical slide rule is constructed of waterproof and durable plastic. It has three clearly labeled scales: speed-time-distance. By adjusting the appropriate dials, values can be independently set into the indexes. With values set into any two scales, the third, or unknown value, will automatically appear at the appropriate index. Directions supplied with the rule should be consulted for details of operation. Note: With the advent of the newer, inexpensive electronic calculators, the nautical slide rule is now obsolescent, but a useful backup tool none the less. (It is virtually indestructible and requires no external power source for operation.) The electronic digital hand-held calculator is also quite satisfactory for navigation purposes, and use of such devices is encouraged. Calculators with engineering or scientific (e.g., ability to do square roots and trigonometric functions) capability are particularly useful. It is also a good idea to place the calculator in a small plastic bag that can be sealed. With practice, the calculator can even be used while inside the plastic bag, which makes you appear eccentric but prevents water damage. (Make sure that you carry spare batteries for the calculator.)

HAND-BEARING COMPASS

A special hand-held compass may be used for taking visual bearings on Aids to Navigation

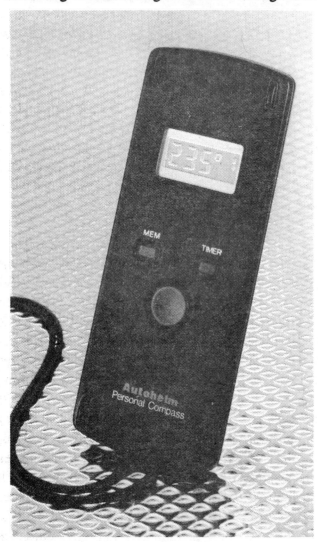

Fig. 4-3. Hand-held Fluxgate Compass. The bearing, 235 degrees, is entered into memory location 1. (Photograph courtesy Autohelm America)

(ATONs) and other vessels. This is not a required tool if the steering compass may be readily used for this purpose. In most cases, however, bearings accurate enough for a precise fix cannot be determined with a steering compass unless the boat is first pointed at the object or the boat is equipped with a pelorus or has been carefully calibrated for beam bearings. This is particularly true if an electronic compass is used as the ship's standard compass. (Depending upon the vessel's design it may or may not be convenient to mount a pelorus.)

The hand-bearing compass may be moved anywhere on the vessel by the navigator, independent of the steering compass. Care should be exercised, however, to ensure that the hand-held compass is not influenced by nearby magnetic fields set up by masses (engines) of ferromagnetic (iron, steel) metals, such as the vessel's standing rigging, rails, anchors, and electrical equipment.

Hand-held compasses now come in a wide variety of sizes, shapes, and prices. The traditional liquid-filled magnetic compass with vane sighting has been joined by other, more novel, compass types. One popular, though still traditional, type is generally termed a "hockey puck," because of the similarity in appearance to its namesake. The hockey puck type is liquid filled, and contains a tritium gas capsule to provide light for reading under conditions of restricted visibility. Additionally, this compass projects the image of the compass card to infinity, so that the compass can be held close to the eye and read, eliminating parallax error. It does take a few seconds for a liquid damped compass to reach equilibrium, however, and requires some practice before accurate bearings can be read from a rolling or pitching vessel.

A new type of hand-held compass is the fluxgate electronic compass illustrated in Figure 4-3. (As discussed in Chapter 2, the fluxgate compass was a revolutionary development of the 1920s and extensively used in aircraft during

World War II. Unlike the traditional compass it does not use magnets, but rather accomplishes the same function by electronically sensing the magnetic field. Rapid innovation has now made this technology accessible in a device that can fit in the palm of your hand!) The particular battery powered device shown in Figure 4-3 features digital readout of bearings (to within plus or minus 2 degrees accuracy when used by an experienced mariner) that are stored in memory whenever a bearing is taken. Several memories are available (up to nine in the model shown in Figure 4-3), so that an entire round of bearings can be taken rapidly while on deck, and later recalled for plotting at the navigator's station. Alternatively, this compass can be controlled so as to display continuous bearing information. The device shown in Figure 4-3 is lighted for night use and also includes a stopwatch for leg timing, estimation of a running fix (see Chapter 6), or other purposes. Although the advantages of this hand-bearing compass are obvious, there are two disadvantages that should be noted. First, this and other fluxgate compasses require a power source. Therefore, extra batteries should be at hand. Second, care should be used with this model fluxgate compass (when taking bearings) to hold it as level as possible, otherwise bearing errors up to several degrees could result. The navigator should practice taking bearings, first under ideal conditions (e.g., in calm or protected waters) and later under more challenging circumstances, before routine use of this hand-bearing compass. Some idea of the sensitivity of this device can be gained by placing it in the "continuous bearing mode" and noting how the digital readout varies with only small movements of the hand. None the less, experienced users can take accurate bearings.

Another more sophisticated variant of the hand-held fluxgate compass is shown in Figure 4-4. This particular device combines a 5 x 30 mm monocular, fluxgate compass, electronic range finder, and timer into one unit. The range finder enables the vessel's "distance off" to be determined by using the known height of an object

sighted (e.g., a lighthouse) and its relative size (as seen in the monocular) to determine the object's range. (Circular LOPs resulting from this type of observation are discussed in Chapter 6.) This particular model contains a gimbal, which minimizes any error arising from failure to hold the compass perfectly level. Additionally, the device enables *average* bearings to be read directly, increasing the accuracy of the bearings taken.

It is often assumed that the hand-held compass is free of deviation. The prudent navigator should take bearings from several locations on the vessel and compare these to the vessel's known position (e.g., on a published range) to test the validity of this assumption and to determine the location(s) on the vessel where the hand-held compass is relatively free of deviation. Particularly on power vessels the mass of metal in the engine may cause appreciable compass deviation if bearings are taken while standing over or near the engine. (This warning is so important that it is repeated elsewhere in the text and study materials.)

BINOCULAR

A good 7 x 50 mm binocular can be useful in locating and identifying visual landmarks and ATONs. For example, the identifying numbers or letters on buoys can often be read using binoculars at a much greater distance than with the unaided eye. (The meaning of the numbers in 7 x 50, is as follows: 7 represents the "power" or magnification of the binocular and 50 mm is the diameter of the objective (front) lens in millimeters.) This is also useful in Search and Rescue (SAR) and for other functions. Avoid binoculars with greater magnification than 7 power, as these are nearly impossible to hold steady enough by hand alone. (There are gyro-stabilized binoculars on the market, but these are out of the price range of the typical boater.) Avoid smaller objective lenses, as these have too limited a field of view and gather too little light to be useful in the operational environment--particularly at night. The 7 x 50 mm is the standard binocular in use by most of the world's navies. It is useful to have rubber-banded binoculars with individual eye-piece focusing. Some mariners prefer to use a model with an illuminated bearing compass.

Remember also that it takes patience and experience to learn to use binoculars effectively. For example, reading the numbers or letters for identification of a buoy is sometimes more difficult than you might think. In conditions of poor visibility or haze, it may be very difficult to establish a positive identification using binoculars-- even at short range. If the reported visibility is good, it may still be difficult to do, particularly if the buoy is backlighted in hazy sunlight. The binocular will only serve to make the silhouette of the buoy larger, rather than making the writing legible. In this weather condition it may be necessary to use other observable cues and contextual information to assist in identification of an object. Suppose, for example, that reference to the chart indicates that a buoy is isolated, without prominent landmarks or other buoys nearby. A sweep of the area with binoculars could verify that no other buoys were able to be seen. This evidence, in concert with estimates of the vessel's probable position or an electronic fix, could be adequate to confirm a provisional identification. Now suppose that the buoy were one of a pair marking the limits of the channel.

Compass

Gimballed fluxgate compass provides 0.5° accuracy. Stores 9 bearings in memory. Displays true or magnetic north. Calculates the change between bearings.

Rangefinder

KVH's Electronic Rangefinder uses known heights and relative size to determine range. Simply press button to match bar segments to size of object and distance is displayed!

Chronometer

Precision quartz crystal clock displays time of day and stores times that bearings were taken. Computes time differences between bearings.

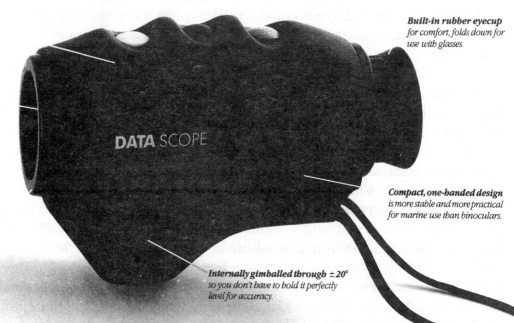

Guaranteed totally waterproof. Rubber buttons and "grip strips" for slip-free hold, even when wet.

5x30 roof prism monocular uses the highest quality optics and permanent focus design. Fully coated lenses for great resolution and brightness.

Illuminated for night viewing.

Built-in rubber eyecup for comfort, folds down for use with glasses.

Compact, one-handed design is more stable and more practical for marine use than binoculars.

Internally gimballed through ±20° so you don't have to hold it perfectly level for accuracy.

Fig. 4-4. Another Hand-held Fluxgate Compass with Integrated Rangefinder. (Photograph courtesy of KVH Industries, Inc.)

The binoculars could be used to locate the other buoy. The point of these examples is to illustrate that several types of information can sometimes be integrated to establish the identification of an unknown object even if it cannot be verified using direct means. Novices are sometimes disappointed that they cannot "see more" through binoculars. But it is important to note that you see "with your mind" as well as through your eyes.

HAND-HELD LEAD LINE

Although much maligned by some, the hand-held lead line may be used to ascertain shallow depths of water, when the depth sounder is not available or usable, such as around a grounded vessel, perhaps from a dinghy. The lead line consists of a line marked in feet or fathoms and a lead weight, hollowed at one end in which tallow can be inserted (called "arming the lead") to gather samples of the bottom. It is difficult to use except in relatively shallow, calm water, at slow speed. None the less, keep a lead line neatly stowed and ready for use at all times in the event the depth sounder becomes inoperative or electrical power is lost and soundings are required.

OTHER PARAPHERNALIA

Other tools that might be considered by the coastal navigator include an optical range finder and a sextant.

As noted, an optical range finder is used to determine the distance between the vessel and an object of known height. In this way a circular line of position (LOP) can be determined as discussed in Chapter 6. Range finders differ in features, cost, and ease of use. It is recommended that experience be gained in using these devices before any purchase decision is made. Many mariners purchase these from glossy Christmas catalogs, try these once or twice, and then, frustrated, later consign these to a garage sale.

A marine sextant is typically used for measuring vertical elevations of celestial bodies for celestial LOPs and fixes--a subject beyond the scope of this text. But, sextants can also be used for measuring horizontal angles. These, in turn, can be employed to fix the vessel's position. In principle, extremely accurate two-angle fixes can be determined using a sextant. The Coast Guard, for example, places its buoys in this manner. However, in practice, it requires both training and experience before reliable positions can be determined from sextant measurement of horizontal angles. Even the selection of the proper objects to sight, so as to maximize the accuracy of the resulting fix, is a sophisticated subject. Readers interested in this topic are directed to the sources listed in the bibliography at the end of this chapter. Suffice it to say that few coastal navigators use a sextant for this purpose. Space and scope constraints preclude a more complete discussion here.

CHARTS AND REFERENCE PUBLICATIONS

Although not, strictly speaking, "tools" of navigation, appropriate nautical charts and navigation reference publications are essential. With respect to charts, ensure that *all* necessary charts are carried and that the largest scale charts are available as noted in Chapter 3. Ensure also that you have the latest editions of the nautical charts, because the use of obsolete charts can be dangerous. Natural and man-made changes, many of these critical, are occurring constantly, and it is essential to have access to the latest information. (The publication, *Dates of Latest Editions, Nautical Charts and Misc. Maps,* is issued quarterly by the U.S. Department of Commerce, National Oceanic and Atmospheric Administration (NOAA), National Ocean Service (NOS) and contains the dates of the latest editions of nautical charts.) Additionally, the charts should be updated by reference to *Notice to Mariners* (see Chapter 10) to insert changes to the charts before a new edition is issued. These updates are important because it may be years before a new edition of a chart is issued. As of this writing, for example, there are numerous charts that are as many as ten years old. Although the number of changes in these older charts may be insufficient to justify publication of a new edition, the likelihood that there are *no* material changes over a ten-year period is small indeed.

Other publications of use by the navigator include the *Light List, Tide and Current Tables,* and the *U.S. Coast Pilots*. These too are discussed in Chapter 10 and should be studied carefully by the navigator as part of the prevoyage planning process and, of course, carried aboard the vessel.

Finally, it is appropriate to include some electronic devices among the navigator's tools. These include a depth sounder and radio navigation apparatus such as radar, RDF/ADF, and loran-C. These latter aids are described in more detail in Chapter 9, but mentioned briefly below.

DEPTH SOUNDER

The depth of water is one of the key factors which a navigator considers in safety of navigation. (It can also be used to provide a "reality check" on positions determined by other means.) Groundings have accounted for approximately 10% of recreational boat incidents in recent years, according to Coast Guard Search and Rescue (SAR) statistics. Although a depth sounder *per se* does not prevent a grounding incident, intelligent use of depth information can help to lower the frequency of these incidents.

The depth sounder is an electronic instrument designed to provide information on a continuous basis through the transmission of pulses of high frequency sound waves that reflect off the bottom and return to the receiver. The reflected waves or echoes are converted to electrical signals and read from a visual scale or indicating device. The sound waves are transmitted by a device called a transducer. The transducer is usually mounted *above* the low point of the hull (often on the stern). Therefore, this distance must be *subtracted* from all readings to determine the actual water depth below the boat's hull or propeller. (Some models of

depth sounders can be adjusted to reflect this condition.)

It is also necessary to *add* the distance from the water line to the transducer in comparing charted soundings (corrected for the state of the tide), with observed depth sounder readings. Water depth is indicated on a screen, by a flashing spot on a circular dial, on a recorder by a trace or, with modern, digital devices, directly as numbers on an electronic (LED or LCD) indica-

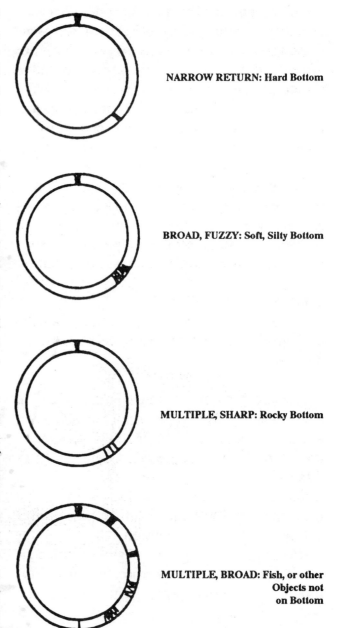

NARROW RETURN: Hard Bottom

BROAD, FUZZY: Soft, Silty Bottom

MULTIPLE, SHARP: Rocky Bottom

MULTIPLE, BROAD: Fish, or other
Objects not
on Bottom

Fig. 4-5. Interpretation of Depth Sounder
Flash Returns.

tor. With practice and experience, you can also tell what the bottom characteristics and conditions are, which is useful in selecting an anchorage. Illustrative readings are shown in Figure 4-5.

More modern depth sounders have a lighted digital display, either a Light Emitting Diode (LED) or a Liquid Crystal Display (LCD), and may combine a variety of other functions in addition to providing depth information. For example, these depth sounders may include a temperature probe to determine sea water temperature, a speedometer to give the vessel's speed through the water (STW), a log to indicate the total distance covered with respect to the water, and a "fish-finder." One example is shown in Figure 4-6 which also features adjustable deep and shallow depth alarms. For example, these alarms can be set to alert the navigator to arrival in shoal waters (the shallow water alarm) or that the anchor is dragging (shallow and deep water alarms). Yet other models also show rudder and trim tab positions, and some include (or can be connected to) voice synthesizers which "call out" depths at an adjustable frequency. (This can be handy if "single handling" and/or if the depth sounder is not located near the helm station in use.) Some of the more elaborate models have the capability to interface with other electronic equipment on board, such as a loran-C, to enable other specialized navigational tasks to be accomplished. There is no attempt in this text to illustrate how to operate these various depth sounders, because the information would be model-specific in most cases and would also quickly become out of date because of the rapid technology advances in the marine electronics field. Refer to the owners' manuals for these details.

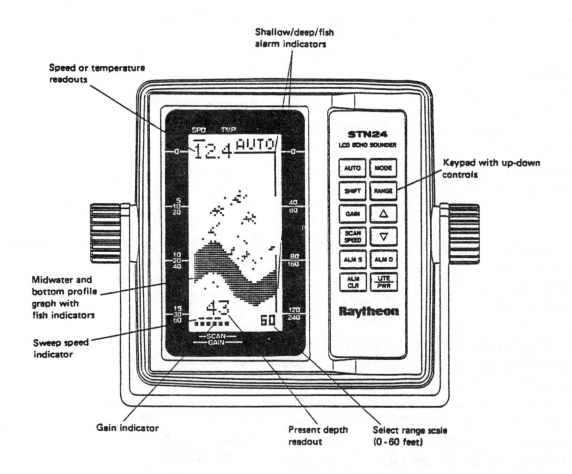

Fig. 4-6. An LCD Echo Sounder with Water Temperature and STW Readouts.
(Illustration courtesy of Raytheon Marine Company)

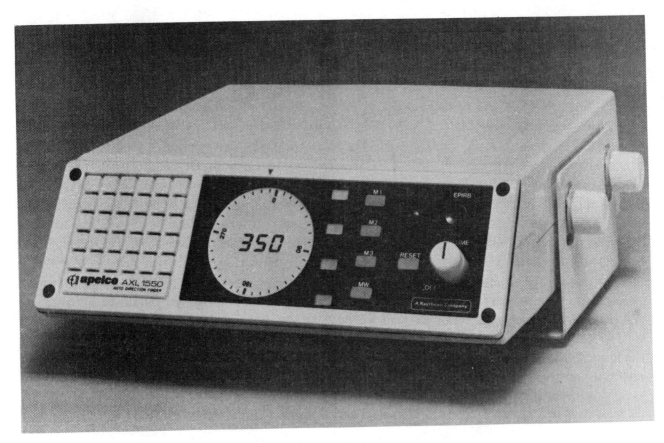

**Fig. 4-7. Apelco AXL 1550 Automatic Direction Finder
(Photograph courtesy Apelco Marine Electronics)**

RDF/ADF

A radio direction finder will allow you to take bearings on certain radio transmitters which are beyond visual range. These are particularly useful when operating in fog or other reduced visibility conditions. There are two basic types of direction finders: those that are operated manually (RDF) and those which take and display the bearings automatically (ADF). Radio bearings are used and plotted essentially in the same manner as visual bearings. Most RDFs display *relative* bearings, but some have an adjustable "bezel" that permits magnetic bearings to be read directly. Care must be taken when using RDF data, however. The accuracy of RDF/ADF signals are adversely affected by a number of factors such as weather (lightning can adversely affect performance), time of day (night effect), metal masts, other antennas, superstructure, etc. Radio signals from land-based stations may also be affected by mountains which may bend the

waves passing over them in such a manner that they appear to be coming from another direction. Also, signals received from very distant stations (hundreds of miles) will have to be corrected when plotted on Mercator charts.

Radio waves, unless refracted (bent) or reflected, travel along great circles on the earth's surface. On Mercator and polyconic projections, great circles (other than the equator and the meridians), are projected as *curved lines* rather than straight lines. The radio waves travel along these curves, *not* the apparent "straight" line between the transmitter and the receiver. RDF/ADF equipment should be calibrated in much the same way as a magnetic compass. Corrections are applied as in compass deviation. It takes a great deal of experience to be able to effectively use RDF equipment for precise navigation. Radio direction finding is discussed more thoroughly in Chapter 9.

VHF-FM DIRECTION FINDER

A VHF-FM Homer (direction-finder homing device), although not generally considered a piloting tool, *per se*, allows zeroing-in on the source of any VHF-FM radio signal being received. Figure 4-7 contains a photograph of one model intended for general civilian use. This unit couples to a conventional VHF-FM receiver and uses a special 4-dipole antenna. Each time a signal is received, the relative bearing of the transmitting station can be measured and displayed on a digital display. Errors in relative bearing are least when the transmitting station is on the homer-equipped vessel's bow, and within plus or minus 5 degrees to 20 degrees for other orientations. (These accuracy figures are specific to each model. However, accuracies are typically greatest at zero relative bearing.) DF gear is especially useful for Search and Rescue (SAR) work to locate the position of a vessel in distress, but can be a useful tool for navigation as well.

LORAN-C

Loran is an acronym that stands for *Long Range Navigation* and, to civilian users, is one of the technology "spinoffs" of World War II. Details of this system are provided in Chapter 9. But, briefly, a loran receiver enables a user to determine a highly accurate position fix within the areas of loran coverage that include (among others) virtually all of the coastal waters off the continental United States. The modern loran receiver is typically integrated with a self-contained navigation computer so that, in addition to the vessel's position, other relevant voyage parameters are able to be displayed. For example, the vessel's speed and course over the ground can be calculated. Additionally, the user is able to establish electronic "waypoints" (which could be buoys, other ATONs, turnpoints, or arbitrary locations) to mark the various legs of the voyage. The loran set can display distance to the waypoint, miles off a direct course to the waypoint (so-called cross track error), average speed over the ground (SOG), velocity to the next waypoint, estimated time until the way-

point is reached (sometimes termed *time to go* [TTG]), current set and drift (see Chapter 7), and a host of other relevant navigational information. Finally, a series of "alarms" can alert the navigator to arrival at a waypoint, penetration of a preselected track, a cross track error of more than a predefined amount or even the fact that the anchor is dragging!

RADAR

Radar, an acronym for *radio detection and ranging*, is also an outgrowth of World War II. Radar is also discussed at length in Chapter 9, but briefly described here. It consists of a transmitter and a highly sensitive receiver. It transmits and receives in rapid succession and, by measuring the time until the reflected signal is received, converts this time to a distance, and shows an electronic image of the radar "target" on a display screen termed a *plan position indicator* (PPI). Radar is used both for navigation, to provide an all-weather electronic image of the vicinity of the vessel, and for collision avoidance. Radar can also be used to detect and warn of areas of precipitation (e.g., rain, hail, or snow). Radar can be coupled with loran and other onboard electronics. Even as recently as a few years ago, the mere thought of including radar in a course designed for small boat navigation would have been foolish. But rapid technological progress has brought down the price of radars to the extent that they are affordable by many small boat operators. The lowest-priced radar sets are in the $1,000 to $2,000 price range as of this writing.

CONCLUDING COMMENTS

The tools and instruments listed above span a great range of uses, sophistication, and prices. (Compare a ten cent No. 2 pencil with a modern radar!) The individual navigator must make the choice of which tools are appropriate to his/her needs and budget. Relevant factors include the size and configuration of the vessel, waters cruised, prevailing weather, and the availability of ATONs. At a minimum, a watch, charts, relevant publications, pencils, plotter, dividers, a hand-bearing compass, a slide rule or calculator, and some device for measuring water depth should be onboard.

Student reaction to the extensive list of equipment presented in this chapter and, indeed, the formal navigation techniques presented elsewhere in this text is sometimes skeptical. A commonly heard remark is to the effect "I don't need all of this gear or to use such formal techniques; I either remain in inland waters or venture at most ten miles off shore." The most cogent response is to note that, according to Coast Guard SAR statistics, fewer than 10% of all SAR cases occur more than ten miles offshore. More than 90% of SAR cases occur on inland waterways or within ten miles of shore. Staying close to shore does not eliminate incidents or the need to navigate with precision.

Indeed, "blue water" sailors know that just the opposite is true. The most accurate navigation is necessary in coastal waters, a point made in Chapter 1..

Of course, mere possession of a sophisticated navigational tool or instrument does not guarantee its proper use or confer immunity from trouble. None the less, the proper tools and instruments used with skill and judgment certainly lower the likelihood of incident. In short, $500 spent on a loran receiver and/or depth sounder is likely to prove a better investment than a $500 refrigerator. Likewise, $10 or $15 spent on a paraline plotter is certainly a better investment than the same money spent on amusing signs depicting the powers of the captain or other nautical equivalents of bumper stickers.

REFERENCES

Note that some of these references present alternative points of view to those offered herein. These are included to lend balance and perspective.

Bowditch, N. *American Practical Navigator, An Epitome of Navigation,* Vol. 1, Defense Mapping Agency, Washington, DC, 1984.

Budlong, J. P. *Shoreline and Sextant, Practical Coastal Navigation,* Van Nostrand Reinhold Co., New York, NY, 1977.

Coote, Capt. T. O. *Yacht Navigation--My Way,* W. W. Norton & Co., New York, 1988.

Eyges, L. *The Practical Pilot, Coastal Navigation by Eye, Intuition, and Common Sense,* International Marine Publishing Co., Camden, ME, 1989.

Maloney, E. S. *Chapman, Piloting, Seamanship and Small Boat Handling,* Hearst Marine Books, New York, NY, 1983.

Markell, J. *Coastal Navigation for the Small Boat Sailor,* Tab Books, Blue Ridge Summit, PA, 1984.

Melton, L. *Piloting with Electronics*, International Marine Publishing Co., Camden, ME, 1987.

Norville, W. *Coastal Navigation Step by Step*, International Marine Publishing Co., Camden, ME, 1975.

Shufeldt, H. H., and G. D. Dunlap, *Piloting and Dead Reckoning*, Second Edition, U.S. Naval Institute, Annapolis, MD, 1981.

Wright, F. W. *Coastwise Navigation,* Jason Aronson Inc., New York, NY, 1980.

Van Heyningen, M. K. van. "The Evolution of the Modern Electronic Compass," *NMEA News,* Jan/Feb 1987.

Chapter 5

Dead Reckoning

Dead Reckoning (DR) is a rather forbidding name given to one of the simplest and most basic techniques of navigation. The origin of this term is lost in antiquity. Some believe that the word "dead" should be written "ded," a contraction for "deduced," because the method *deduces* the future position of a vessel from a present (or past) known position and knowledge of the course steered and speed maintained. Others believe that the term originated with the activity of throwing a piece of wood (a so-called Dutchman's log) in the water from the vessel's bow, and measuring the length of time taken for the vessel's stern to pass the log (which was, by hypothesis, "dead" in the water) to form a crude estimate of the vessel's speed through the water. Still others with a more macabre sense of humor believe that "dead" is used to describe your condition if you don't follow this procedure carefully!

Whatever the origin of the term, professional navigators believe that DR is one of the most important navigational techniques. Piloting, electronic navigation, or celestial navigation are not in themselves complete systems of navigation -- just names given to describe ways of checking the accuracy of DR positions. It is important to remember that sophisticated electronics can (and do) fail, cloud cover can prevent observation of celestial bodies, and poor visibility can prevent aids to navigation (ATONs) or other visual references from being seen and identified. In such circumstances it is particularly important to be able to estimate a vessel's position. An estimate derived from DR may be all that is available.

DR is a relatively simple, some would even say "crude," method of navigation. Crude though it may be, history shows that it is possible to accomplish great feats of navigation solely by means of DR. The great Genoese navigator, Christopher Columbus, for example, was by all accounts a superb DR navigator, and his historic voyages were effected almost solely by the use of DR. Even today, with all the advances in the art and science of navigation, from computers to use of navigational satellites, the ability to maintain a competent DR plot is considered one of the essential skills of the navigator.

This chapter provides the basics of DR, nomenclature, symbols, conventions (rules) for preparing DR plots, and a discussion of how a vessel's speed curve is prepared and used. The material in this chapter is closely related to that presented in Chapter 6; so it is a good idea to read through both chapters briefly before studying this chapter.

NOMENCLATURE AND PLOTTING CONVENTIONS

Much of the material in this (and the next) chapter(s) is concerned with nomenclature and conventions for constructing DR plots. There is, unfortunately, no universal agreement on these definitions and conventions. Plotting symbols employed in Great Britain, for example, differ substantially from those used in the United States or Canada. (Once again we appear to be divided by a common language.) Even within the United States, there are differences in practice and convention--as any careful comparison of the excellent texts given in the bibliography for this chapter will reveal. Nonetheless, U.S. practice is fairly well standardized and these conventions will be presented here.

Definitions and conventions are sometimes tedious reading, and many a student is tempted to try expedient "shortcuts," or to become impatient with an instructor who "nitpicks." Resist this temptation! It is important that a common set of definitions is employed, and likewise important that common plotting conventions are used. After all, when you hand over the watch to another navigator, it is essential that he/she be able to understand chart notations, the log, and other pertinent voyage information. Take the time to be disciplined, to prepare neat plots, and to record all pertinent information when obtained. The midnight to 4 AM watch is no time to have to reconstruct earlier plots or to sort out whether a particular chart notation represented a DR position, estimated position, or fix! As you gain experience (or develop a "seaman's eye" as discussed in Chapter 11) you will be better able to judge just how much information to record, and the appropriateness of various shortcuts. For the present, take the time to study this material carefully and to work sufficient examples in the student study guide (SSG) until the preparation of DR plots is "second nature."

UNITS, SIGNIFICANT FIGURES AND PRECISION

Before discussing DR and plotting conventions, it is useful to address the question of accuracy, precision, and significant figures used in small boat navigation. These are related but distinct concepts. Accuracy refers to the closeness of a measured or estimated value to the true (but often unknown) value. Precision correctly refers to the *repeatability* of a measurement, but is used here to denote the "fineness" of the degree of measurement, or number of decimal places if you will. Table 5-1 presents the generally accepted limits of precision used for small boat navigation. A vessel's speed (and related speed terms defined in this chapter), for example, is generally taken to the nearest 0.1 knot

(or statute mile per hour where this unit is employed). Thus, the value 4.0 knots is written to distinguish it from, say, 3.9 knots or 4.1 knots. In a technical sense 4 knots as written means any number between approximately 3.5 and 4.5 knots and, therefore, is different from 4.0 knots. Those who insist on being formally correct label charts with the precision of the measurements shown in Table 5-1. This text is less formal and, for example, would use 4 knots and 4.0 knots interchangeably (it being understood that, unless otherwise specified, speed is measured to the nearest 0.1 knot). (In some of the numerical examples presented in this text a greater number of decimal places may be shown to enable the reader to follow the calculations or to avoid roundoff error. In the end, however, all values should be rounded to the limits given in Table 5-1.)

DEAD RECKONING DEFINED

The practice of estimating position by advancing a known position for courses and distances run is called *dead reckoning* (DR). It is generally accepted that the *course* (C) known to have been *steered* and the *speed* (S) or *speed through the water* (STW) will be used in the preparation of a DR plot. All directions plotted on the chart will be **TRUE**. The DR plot is always started from a known position and always *restarted* at the time another known position is determined.

The effects of current and wind drift are *not* considered in determining a position by dead reckoning. Such a position is termed a **dead reckoning position** (DR position). The term dead reckoning is sometimes erroneously used to refer to the determination of a predicted position by use of the course and speed *expected* to be made good over the ground taking into consideration the effects of wind and current. Although positions determined by consideration of these other factors may be superior in some respects, they are properly termed **estimated positions** (EP), and not DR positions.

TABLE 5-1. STANDARDS OF PRECISION USED IN SMALL CRAFT NAVIGATION.

Generic Concept	Illustrative Quantities	Measured or Reported to
Position	Latitude Longitude	Nearest 0.1'
Direction	Course/Heading Bearing Deviation Variation Current Set	Nearest whole degree
Speed	Speed Speed through Water Speed of Advance Drift	Nearest 0.1 knot or statute mile per hour
Distance	Distance Cross Track Error	Nearest 0.1 nautical or statute mile unless otherwise specified
Time	Time to Go Fix Time Estimated Time of Arrival	Nearest minute unless otherwise specified

DR plots are used for two basic purposes.

First, a DR plot is used for overall *voyage planning.* Voyage planning includes the determination of the overall course(s) and speed(s) to be run, identification of *checkpoints* or *waypoints* where courses or speeds are to be changed or the vessel's position determined, fuel or amenity stops, points of interest, etc. In short, the voyage plan describes the intended trip in general terms sufficient for planning purposes. These plans are scoped in enough detail to ensure adequate fuel reserves (see Chapter 11) and safe passage. The plan is best made in the comfort of your home or office, or on the vessel while still at the dock.

Second, a DR plot is maintained while underway to reflect the vessel's actual progress and position. This *tactical* DR plot reflects all the factors that may alter plans--a late start, unplanned diversions, winds or currents different than anticipated, etc. This on-the-water tactical DR plot may not be as elaborate or neat as the voyage plan (or *planning plot*) but makes up in accuracy for what it loses in appearance. Both types of plots are included in this discussion.

ELEMENTS OF DEAD RECKONING

In the process of dead reckoning, courses are drawn on the chart as solid lines from a known starting position called a *fix* or *point of departure.* Course lines are identified by their true direction, which is written preceded by a "C" on top of, and parallel to, the course line in the usual three digits (e.g., 000 for 000° - True North); the degree sign (°) is implicit and is not written.

Beneath the course line is written the speed being run by the vessel. As noted, the vessel's speed is normally written in nautical miles per hour, knots using an "S" followed by one, two, or three digits. Speed can generally be measured to the nearest tenth of a knot and so one decimal place is used. The speed may also be indicated in statute miles per hour if distances are customarily measured in statute miles on the chart being used. The abbreviations kn, kt (or mph) is not necessary and is not written.

The position at which the vessel would be expected to be, after running a specified course at a specified speed for a particular length of time (expressed in hours and minutes), is calculated and the resulting distance is marked off on the course line, and the DR position is plotted. The DR position is labeled by a dot surrounded by a *semicircle* (or partial circle), and the time, using the 24-hour system, is written on the chart at an angle to the horizontal.

BEGINNINGS: ILLUSTRATIVE DR PLOTS

Figure 5-1 shows an illustrative DR plot that might be suitable for a power vessel. This plot shows a portion of a voyage in Buzzards Bay on the 1210-Tr chart. At 1:00 pm (1300), the vessel takes *departure* from buoy "BR" (Qk Fl G) north of Quicks Hole. A full circle is used as the symbol for departure (or a fix), with the figure 1300 (to denote the time) written parallel to one of the chart axes. The vessel proceeds on course 000 true at a speed of 6.1 knots as shown by the labels above and beneath the course line respectively. (As discussed below, the direction is taken to be with respect to true north unless otherwise specified; so it is not necessary to use a special chart label to denote true. Likewise, as noted above, "degrees" are understood to be the unit of angular measurement unless otherwise specified; so no degree symbol is employed.) A DR position is plotted at 1335, written at an angle to the course line, to show the time when the vessel changes course (or will change course) to 057. The DR position is shown by the semicircle. For route segments that involve course changes, as is

the case in Figure 5-1, a partial circle is used. At 1426, another DR position is plotted where the vessel changes course to 152 (speed maintained at 6.1 knots). At 1447, another DR position is plotted at the course change to 228 for the return trip. At 1518 the vessel's speed is slowed to 4 knots (written 4.0 on the DR plot), shown by the semicircle, etc. This simple DR plot shows the DR positions, course legs, times, and speeds for each leg of the voyage.

For clarity, the turnpoints in the DR plot shown in Figure 5-1 were drawn in the "open water." In well-marked waters, it is convenient to plan course "legs" so as to begin or end at or near buoys, along the lines defined by ranges, or at other locations where the vessel's position is easily determined. For example, the 1426 turnpoint shown might be difficult to verify in practice (without loran or other electronic aid aboard). But that is getting ahead of the story. The purpose of Figure 5-1 is simply to illustrate DR plotting conventions.

Figure 5-1 illustrates many of the symbols and conventions employed for DR plots. Normal practice is to start the plot with a point of departure, denoted by the circle. Courses and speeds are appropriately labeled, and DR positions (and times) are plotted *at each course or speed change.* Although not shown on Figure 5-1 to avoid a cluttered appearance, DR positions would also normally be plotted at regular intervals (every hour or every half hour) and whenever a fix or line of position (see below) is determined.

Figure 5-2 shows another DR plot. Here there are no planned course or speed changes, and DR positions are shown on the hour and half hour as would be more typical for small craft navigation in pilot waters. At 4:15 pm (1615) the vessel is able to fix its position by taking three bearings on land-based objects. (Fix labels and plotting techniques are discussed in Chapter 6). Accordingly, the known position represented by the fix is plotted (as a circle). For reasons that will be apparent in Chapter 7 on current sailing,

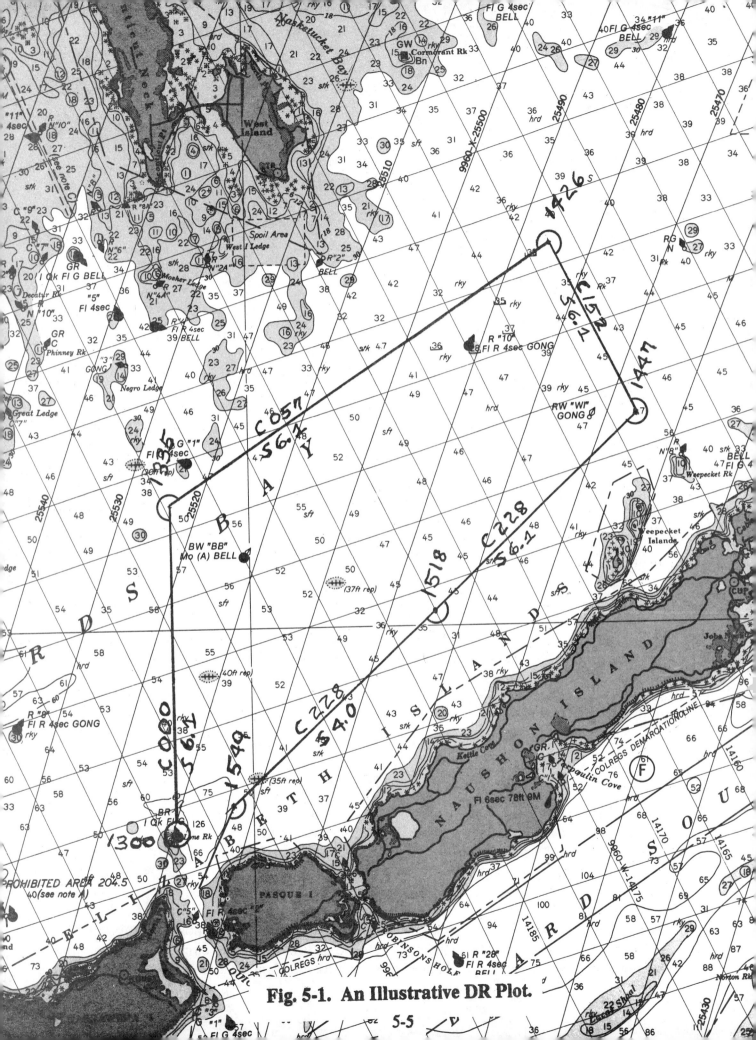

Fig. 5-1. An Illustrative DR Plot.

5-5

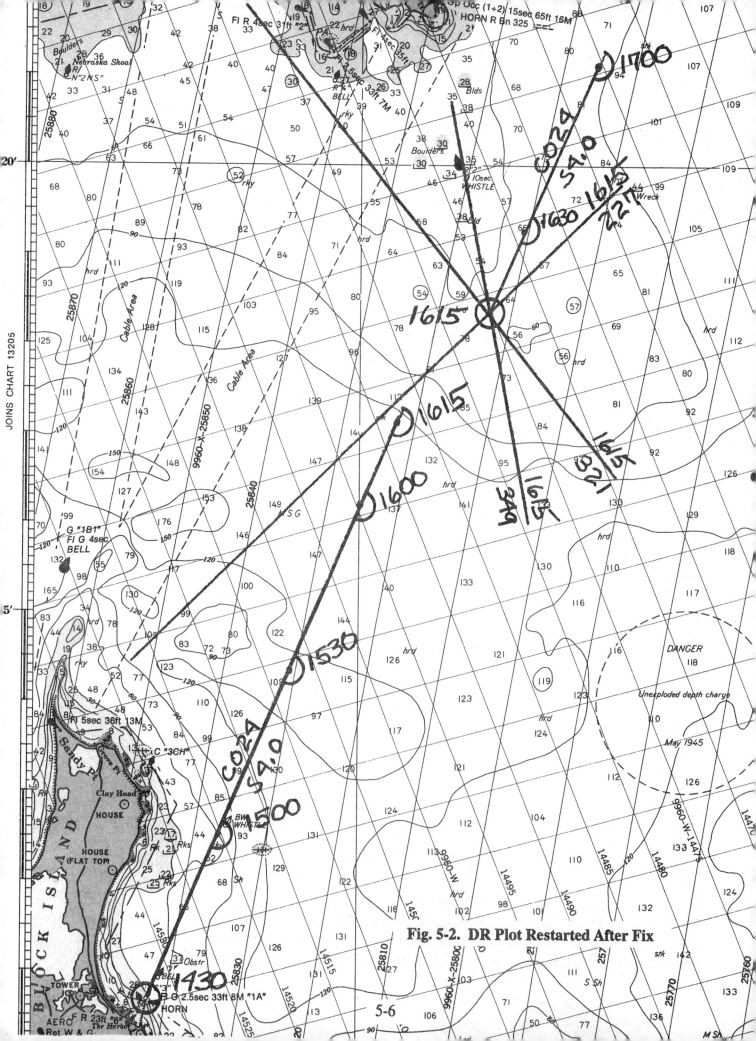

Fig. 5-2. DR Plot Restarted After Fix

5-6

TABLE 5-2. AN ILLUSTRATION OF A SHIP'S LOG FORMAT

DATE:　　　　　　VESSEL:　　　　　　　　　NAVIGATOR:

	Position		Course			Speed		
Time	L:	Lo:	Compass	Magnetic	True	RPM	STW	Remarks

a DR position is also plotted at the time of the fix. Finally, the *tactical* DR plot is *renewed* (started again) from the fix determined at 1615 and *not* from the 1615 DR position. The practice of restarting a tactical DR plot at a fix increases the accuracy of subsequent DR positions, because errors arising from factors neglected in the preparation of the DR plot are not cumulative.

SHIP'S LOGS -- A COMPLEMENT TO THE TACTICAL DR PLOT

The above examples show that a properly prepared DR plot can be both self-contained and informative. Even so, most mariners find it convenient to prepare entries for a ship's log book. There are probably as many proposed formats for pages in a ship's log book as there are textbooks on navigation, but the essentials of the log are summarized in Table 5-2. In addition to the "header" entries, columns are provided for time, position (latitude, longitude), course (compass, magnetic, true), engine speed (revolutions per minute, RPM), vessel speed, LOP, or fix data, and a space for remarks. (Remarks could include weather information, a brief discussion of the impertinence of Mr. Christian, etc.). The time honored ship's log is the official record of the voyage. Later in Chapter 7 on current sailing, a somewhat more elaborate worksheet is presented, but the bare essentials are shown in Table 5-2.

The log book is a complement to the tactical DR plot. It provides space for noting relevant calculations (in the remarks section), and other information that is not shown on the DR plot. Normally, the log book entries and the tactical DR plot are prepared at the same time. In some circumstances, for example, on long distance cruises, the helmsman will make entries into the ship's log, and the navigator or captain will update the DR plot at a later time. But normally, the entries in the ship's log and the updating of the tactical DR plot are contemporaneous.

DR PLOTS FOR SAILING VESSELS

(This section is somewhat more technical and may be omitted without loss of continuity.) The preparation of DR plots for sailing vessels presents some novel aspects. This is because, unlike power vessels which can choose courses and speeds almost at will, sailing vessels have some unique operating restrictions. In particular, sailing vessels cannot sail directly against the wind nor, for that matter, usually any closer than within approximately plus or minus 35 to 45 degrees of the direction from which the wind is blowing. The sailing vessel's speed through the water is a complex function of the boat length, design, sail trim, sea state, wind speed, and direction of the wind relative to the course. (For a fixed wind direction, the relation between boat speed through the water and course is described by a so-called polar diagram that varies with the wind speed and is unique to each vessel design.) Therefore, when proceeding in an upwind direction, the sailor traverses the overall course in a series of "tacks"--short legs off the wind an appropriate number of degrees. The determination of the proper angle of these tacks relative to the desired overall track line is a matter for optimization. Small angles act to minimize the extra distance covered, but boat speed is adversely affected if the vessel sails too close to the wind. Large angles increase the average speed through the water but also increase the total distance that needs to be covered relative to the rhumb line course. For any given vessel, prevailing wind, and current, there is an optimal tack sequence that minimizes the time taken to travel between any two points. The determination of this optimal sequence is a very sophisticated topic well beyond the scope of this course in navigation, but is addressed (at least implicitly) in some of the texts referenced at the end of this chapter.

For purposes of this chapter, it is sufficient to note that the various tacks can be diagrammed on a DR plot, which presents a "hemstitched" appearance as shown in Figure 5-3. This figure assumes that the desired track is exactly upwind

(e.g., overall course is 090 and the wind is from 090) and that the vessel does not sail any closer to the wind than 45 degrees. In this illustration each separate tack is identified with course, speed, and DR positions at the turn points. In this case, the DR positions on the hour and half hour coincide with the turn points. Additionally, DR positions should be plotted whenever a fix, running fix, or LOP is determined. If the tacks are short as would be the case, for example, in a narrow river, this detail is generally omitted and factored instead into a reduced speed through the water. But, if the tacks are of appreciable length, diagrams such as shown in Figure 5-3 should be used. In "blue water" or ocean sailing, depending upon the circumstances, individual tacks could be quite long, a matter of several hours or even days. In such cases it would be particularly important to plot these tacks as actually sailed. On courses that are generally downwind, the sailing vessel would be functionally equivalent to a power vessel, and so, too, would be the resulting DR plots.

It is important to note that, when a sailboat has to tack upwind, the actual distance sailed between any two points can be substantially greater than the rhumb line (straight line) distance. If a sailboat were forced to tack at an angle, theta, to the desired track line, the actual distance covered compared to rhumb line distance will be increased by a factor $1/\cos[\text{theta}]$. Thus, for example, if theta were 45 degrees--as it is in the illustration in Figure 5-3, the actual length of the "hemstitched" or "zig-zag" course through the water would be greater than the rhumb line distance by some 41%. Consequently, the speed made good (absent current or leeway) along the rhumb line would be only approximately 71% of the speed through the water. In fact, the actual situation is somewhat "worse" than the idealized diagram in Figure 5-3 would indicate. This is because the wind tends to blow the boat farther downwind of the course steered. The angle between the course steered and the course over the ground due solely to wind effects is termed "leeway" and can amount to 5 degrees

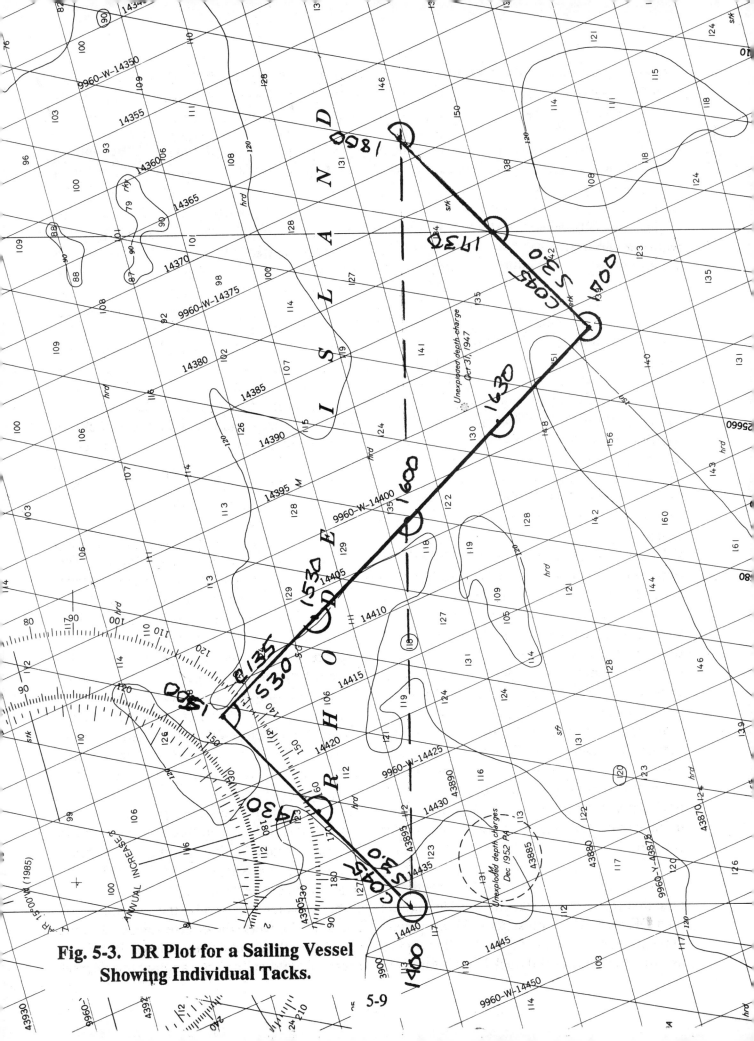

Fig. 5-3. DR Plot for a Sailing Vessel Showing Individual Tacks.

or more. (Leeway or current would not be shown on a DR plot but would affect the overall ground speed attained. Power vessels are also affected by leeway, which can be particularly important for slow-moving vessels with a large surface area above the water line. Consult the references at the end of this chapter for details.) Sailboats take longer to complete a voyage than power craft, not only because of their hull design and generally slower speeds through the water, but also because of the additional track length required for tacking upwind. Because the extra distance covered can be material in certain circumstances, it is necessary to go to the trouble of factoring tacks into the DR plot. Laying out the tacks is also important to ensure that the sailing vessel remains in safe waters. If there is not sufficient safe water (sea room) to accommodate these tacks the sailing vessel has little alternative but to await more favorable winds or turn on the "Iron Genoa" (engine).

Finally, winds are often quite variable and, therefore, the tacks may have to be adjusted from those originally planned. Consequently, the navigator aboard a sailing vessel may have to make frequent revisions to the DR plot to "stay with the vessel." Navigators aboard power vessels also have to adjust DR plots, but with less frequency. Little wonder then that sailboat navigators get to stay in practice!

DEAD RECKONING TERMS DEFINED AND ILLUSTRATED

There are several important terms used in the practice of dead reckoning. Their definitions are nearly universal among navigators and should be learned and understood. These terms are defined and explained below:

Course (C). Course is the average heading and the horizontal direction in which a vessel is intended to be steered, expressed as the angular distance relative to north, usually from 000° at north, clockwise through 359° from the point of departure or start of the course to the point of arrival or other point

of intended location. The reference direction is true and if so used, need not be labeled. However, some navigators find it more convenient to also use magnetic courses. These magnetic courses are labeled after the three digit direction with the letter "M."

Others have advocated going one step further and indicating compass courses, labeling them with the letter "C." This practice is to be discouraged, since a compass course depends upon the value for deviation on that heading. Deviation can and often does change with time as discussed in Chapter 2.

The result is that course lines left on charts for long periods of time may bear no relation to the correct value if they have been labeled as compass courses and the deviation has changed.

Course of Advance (COA). This indicates the direction of the *intended* path to be made good *over the ground.*

Course Over Ground (COG). This indicates the direction of the path actually followed by the vessel over the ground, usually an irregular line.

Course Made Good (CMG). This indicates the single resultant direction from a point of departure to a point of arrival at a given time. (Synonym, Track Made Good)

Current. The horizontal velocity (speed and direction) of water over ground. (See Chapter 7 for a more complete definition.)

Dead Reckoning (DR) Position. A position determined by dead reckoning.

Dead Reckoning Plot. A DR plot is the charted movement of a vessel as determined by dead reckoning.

Drift. The speed in knots at which the current is moving. Drift may also be indicated in statute miles per hour in some areas -- the Great Lakes for example. This term is also commonly used to mean the speed at which a vessel deviates from the course steered due to the combined effects of external forces such as wind and current.

Estimated Position (EP). An improved position based upon the DR position and which may include, among other things, factoring in the effects of wind and current, or a single line of position.

Line of Position (LOP). A line of bearing to a known origin or reference, upon which a vessel is assumed to be located (see Chapter 6, Line of Position). An LOP is determined by observation (visual bearing) or measurement (RDF, loran, radar, etc.). An LOP is assumed to be a straight line for visual bearings, or an arc of a circle (radar range), or part of some other curve such as hyperbola (loran). LOPs resulting from visual observations (magnetic bearings) should be converted to true bearings prior to plotting on a chart.

Fix. A known position determined by passing close aboard an object of known position or determined by the intersection of two or more lines of position (LOPs) adjusted to a common time, determined from terrestrial, electronic, and/or celestial data (see Chapter 6). The accuracy, or quality of a fix, is of great importance, especially in coastal waters, and is dependent on a number of factors.

LOPs must be based on known and/or identified sources. Buoys and other floating objects are not recommended for determination of fixes. (This is discussed in more detail elsewhere.) The angle between the intersecting LOPs is important. The ideal is 90°. If the angle is small, however, a slight error in

measuring or plotting will result in a relatively large error in the plotted position. LOPs from visual bearings to nearby objects are preferable to those obtained from objects at a distance.

The most accurate visual fix is obtained from three objects above the horizon 50° to 70° (or 110° to 130°) apart in azimuth. *A dead reckoning plot is always renewed at a fix or running fix.*

Heading (HDG). The instantaneous direction of a vessel's bow. It is expressed as the angular distance relative to north, usually 000° at north, clockwise through 359°. Heading should not be confused with course. Heading is a constantly changing value as a vessel yaws back and forth across the course due to the effects of sea, wind, and steering error. Heading is expressed in degrees of either true, magnetic, or compass direction.

Position. On the earth this refers to the actual geographic location of a vessel defined by two parameters called coordinates. Those customarily used are latitude and longitude. Position may also be expressed as a bearing and distance *from* an object the position of which is known.

Running Fix (RFIX). A fix obtained by means of LOPs taken at different times and adjusted to a common time. This practice involves advancing or retiring LOPs as discussed in Chapter 6.

Set. The direction *towards* which the current is flowing. This term is also commonly used to mean the direction towards which a vessel is being deviated from an intended course by the combined effects of external force such as wind and current.

Speed (S). The rate at which a vessel advances relative to the water over a horizontal distance. When expressed in terms of nautical miles per hour, it is referred to as knots (kn or kt). One knot equals approximately 1.15 statute miles per hour.

Speed Made Good (SMG). Indicates the overall speed actually accomplished relative to the ground along the course line.

Speed of Advance (SOA). Indicates the speed intended to be made relative to the ground along the track line.

Speed Through the Water (STW). The apparent speed indicated by log-type instruments or determined by use of tachometer and speed curve or table, at a particular point in time, along the course line.

Speed Over Ground (SOG). The actual speed made good at any instant in time along the course being steered.

Track (TR). The intended or desired horizontal direction of travel *with respect to the ground.* (Synonym, Intended Track, Trackline)

SUBTLETIES IN THE DEFINITIONS LISTED ABOVE

On quick reading, many of the terms listed above may appear quite similar--and, indeed, some are nearly identical. But, there are some subtle differences that are drawn. This section explores some of the similarities and differences among the above terms.

The basis for distinction among some of these terms relates to the *difference between average and instantaneous values.* For example, course relates to the average direction of travel. A helmsman may attempt to maintain a course of 090 degrees, but for a variety of reasons (e.g., motion of the sea, collision avoidance, etc.) the *heading* of the vessel might vary from 080 to 100 degrees. The course steered may average 090, but at a given instant in time the heading might be 097. The average of the heading values will equal the course steered, however. The reader

may be puzzled by the subtlety: is this a distinction without difference? Emphatically not! The course (090 in this illustration) is the appropriate variable to be plotted on the DR plot. But, suppose a relative bearing of an ATON were observed to be 045 degrees while the vessel was heading 097. You would want to add the vessel's magnetic heading (not the course) to the relative bearing to calculate a magnetic bearing (142 degrees in this example assuming no deviation). When taking such a bearing and calling "mark" to the helm, you want the helmsman to answer 097 (the heading), not 090 (the course) -- hence the need to distinguish between these concepts. Not all such distinctions are equally meaningful, however. The distinction between speed (average speed) and speed through the water (instantaneous speed) is less important for most applications and, therefore, these terms are used interchangeably in this text. Strictly speaking it is speed, rather than STW that should be shown on the DR plots, but this distinction is academic.

The basis for distinction between other concepts defined above is the *plane of reference.* Course, for example, is defined relative to the average heading. But, CMG refers to the average progress relative to the ground or earth. Likewise, speed is defined relative to the water, whereas SMG is relative to the ground. You steer a course and maintain a speed, but these are elements of *relative motion.* The CMG and SMG refer to the vessel's *actual progress relative to the earth* and hence refer to what is termed *true motion.* (The difference between these two concepts is accounted for by current--the horizontal flow of water relative to the earth as is discussed in Chapter 7 on current sailing.) As with CMG and SMG, COG and SOG are defined relative to the ground, but COG and SOG relate to the actual (often irregular) path of the vessel's progress with respect to the earth while CMG and SMG relate to the average course and speed traveled with respect to the earth. As a practical matter, COG and SOG are relatively unimportant--CMG and SMG are the key terms here.

The basis for distinction between yet other similar terms defined above refers to the distinction between *anticipated or planned events and actual events*. The terms track and COA are synonymous and refer to the planned route for the vessel with respect to the ground. So, too, does CMG, but the distinction between these terms is that COA is an *intended* path, whereas CMG is what has *actually* occurred. Thus, on the basis of forecast or estimated currents, a course may be set in order to achieve a certain track or COA, but the net result with the actual currents is the CMG. If the forecast or estimate was accurate, then the COA and CMG will be virtually identical. Otherwise these will be different, and the difference is meaningful. Similarly, the SOA is the intended or estimated speed along the track with respect to the ground, but the SMG is the actual "ground" speed after the fact.

In subsequent chapters the meaning and use of these terms will become more familiar. For purposes of this chapter, the key terms needed are speed, course, DR position, LOP, and fix or departure.

ACCURACY OF DR PLOTS

Students frequently ask about the accuracy of DR plots, so it is appropriate to address this topic. Unfortunately, there are no "hard and fast" rules or even useful "rules of thumb" for determining the accuracy of a DR position. In broad terms, the factors contributing to error in DR positions include all the elements of current (see Chapter 7) such as current, leeway, helmsman's errors, etc. More to the point, it is only the effects of these factors over the time period since the vessel's last known position that are relevant. Therefore, to a large degree, the navigator can control the accuracy of the DR positions by taking more frequent fixes. Other factors being equal, the accuracy of DR positions will be twice as good if fixes are taken every 30 minutes than if these are taken hourly. Fixes should not be viewed as "happenstance" or chance occurrences, but rather should be deliberately planned for in any voyage considering the loca-

tion of ATONs, other suitable charted features, and available navigation equipment on board the vessel (e.g., RDF, loran, radar). When you examine a chart and lay out a course to your destination, get in the habit of preplanning fix opportunities. Indeed, the availability of suitable fix opportunities should be one of the important factors in route selection. This subject is developed more thoroughly in Chapter 6.

DR position accuracy is also related to the care taken by the navigator in the preparation of the DR plot and the helmsman's skill and interest in maintaining the assigned course. In the age of electronics, where a fix can be taken with no more effort than reading a loran display, there is a temptation to pay less attention to more traditional methods of navigation. Over-reliance on automated systems should be avoided, however. It deprives the navigator of the opportunity to maintain necessary skills, and as any boater should know, automated systems can fail. Columbus could certainly have benefited from loran, SATNAV (a satellite based navigation system), and radar. But, odds are he would have been a better navigator than most of us equipped with the same tools because he knew well how to live without these advances.

SUMMARY OF THE "RULES" CONSTRUCTION OF DR PLOTS

At this point it is appropriate to summarize some of the key conventions in the preparation of DR plots.

First, with respect to symbols:

1. The circle with a dot inside is used to denote a known position--either departure, a fix, or running fix. (An additional symbol and supplemental fix conventions are introduced in the next chapter.) All DR plots begin with this symbol. The time (4 digits and 24-hour time) is written next to the known position, preferably parallel to one of the chart axes.
2. Courses are drawn with a solid line. The course steered is written above the line be-

ginning with a capital "C" and followed by the true course (in degrees to three digits without the degree symbol). If a magnetic course is written the letter "M" should follow. Refrain from writing compass courses on the chart, although these should be noted in the ship's log.

3. The speed or speed through the water (STW) should be written beneath the course line beginning with a capital "S" and the speed to one decimal place if known.

4. DR positions are denoted with a semicircle (or partial circle) with a dot inside, and the time (4 digits and 24-hour time) noted at an angle to the course line written nearby.

Second, with respect to plotting conventions:

1. DR positions are to be based solely on the course steered and STW using time--speed--distance calculations (see below), and not upon any allowance for current or leeway.

2. DR positions should be plotted at appropri-ate time intervals (generally every hour or every half hour on the hour and half hour).

3. DR positions should also be plotted when-ever a fix, running fix, or LOP is determined.

4. DR positions should also be plotted when-ever a course or speed change takes place. In the event that numerous course or speed al-terations, fixes, or LOPs are performed, the hourly or half-hourly DR positions may be omitted for clarity.

5. A new DR plot should be started whenever a fix or running fix is obtained.

Third, and more generally:

1. Make every effort to produce a neat, unclut-tered, and easy-to-understand plot. Meas-ure courses and distances carefully.

2. Keep the plot up-to-date by recording and annotating fixes and LOPs, etc., as these are taken. Note relevant data and appropriate remarks in a log as well as maintaining the plot on the nautical chart.

RULES FOR DR PLOT

☑ DR BASED ONLY ON COURSE AND STW

☑ DR POSITIONS PLOTTED AT CONVENIENT TIME INTERVALS, E.G., EVERY 30 OR 60 MIN.

☑ DR POSITIONS PLOTTED WHENEVER A FIX, RUNNING FIX, OR LOP IS DETERMINED

☑ DR POSITION PLOTTED WHENEVER A COURSE OR SPEED CHANGE OCCURS

☑ A NEW DR PLOT SHOULD BE STARTED WHENEVER A FIX OR RUNNING FIX IS OBTAINED

REPRISE: VOYAGE PLANS AND TACTICAL DR PLOTS

Earlier it was noted that DR plots were prepared both for planning purposes (the voyage plan) and to keep track of the vessel's actual progress (the tactical DR plot). Now that the details of DR plots have been covered, it is appropriate to discuss these plots and their purposes again.

The voyage plan is prepared prior to leaving the dock. It is a complete DR plot, covering the entire length of the planned voyage, prepared in sufficient detail to ensure that enough fuel is carried, enroute and arrival time estimates are approximately correct, a safe routing is chosen, and other planning objectives are satisfied. But, because no fixes or lines of position are available at the time that this DR voyage plan is prepared, this plot contains only DR positions (not fixes or lines of position), courses, and other annotations deemed suitable by the navigator. Both times and positions shown on this DR plot may later turn out to be in error. In particular, because the starting time is often uncertain, the navigator may find it more convenient to represent time as elapsed time (e.g., hours and minutes after trip start), rather than clock time.

The tactical DR plot is prepared "as you go" and reflects the actual starting time, actual fixes when determined, and the vessel's actual (as opposed to planned) progress. The tactical DR plot is updated and started again after each fix and shows DR positions at fixes and whenever an LOP is determined. On a voyage with many "legs" where numerous course or speed changes are planned, it is generally not convenient to replot the entire subsequent voyage on the tactical plot whenever a fix is determined, because the nautical chart could become impossibly cluttered. (Moreover, much of this work may be wasted, because additional fixes require renewing the tactical DR plot.) Therefore, the navigator usually plots only the next (few) DR position(s) in sequence on the tactical plot. In short, the navigator uses the tactical DR plot simply to monitor progress and "stay ahead of the vessel." The original DR voyage plan serves as a reference plot if needed. Of course, if the tactical DR plot shows the vessel to be "impossibly" behind schedule or out of position, it may be necessary to rethink and revise the entire plan in the light of these developments. For example, the fuel calculations in the voyage plan may be predicated on the assumption of "catching" an incoming tide (which will stretch the available fuel as discussed in Chapter 11), whereas the actual progress may mean that adverse currents will be encountered. In this situation, it may be wise to redo the fuel budget to ensure that sufficient fuel remains and, if necessary, divert to alternates to take on additional fuel. Alternatively, courses may have to be recalculated (see Chapter 7) if currents turn out different than anticipated.

It is a matter of judgment and individual choice how these plots are prepared and used. Some navigators lay out the original voyage plan on the chart and maintain the tactical plot on a transparent overlay. Others may use separate charts for this purpose (a slightly expensive option). Yet others use plotting sheets (available in blank pads with only latitude and longitude shown). Finally, some navigators "rough out" the voyage plan on a series of worksheets and draw the tactical DR plot only on the nautical chart (this practice requires that there is sufficient space on the vessel for plotting). With experience, a satisfactory method can be chosen.

TIME, SPEED, AND DISTANCE

Dead reckoning is accomplished by calculating distance (D) run, or to be run, speed (S) of the vessel, and time (T) of the run. Distance is measured to the nearest tenth of a nautical mile, speed to the nearest tenth of a knot, and time to the nearest minute. If any two of these three quantities are known, the third can easily be computed using the three forms of the basic time - speed - distance formula shown below:

$$D = \frac{S \times T}{60}, \qquad \text{written } D = ST/60$$

Where:
- D = Distance, nautical miles
- S = Speed, kn
- T = Time, minutes

or

$$S = \frac{60 \times D}{T}, \qquad \text{written } S = 60\,D/T$$

or

$$T = \frac{60 \times D}{S}, \qquad \text{written } T = 60\,D/S$$

It is important to note that the time used in the above equations is the time of the run, or the interval of time between two DR positions. Since DR positions are to be labeled with their appropriate time, the interval is easy to determine. As noted above, time is indicated in the twenty-four hour system, where 1:00 PM, for example, is 1300. To determine the interval between two times, simply subtract the smaller time from the larger, by hours and minutes.

Remember, however, that there are 60 (and not 100) minutes in each hour. If you do not have enough minutes from which to subtract, "borrow" 1 hour or 60 minutes. If you cross into another day, and pass 2359, reverting back to 0000, then borrow 24 hours from that day, and add them to the old day to make the calculation. Examples of time--speed--distance (TSD) calculations are provided below to illustrate the process of computation and determination of the proper time interval.

Example #1. Solving for distance when speed and time are known: Suppose you are running at 10 knots, how far will you travel in 20 minutes?

1. Since speed and time are known, the formula to use is: $D = ST/60$

2. Insert the values for S, speed = 10 knots, T, Time = 20 minutes: $D = (10)(20)/60$

3. Carry out the arithmetic:
   $D = 200/60 = 3.3$ nautical miles

Example #2. You can make it from your station to the shipping channel in 3 hours and 45 minutes if you maintain a speed of 10 knots. What is the distance to the shipping channel?

1. You must use minutes to solve the TSD formula. Convert the 3 hours to minutes. To do this, multiply 3 hours by 60 (60 minutes in an hour), which is 180 minutes, and then add 45 minutes. Time (T) is 225 minutes.

2. Write down the appropriate formula:
   $D = ST/60$

3. Compute using information you have for the appropriate letter:
   $D = (10 \text{ kn})(225 \text{ minutes})/60$
   $D = 2250/60 = 37.5$ M (nearest tenth)

Example #3. Solving for speed when time and distance are known. Assume that it took you 40 minutes to travel 12 miles, what is your speed?

1. Since distance and time values for D, Distance = 12 miles, T, Time = 40 minutes: $S = (60)(12)/40$

2. Carry out the arithmetic:
   $S = 720/40 = 18.0$ knots

Example #4. A second problem solving for speed when distance is known and time can be calculated: Your departure time is 2030. The distance to your destination is 30 miles. You want to arrive at 0000 (2400). Obtain the speed you must maintain.

1. Find the time interval between 2030 and "2400" (2400 will not be displayed on a 24-hour clock. Nonetheless, 0000 is logically equivalent to 2400). To do this subtract 2030 from 2400. Remember you are subtracting "hours" and "minutes." Determine the time interval as follows (note that 23 hours and 60 minutes is equivalent to 24 hours and 00 minutes).

hr	min	hr	min
24	00	23	60
hr	min	hr	min
-20	30	-20	30

| | | 3hr | 30 min |

2. Remember you use minutes to solve the TSD equation. Convert the 3 hours to minutes. To do this, multiply 3 hours by 60 (60 minutes in an hour), which is 180 minutes. Add the 30 minutes remaining from Step 1. Time (T) = 210 minutes.

3. Write down the appropriate formula.
   $S = 60D / T$

4. Compute using information you have for appropriate letter.
   $S = (60) (30 \text{ miles}) / 210 \text{ minutes}$

5. $S = 1800 / 210 = 8.6$ knots (as rounded to the nearest tenth)

Example #5. Solving for time when speed and distance are known: You are cruising at 15 knots and have 12 miles to cover before arriving on station. How long will it take before you arrive at your destination?

1. Since distance and speed are known, use this formula:
   $T = 60 D/S$
   $D = 12 \text{ miles}$
   $S = 15 \text{ knots}$

2. Substitute appropriate values for D, Distance = 12 miles, S, Speed = 15 knots:
   $T = (60) (12) / 15$

3. Carry out the arithmetic:
   $T = 48 \text{ minutes}$

SPEED CURVE

In order to be able to do TSD calculations, it is necessary to be able to have an accurate value for speed. Even if the small craft is equipped with a log of some kind to provide speed indication directly, this device must be calibrated against known speeds to determine any deviation of the indicated speed from actual speed. For boats equipped only with engine speed indicators (tachometers) some means must be provided to convert engine RPM (revolutions per minute) into speed through water. The mechanism used to accomplish calibration of speed logs or tachometers in terms of actual speed through the water is the development of the speed curve, a graphic plot of observed speed versus RPM.

The procedure is simple. A measured distance (often, but not necessarily, one nautical mile) is run at various engine speeds (RPM), in both directions over a set course, and the speeds measured (calculated from the TSD formula). Ideally the speed curve is developed on a day when the wind is calm to eliminate wind effects.

The purpose of running the course in both directions is to average out the effects of any current to produce an estimate of the vessel's speed through the water. A plot is made of RPM, usually in increments of 250 RPM, 500 RPM (or other convenient interval) over the range of available engine speeds, against the average measured speed. The resulting curve can be used to predict the resulting speed for any RPM, or the appropriate RPM for any desired speed. As a by-product for planing boats, the planing point is clearly evident, and the most economical speeds are quickly indicated. This subject is explored in Chapter 11.

It is important to realize, however, that such a speed curve is valid only for the conditions as tested. If the hull is degraded by additional drag from marine encrustations, for example, the speed curve applying to the clean hull is invalid, and the hull must be restored to initial conditions or a new curve must be developed for the new conditions. For smaller craft, which are sensitive to load, it may be necessary to develop separate speed curves for different load conditions (e.g., fuel carried and crew aboard).

TABLE 5-3. ILLUSTRATIVE SPEED TABLE.

COURSE DESCRIPTION:_____

COURSE LENGTH: 1.00 NAUTICAL MILES

DATE:
VESSEL:
HULL CONDITION:
FUEL QTY:
WATER QTY:
NUMBER CREW:

| RPM | "OUT" LEG | | | "BACK" LEG | | | AVERAGE SPEED (KNOTS) | CALCULATED CURRENT (KNOTS) |
	MIN	SEC	CALCULATED SPEED (KNOTS)	MIN	SEC	CALCULATED SPEED (KNOTS)		
250	22	24	2.7	19	35	3.1	2.9	0.2
500	20	30	2.9	17	55	3.3	3.1	0.2
750	18	6	3.3	15	48	3.8	3.6	0.2
1000	15	15	3.9	13	15	4.5	4.2	0.3
1250	12	15	4.9	10	35	5.7	5.3	0.4
1500	9	45	6.2	8	20	7.2	6.7	0.5
1750	7	49	7.7	6	45	8.9	8.3	0.6
2000	6	23	9.4	5	35	10.7	10.1	0.7
2250	5	14	11.5	4	44	12.7	12.1	0.6
2500	4	1	14.9	3	45	16.0	15.5	0.5
2750	3	23	17.7	3	13	18.7	18.2	0.5
3000	3	23	17.7	3	12	18.8	18.2	0.5

NOTE THAT SPEEDS, AND NOT TIMES, ARE AVERAGED. SPEEDS ARE AVERAGED TO THE NEAREST 0.1 KNOT. CURRENTS ARE CALCULATED AS WELL, NOT FOR SPEED CALCULATION PURPOSES BUT RATHER TO ENSURE THAT THE COMPUTATIONS ARE PLAUSIBLE. NOTE HERE THAT ESTIMATED CURRENTS FIRST INCREASE, THEN DECREASE SLIGHTLY, AS MIGHT BE EXPECTED WITH A TIDAL CURRENT.

The speed curve is developed as follows:

1. A measured mile or other measured course is located on the chart or laid out on the shore so that it is visible in an area safe enough for conducting speed trials. Usually, each end of the speed course is denoted by visible range markers, for example, diamond shapes at one end, and squares or circles at the other. These ranges form perpendiculars to the measured distance course to be run. Alternatively, natural ranges, ATONs, etc., can be used, but the distance between these must be measured on the chart.

2. A table is made up prior to conducting any speed runs. The table consists of several columns: RPM, time of run in initial direction, calculated speed in initial direction, time of run in reciprocal direction (in min-

utes, or minutes and seconds), calculated speed in reciprocal direction, and the average of the two speeds. For this discussion, rows are indicated for increments of 250 RPM engine speed from 250 RPM up to the maximum permissible engine RPM. The rest of the columns will be filled in during the speed trial.

3. The speed trial is conducted. The boat is taken out to the course, which is determined from the chart, and the direction converted from true to compass for the initial course and from true to compass for the reciprocal course. (Note that each course is developed individually. Remember, the deviation depends on the compass or magnetic heading, and reciprocal headings do not necessarily have the same deviation!)

When the boat is approaching the speed course, it is brought up to the RPM desired, and turned on to the course. A stop watch or chronograph is started when the vessel at speed crosses the first range and continued until the vessel crosses the second range, when it is stopped. The time is noted on the table, the resulting speed calculated, and the reciprocal course is then run. (If seconds are recorded, these must be converted to decimal minutes by dividing by 60 and adding this fraction to the minutes.) Again, the watch is started upon crossing the range and stopped when crossing the next range. The time is again noted, and the resulting speed calculated and entered into the table. The two speeds are averaged and the resulting value entered into the last column in the table. Speed runs are done in each direction to

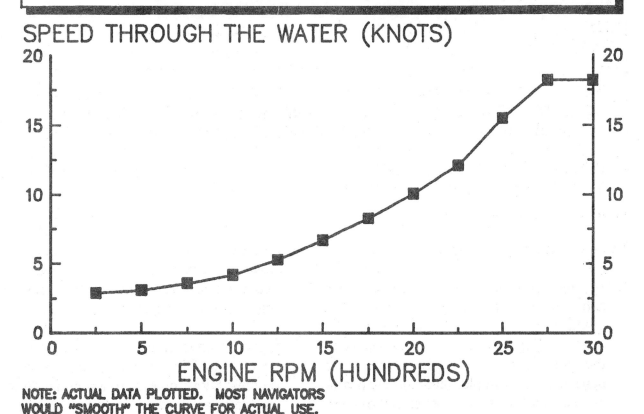

FIGURE 5-4. ILLUSTRATIVE SPEED CURVE BASED ON DATA TAKEN FROM TABLE 5-3.

SPEED THROUGH THE WATER (KNOTS)

ENGINE RPM (HUNDREDS)

NOTE: ACTUAL DATA PLOTTED. MOST NAVIGATORS WOULD "SMOOTH" THE CURVE FOR ACTUAL USE.

account for the effects of any current. Thus, you end up with a so-called "out" and a "back" leg (terms such as "upwind" or "downwind" are sometimes used). *The speeds for each leg are calculated and these speeds averaged. Do not average times and then calculate a single speed.* As a plausibility check on the speed curve, compare the calculated current with the estimated current using the methods of Chapter 8.

4. The process is continued for each value of RPM desired, until the table is completely filled out (see Table 5-3).

5. The speed curve is then developed. A graph is drawn in an X-Y coordinate system (see Figure 5-4). The X, or horizontal axis, is calibrated for RPM, and the Y, or vertical axis, is calibrated for speed in knots. The values of RPM and Speed are plotted for each pair of RPM/Speed values in the table. Any symbol can be used for the plot. A "smooth" curve may be developed (possibly by "eye") through the data points, to refine the estimates, but this is omitted here. Either the graph or the table may be used, subsequently, to determine the speed which would result for a specific RPM or the RPM which must be made to accomplish a specific speed. Note that the speed indicated from the curve is speed through the water (STW), not speed over the ground. This speed can be used in the TSD calculations to develop your DR plots.

If your vessel is equipped with loran, many of the above steps can be simplified. All (or nearly all) lorans in production today have an option of reading speed over the ground (SOG) directly. All that is necessary is to run the out and back legs as discussed above and read the SOG or SMG directly from the loran display. The out and back leg speeds are averaged as discussed in step 3, above. However, care must be used to ensure that the correct speed is taken from the loran. (Most lorans have the capability to display several speeds including, for example, SOG, SMG, velocity towards destination, and velocity along route. SOG comes the closest to that required for development of a speed curve.) Additionally, depending on the loran's quality and such technical features as the averaging time for calculation of SOG, the loran's estimate may be less precise than if the "timed speed run" method discussed above is employed. Some navigators do not recommend use of loran for this reason.

REFERENCES

Anderson, J. *Exercises in Pilotage,* David & Charles, London, England, 1987.

Bowditch, N. *American Practical Navigator, An Epitome of Navigation,* Vol. 1, Defense Mapping Agency, Washington, DC, 1984.

Collinder, Per. *A History of Marine Navigation,* St. Martin's Press Inc., New York, NY, 1955, pp. 122, *et seq.*

Gotelle, P. *The Design of Sailing Yachts,* International Marine Publishing Co., Camden, ME, 1979.

Henderson, R. *The Racing Cruiser,* Reilly and Lee Books, Chicago, IL, 1970.

Hobbs, R. R. *Marine Navigation 1, Piloting,* Second edition, Naval Institute Press, Annapolis, MD, 1974.

Johnson, P. *Ocean Racing and Offshore Yachts,* Second edition, Dodd Mead & Co., New York, NY, 1972.

Kane, G. R. *Instant Navigation,* Second edition, Associated Marine, San Mateo, CA, 1984.

Maloney, E. S. *Dutton's Navigation and Piloting,* 14th edition, Naval Institute Press, Annapolis, MD, 1985.

Marchaj, C. A. *Aero-Hydrodynamics of Sailing,* Revised and Expanded Edition, International Marine Publishing Co., Camden, ME, 1988.

Marden, Luis. "The First Landfall of Columbus," *National Geographic,* Vol. 170, No. 5, November, 1986, pp. 572, *et seq.*

Mixter, G. W. (edited by D. McClench) *Primer of Navigation,* Fifth edition, Van Nostrand Reinhold Company, New York, NY, 1967.

Pocock, M., *Inshore-Offshore, Racing, Cruising, and Design,* Nautical Books, London, England, 1986.

Saunders, A. E. *Small Craft Piloting and Coastal Navigation,* Alzarc Enterprises, Scarborough, Ontario, Canada, 1987.

Shufeldt, H. H., and G. D. Dunlap. *Piloting and Dead Reckoning,* Second edition, Naval Institute Press, Annapolis, MD, 1981.

Toghill, J. *The Yachtsman's Navigation Manual,* John de Graff, Clinton Corners, NY, 1975.

U.S. Power Squadron. "Director's Staff Memorandum No. 8C," January, 1987.

Waters, D. W., *The Art of Navigation in England in Elizabethan and Early Stuart Times,* Yale University Press, New Haven, CT, 1958.

Chapter 6

Piloting

This chapter follows directly the discussion of dead reckoning and amplifies and expands upon the material presented in Chapter 5. As noted, DR is used to project the position of the vessel at some future time using information on the course steered and speed maintained. If the helmsman steers a straight and accurate course and maintains a constant speed, and water current and/or wind can be neglected, the DR position will be quite accurate. However, these ideal conditions seldom prevail exactly and DR positions need to be checked for accuracy and updated as necessary. In principle, these accuracy checks can be made by several means, such as by visual reference to charted objects (termed *piloting*), electronic measurements (termed *electronic navigation*), and by reference to celestial bodies (termed *celestial navigation*). In coastal (sometimes termed *pilot*) waters, visual reference to charted features (both natural and man-made) is convenient and commonly used. The essence of piloting is to continually check, refine, and update DR positions by visual means, to determine a sequence of fixes and to calculate such revisions to the vessel's course or speed as are necessary to complete the voyage in a safe and efficient manner.

The principal objective of this chapter is to show how positions can be determined by visual reference to charted objects. However, material on position fixing by electronic means is also introduced in this chapter to familiarize the reader with the relevant nomenclature, notation, and procedures. Additional information is provided in Chapter 9.

Because fixes are presumed to be more accurate than DR positions, students often ask why mariners take the trouble to maintain DR plots. This question was addressed implicitly in Chapter 5, but it is worthwhile to restate the answer here. There are basically two important reasons why DR plots are necessary. *First, a fix, no matter how accurate, is simply a determination of a vessel's position at an instant in time.* By itself, a fix cannot be used to determine or estimate a vessel's future position--as is done by DR. *Second,* although it is recommended that a vessel's position be fixed frequently--particularly in pilot waters where it is necessary to ensure that the vessel does not stray into danger--*opportunities for fixes may be limited.* Fog or other weather phenomena that cause poor visibility may prevent frequent fixes, for example. Additionally, in certain parts of the country the shoreline may be nearly featureless and aids to navigation (ATONs or NAVAIDS) few and far between. In such circumstances DR positions may be all that are available. Therefore, even though DR positions may be inaccurate and should be checked at suitable intervals, the preparation of DR plots is essential to prudent navigation.

For the most part, the material in this chapter is not difficult, either in principle or in practice. Nonetheless, accident statistics on Search and Rescue (SAR) cases from the Coast Guard indicate that many distressed mariners do not know their position with any accuracy. Inaccurate or incomplete position information not only contributes to accidents (e.g., groundings and running out of fuel) but also delays rescue, because Search and Rescue Units (SRUs) must waste time searching for the scene of distress. Therefore, it is particularly important that this material be mastered.

Aside from the obvious safety element, there are many other benefits to being able to determine position rapidly and accurately. In general, these relate to the comfort and efficiency of the voyage. A captain who knows his/her position at all times is a more confident captain, and so are any guests aboard. The determination that the vessel is not on the preplanned track means that corrective action can be initiated promptly and voyage length and fuel consumption can be reduced.

For all these reasons the material covered in Chapters 5 and 6 is essential for every mariner and, in a very real sense, constitutes the core of the ACN course. Take the time to read and reread these chapters thoroughly and to work out the problems in the Student Study Guide.

PILOTING DEFINED

Piloting is navigation involving frequent or continuous reference to charted landmarks, ATONs, and depth soundings. It is, in essence, a frequent or continuous comparison of the physical features of the earth's surface (including man-made features) and their relationships to those same features as these are indicated on the chart to reconstruct the same relationships of direction, angular differences, and distances to establish the position of the vessel.

The charted features include those of natural origin, such as promontories, hill and mountain tops, and fixed, man-made objects such as towers of various types, buildings, smoke stacks, cooling towers, lighthouses, and other structures. Also included in these fixed features would be "invisible" aids to navigation such as active radio beacons (RBn.), radio direction finding stations, and loran chains, as well as passive radar reflectors (Ra Ref.). Properly speaking, the use of radio beacons and the like falls in the category of

electronic navigation, but is discussed here as well as in Chapter 9.

Buoys and other floating, nonfixed aids to navigation are also used in piloting, but the navigator should treat these aids with some caution since they are susceptible to accidental damage (sinking) or relocation (dragging) and cannot be guaranteed to be on station at all times.

Piloting is an important part of small craft navigation and demands the constant attention of the navigator, who should be continuously analyzing the present to plan for the future, and who should use every means available to ascertain hazards to navigation and to locate the vessel's position both accurately and often to avoid danger and arrive safely at the intended destination.

THE LINE OF POSITION (LOP)

A *line of position* (LOP) is a line established by observation or measurement on which a vessel can be expected to be located. A vessel can be at an infinite number of positions along any single LOP. In piloting an LOP may be established by a measured bearing to a known and charted object, or by an alignment of two visible and charted objects, or by a measured distance from a charted object. In the case of bearings, LOPs are straight lines. In the case of distances, LOPs are circles, and sometimes referred to as circles of position (COP). LOPs are used in this text to refer to both. These methods for determination of LOPs are discussed below. LOPs can also be determined by electronic means, such as radar, loran, and RDF.

LOP BY BEARING FROM CHARTED OBJECT

One of the simplest and most common LOPs is developed from a single bearing on a charted object. The bearing can be taken using a pelorus (see Chapter 2), or a hand-bearing compass, or by orienting the boat so that the resulting relative bearing is dead ahead (000R), abeam (090R or 270R) or astern (180R). Bearings so deter-

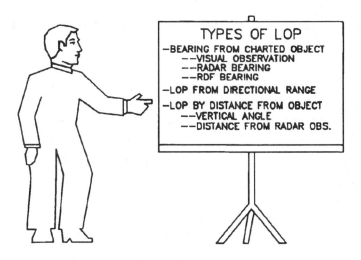

TYPES OF LOP
-BEARING FROM CHARTED OBJECT
  --VISUAL OBSERVATION
  --RADAR BEARING
  --RDF BEARING
-LOP FROM DIRECTIONAL RANGE
-LOP BY DISTANCE FROM OBJECT
  --VERTICAL ANGLE
  --DISTANCE FROM RADAR OBS.

mined could be compass bearings if the ship's compass is used, magnetic bearings if a hand-bearing compass is used from a location where it is free of deviation, or relative bearings if a pelorus is used. If a relative bearing is taken, it must be converted to a true bearing by first determining the compass heading at the instant of the relative bearing observation, correcting this compass heading to a magnetic heading by applying deviation and then to a true heading by allowing for variation as discussed in Chapter 2. The relative bearing is then added to the vessel's true heading to determine the true bearing of the object.

The true bearing is plotted on the chart to the object as a solid line. (To distinguish the LOP from the course line, it is recommended that LOPs be drawn lightly and course lines more heavily.) However, it is not necessary to draw the entire line from the charted object to the probable location of the vessel. Drawing a segment within the area of the expected position of the vessel is sufficient and saves having to make chart erasures if the chart is to be reused. The vessel is somewhere on the LOP. This line of position is labeled on its top with the time of the observation (using four digits in the 24-hour system) and may be labeled on the bottom with the *true* bearing *from the vessel to the object*. The process is illustrated in Figure 6-1.

1. The vessel is steering a course of 264° true, speed 4.0 knots. The Point Judith Light is

visible off to starboard. It is clearly visible from the vessel and is easily identified on the chart by its characteristics (magenta overlaying a dot within a circle, and the legend: Gp (Occ (1+2) 15 sec 65 ft 16 M). At 1015 the vessel is on a compass heading of 274C, when the lighthouse is observed with a pelorus (see Chapter 2) bearing 073R (73° to starboard of the bow). The heading, relative bearing, and the time are recorded in the vessel's log: time, 1015; heading, 274C; relative bearing, 073R. The navigator corrects the compass heading to a true heading (TH) using the deviation for that compass heading observed from the deviation table or deviation curve (assume that the compass deviation is 5° E on a heading of 274C), and applies the local variation (assume that the variation is 15°W) using the method discussed in Chapter 2:

DIRECTION	HEADING	MEMORY AID
Compass	274C	CAN
Deviation	+ 005E	DEAD
Magnetic	279M	MEN
Variation	- 015W	VOTE
True	264T	TWICE
	AT ELECTIONS?	

2. The true bearing (TB) of the object from the boat is then determined by adding the relative bearing (RB) (073R) to the true heading (TH) (264):

**TRUE BEARING OF OBJECT
FROM VESSEL:**

TH + RB = TB
264 + 073 R =   337

3. The line of position is plotted from the lighthouse on a bearing of 337, and labeled with the time of observation (1015) on top and the true bearing *from the vessel to the object* (337) underneath the line. The vessel is assumed to be located somewhere on that line. Conventional practice would be to plot a 1015 DR position whenever an LOP is determined.

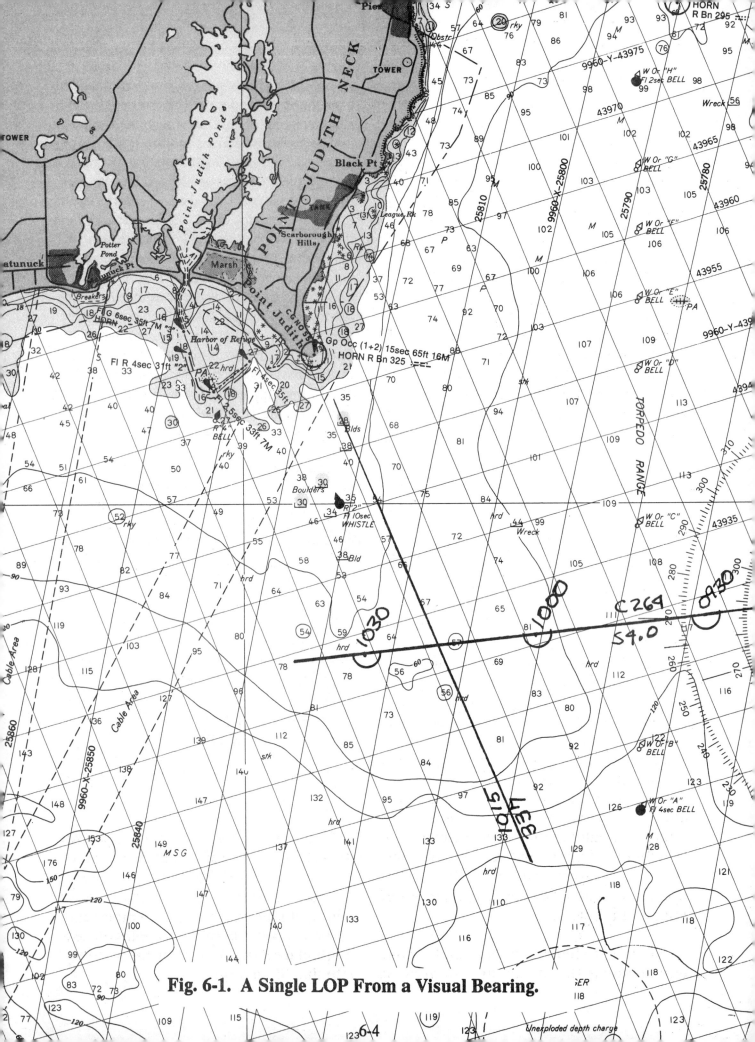

Fig. 6-1. A Single LOP From a Visual Bearing.

Therefore, a 1015 DR position should also be plotted in Figure 6-1.

ACCURACY OF LOPs

It is customary to regard visual LOPs as being highly accurate--that is, to assume that the vessel's position must be located exactly along a LOP. This convention is followed here. But, it is important for the mariner to be aware that the possibility of error always exists in the determination of LOPs. An LOP determined by conversion of a relative bearing, for example, is subject to several errors. The error in the measurement of the relative bearing itself could easily be of the order of 1 or 2 degrees, even if a pelorus is used. The relative bearing is added to the ship's heading to determine a true bearing (after conversion of the heading from compass to true). The ship's heading is not known with certainty, and errors of 2 degrees or so would not be regarded as uncommon. (All the more so if the navigator and the helmsman are the same person!) The conversion process from relative to true bearings, even though it is only a simple matter of addition and/or subtraction, introduces the possibility of additional errors. Leaving aside outright blunders, such as applying the deviation appropriate to the relative *bearing* rather than the ship's *heading* or errors in addition, the vessel's compass is not perfectly accurate (particularly if the sea is other than flat calm) and the deviation table is only approximate. Thus, bearing errors of 2 or 3 degrees would not be thought of as unusual--even more if the seas do not cooperate. Finally, the LOP needs to be plotted on a chart for position determination. Plotting errors of 1 degree or more can occur, so the maximum possible error in a vessel LOP as plotted could easily be at least 3 or 4 degrees. Many of these errors are random, rather than systematic, and would tend to "cancel out." Although the probable error is less than the maximum possible error, it is a mistake to believe that the overall error is negligible.

For these and other reasons, visual LOPs are only approximate, perhaps no more accurate than to within plus or minus 3 degrees on a small vessel. Electronic LOPs developed by radar and radio direction finders (RDF) are also subject to bearing error, a subject discussed more fully in Chapter 9. To avoid chart clutter, it is generally appropriate to use the best estimate of the LOP and plot this alone rather than attempt to calculate possible error limits (confidence intervals) and plot these on the chart. None the less, it is important to keep these errors in mind and to take steps to minimize them by careful measurement and judicious selection of objects for observation. Additionally, it is important to recognize and allow for these errors in voyage planning. For example, courses should not be laid out so as to pass close to hazards to navigation unless otherwise unavoidable. Rather, an ample safety factor should be incorporated to ensure that the vessel remains in safe water.

LOP BY DIRECTIONAL RANGE

A *directional range* consists of two objects in line, one behind the other, and defines a unique direction and a *range line* (the line drawn through the two objects). (British nomenclature for a range is a *transit*.) Ranges can provide highly accurate visual LOPs and can be used in compass calibration as discussed in Chapter 2. They are also helpful in steering difficult channel approaches. The objects may be man-made, e.g., range markers for a channel, a steeple, and a tank, etc., or natural, e.g., two tangents of land (taken carefully to account for slope of land and curvature of earth's surface), a large rock and a waterfall, etc., or a combination of both. The important factor is that objects in range have to be charted to be used in piloting.

Range markers designed as NAVAIDS place the taller of the markers behind the shorter marker viewed along the course line. The *top object* appears to be to the *left* of the lower object when the observer is *left* of the line determined by the range, and the *top object* appears to be to the *right* of the lower object when the observer is to the *right* of the range.

Fig. 6-2. A Range LOP Determined By a Charted Tank and Tower. Only the Time is Noted.

An LOP by range is the easiest LOP to determine and among the most accurate. Because no calculation is required, only the time need be noted and indicated on the chart. A range LOP is illustrated in Figure 6-2. Here, the navigator noted that a charted tank and a tower were in range at 1700. The range line was *lightly* drawn on the chart and labeled on top with the time. The direction need not be indicated since it is already uniquely defined on the chart, and further measurement, and labeling is unnecessary.

LOP BY DISTANCE FROM CHARTED OBJECT

Distance to an object can be determined by measurement using a radar observation, by measurement of vertical angle by use of a **SEXTANT** or **STADIMETER,** or by a rangefinder. In this case, however, the LOP is a *circle rather than a straight line.* the resulting circle or arc of position is labeled with the time and the distance. The time is placed on the "top" of the "line," the distance, "below," *as the circle appears in the area of the labeling.*

DISTANCE BY VERTICAL ANGLE

(This section is more technical and can be omitted without loss of continuity.)

A sextant is used to measure the vertical angle of a charted object of known height. The distance in nautical miles to the object is simply the height of the object (from the *water level* to the height of the *light source* -- not the top of the structure -- for a lighthouse) divided by the tangent (tan) of the angle measured (H), and divided by 6076 (to convert ft. to nautical miles), or:

$$d = \frac{h}{6076 \tan H}$$

This calculation can be performed on electronic calculators or (less conveniently) by the use of trigonometric and logarithmic tables. As an example, suppose a light of height 85 ft were observed to have a vertical angle of 0.53° (31.8 minutes, remember to convert to decimal de-

grees by dividing minutes by 60). For this angle H, tan H = 0.00925, h = 85 ft (neglecting the difference between the chart datum for heights and the height of the tide) and:

$$d = \frac{85}{6076 \times 0.00925} = 1.5 \text{ M}$$

After the range to the object is determined, a circular line of position is drawn on the chart around the object (or an arc is swung from the object if it is clearly apparent as to which direction the vessel lies) using the drafting compass set on that range from the latitude scale on the chart. This circular LOP is labeled with the time and with the distance (1.5 M--the distance units are implicit and are not normally labeled). The vessel is assumed to be somewhere on the circle or the arc.

DISTANCE BY RADAR OBSERVATIONS

Using a radar, the object is identified on the *plan position indicator* (PPI), the radar "scope" or "screen." The *fixed range markers* (FRM) or the *variable range marker* (VRM) are used to determine the range of the object from the vessel. This is illustrated in Figure 6-3, where the light on the NW tip of Gay Head provides a "recognizable" radar target at range 2.5 M. (See Chapter 9 for a discussion of radar detection and identification of targets. The light, *per se,* is unlikely to be detected on radar, but the western end of the island at Gay Head would have a characteristic radar signature.) A circular (or arc in this case) line of position is then scribed around the object on the chart using the drafting compass set to the distance (here, 2.5 M) using the latitude or bar scale. The circle is labeled with the time (1800) above the line and the distance (2.5) below the line. The arc is drawn to cover the possible positions of the vessel. The vessel is somewhere on this circle (or arc).

PRACTICAL POINTERS FOR DETERMINATION OF LOPs

Before discussing how fixes are determined, it is useful to provide some brief practical pointers on the selection of objects for determination

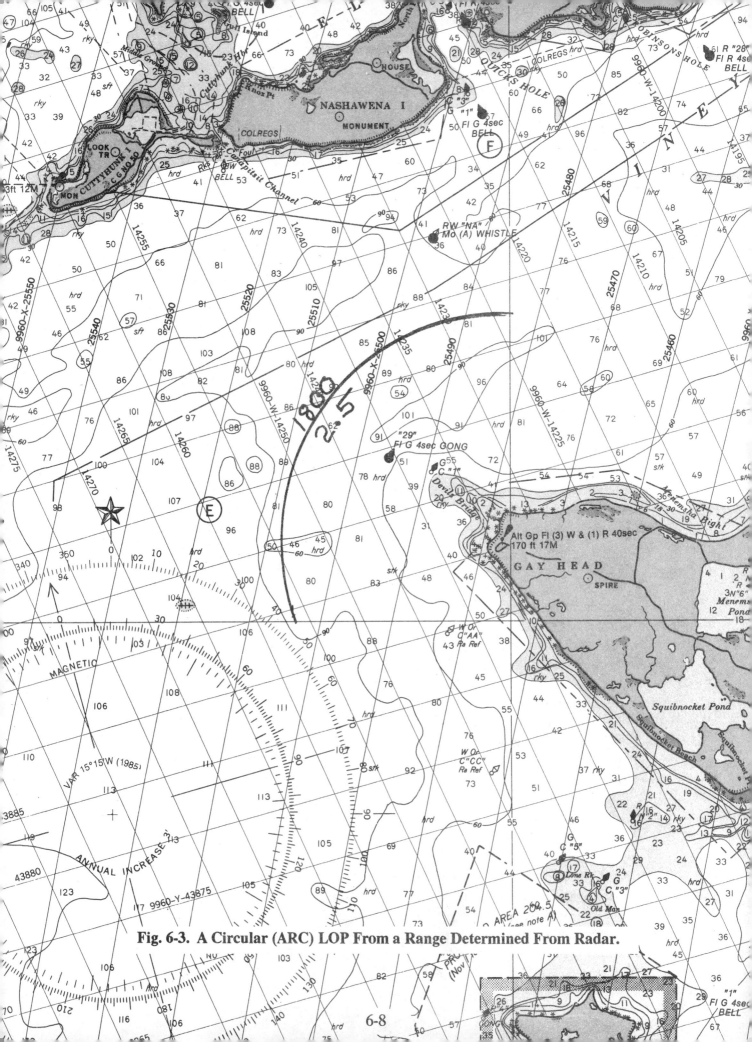

Fig. 6-3. A Circular (ARC) LOP From a Range Determined From Radar.

TABLE 6-1. LATERAL ERRORS AS A FUNCTION OF BEARING ERROR AND THE DISTANCE TO FIX SHOW IMPORTANCE OF SELECTING NEARBY OBJECTS FOR FIXES. TABLE ENTRIES SHOW LATERAL ERROR IN YARDS.

DISTANCE TO OBJECT		BEARING ERROR IN DEGREES						
NAUTICAL MILES	YARDS	1	2	3	4	5	7.5	10
0.125	250	4	9	13	17	22	33	44
0.250	500	9	17	26	35	44	66	88
0.375	750	13	26	39	52	66	99	132
0.500	1,000	17	35	52	70	87	132	176
0.625	1,250	22	44	66	87	109	165	220
0.750	1,500	26	52	79	105	131	197	264
0.875	1,750	31	61	92	122	153	230	309
1.000	2,000	35	70	105	140	175	263	353
1.125	2,250	39	79	118	157	197	296	397
1.250	2,500	44	87	131	175	219	329	441
1.500	3,000	52	105	157	210	262	395	529
1.750	3,500	61	122	183	245	306	461	617
2.000	4,000	70	140	210	280	350	527	705
2.500	5,000	87	175	262	350	437	658	882
3.000	6,000	105	210	314	420	525	790	1,058
3.500	7,000	122	244	367	489	612	922	1,234
4.000	8,000	140	279	419	559	700	1,053	1,411
5.000	10,000	175	349	524	699	875	1,317	1,763
7.500	15,000	262	524	786	1,049	1,312	1,975	2,645
10.000	20,000	349	698	1,048	1,399	1,750	2,633	3,527
12.500	25,000	436	873	1,310	1,748	2,187	3,291	4,408
15.000	30,000	524	1,048	1,572	2,098	2,625	3,950	5,290
17.500	35,000	611	1,222	1,834	2,447	3,062	4,608	6,171
20.000	40,000	698	1,397	2,096	2,797	3,500	5,266	7,053

of LOPs. In some cases, identifiable objects are few and far between and the navigator has little choice but to use any possible opportunity. In others, however, such as in the waters covered by the 1210-Tr chart, there is an abundance of charted objects suitable for LOP determination or position fixing, and some thought should be given to selecting those that are "best." As the mariner becomes familiar with the area, the identification of objects suitable for determination of LOPs or fixes becomes "second nature." But, for unfamiliar waters it is important to study the applicable nautical chart(s) and other relevant publications to plan for LOP opportunities.

First, the object(s) selected for the LOP must be charted and readily identifiable. Land features,

such as isolated and uncovered rocks or rocky bluffs can sometimes be used to advantage, but beware of gently sloping shorelines, because these are not always distinct (particularly if radar is used) and may change apparent position with the height of the tide. Man-made structures, such as standpipes, water towers, radio towers, cupolas, or spires on buildings, as well as ATONs, can be readily used. The architects of the nautical chart have decided which objects to chart based on their possible navigational utility. However, examine the chart closely to ensure that the object selected cannot be mistaken for another. In this connection, isolated objects can sometimes be easier to see and identify than those in close proximity. The key point here is that an object has to be *both detected and identified* in order to

TABLE 6-2. THE DISTANCE TO THE VISIBLE HORIZON IN NAUTICAL MILES AS A FUNCTION OF THE OBSERVER'S HEIGHT OF EYE IN FEET AND OBJECT HEIGHT IN FEET SHOWS THE IMPORTANCE OF SELECTING TALL OBJECTS FOR LOP DETERMINATION.

HEIGHT OF OBJECT (FT.)	HEIGHT OF EYE IN FEET							
	0.0	2.5	5.0	7.5	10.0	15.0	20.0	30.0
0.0	0.0	1.8	2.6	3.2	3.7	4.5	5.2	6.4
2.5	1.8	3.7	4.5	5.1	5.5	6.4	7.1	8.3
5.0	2.6	4.5	5.2	5.8	6.3	7.1	7.8	9.0
7.5	3.2	5.1	5.8	6.4	6.9	7.7	8.4	9.6
10.0	3.7	5.5	6.3	6.9	7.4	8.2	8.9	10.1
12.5	4.1	6.0	6.8	7.3	7.8	8.7	9.4	10.5
15.0	4.5	6.4	7.1	7.7	8.2	9.1	9.8	10.9
17.5	4.9	6.7	7.5	8.1	8.6	9.4	10.1	11.3
20.0	5.2	7.1	7.8	8.4	8.9	9.8	10.5	11.6
22.5	5.5	7.4	8.2	8.8	9.2	10.1	10.8	12.0
25.0	5.8	7.7	8.5	9.1	9.5	10.4	11.1	12.3
27.5	6.1	8.0	8.8	9.3	9.8	10.7	11.4	12.5
30.0	6.4	8.3	9.0	9.6	10.1	10.9	11.6	12.8
35.0	6.9	8.8	9.5	10.1	10.6	11.5	12.2	13.3
40.0	7.4	9.2	10.0	10.6	11.1	11.9	12.6	13.8
45.0	7.8	9.7	10.5	11.1	11.5	12.4	13.1	14.3
50.0	8.3	10.1	10.9	11.5	12.0	12.8	13.5	14.7
55.0	8.7	10.5	11.3	11.9	12.4	13.2	13.9	15.1
60.0	9.1	10.9	11.7	12.3	12.8	13.6	14.3	15.5
65.0	9.4	11.3	12.0	12.6	13.1	14.0	14.7	15.8
70.0	9.8	11.6	12.4	13.0	13.5	14.3	15.0	16.2
75.0	10.1	12.0	12.7	13.3	13.8	14.7	15.4	16.5
80.0	10.5	12.3	13.1	13.7	14.2	15.0	15.7	16.9
85.0	10.8	12.6	13.4	14.0	14.5	15.3	16.0	17.2
90.0	11.1	12.9	13.7	14.3	14.8	15.6	16.3	17.5
95.0	11.4	13.3	14.0	14.6	15.1	15.9	16.6	17.8
100.0	11.7	13.5	14.3	14.9	15.4	16.2	16.9	18.1
110.0	12.3	14.1	14.9	15.5	16.0	16.8	17.5	18.7
120.0	12.8	14.7	15.4	16.0	16.5	17.3	18.0	19.2
130.0	13.3	15.2	16.0	16.5	17.0	17.9	18.6	19.7
140.0	13.8	15.7	16.5	17.0	17.5	18.4	19.1	20.3
150.0	14.3	16.2	16.9	17.5	18.0	18.9	19.6	20.7
175.0	15.5	17.3	18.1	18.7	19.2	20.0	20.7	21.9
200.0	16.5	18.4	19.2	19.8	20.2	21.1	21.8	23.0

provide a valid LOP. In some cases, for example, with municipal water towers the object can be readily identified by writing (the town's name) or other distinguishing marks on the side. In other cases a unique color or color pattern may make some objects easy to recognize. (Local knowledge can be a great help.) The nautical chart or US Coast Pilot (see Chapter 10) often contains information that can determine the suitability of objects for position determination.

For example, the 1210-Tr chart notes that the Gay Head Light shown in Figure 6-3 cannot be seen (and, therefore, would not be usable) in the area south of Nomans Land. Identification of objects using radar (discussed in Chapter 9) rather than visual means requires some experience in interpretation of radar images. Remember, also, that different visual cues are important for recognition of objects at night compared to daytime viewing conditions. Lighted ATONs are often preferable because the color and characteristics of the light provide more positive identification during the hours of darkness.

Second, choose objects that are as close as possible to the vessel's position in preference to those that are located farther away. Remember, a 1 degree error in determining an object's bearing translates approximately to an error of one mile off in 60 (lateral error). Table 6-1 illustrates this point. It shows the lateral error in yards as a function of the distance off (in nautical miles or yards) and the error in determining an object's bearing. Thus, for example, a bearing error of 3 degrees translates into a lateral error of only 13 yards if the object observed is 1/8th of a mile distant, but more than 2,000 yards if the object is 20 nautical miles away. Nearby objects are also easier to see and identify, particularly under conditions of restricted visibility.

Third, choose objects that are taller in preference to those that are shorter. The ease with which an object can be detected and identified is a complex function of the prevailing visibility, shape of the object, color contrast compared to the surroundings, and other factors. But it is also a function of height of the object, a subject explored in more detail in Chapter 9. The distance to the visible horizon (arising from atmospheric refraction and the curvature of the earth) is a function of the observer's height of eye and the height of the object, as shown in Table 6-2. Thus, for example, an observer on a vessel with a height of eye of 7.5 feet could, under ideal conditions, see an object of height 10 feet as many as 6.9 nautical miles away. If the object were 100 feet high, it might be seen at a distance of 14.9 nautical miles. (This is yet another reason why small buoys are difficult to see.) Actual distances of visibility could be smaller than shown in the table (which is based solely on average atmospheric refraction and the earth's curvature) but, in no event, would be much larger than shown in this table. In any event, Table 6-2 shows the potential benefits of looking for taller objects. It is sometimes useful to draw an arc or circle of the distance to the visible horizon on the chart to determine the maximum range at which key objects can be seen.

Fourth, as noted above, try to use fixed rather than floating structures for determination of LOPs. Buoys can be sunk or off station. This guidance is not intended to be an *absolute* prohibition against use of buoys for determining an LOP or position fixing. In some cases, buoys may be the only objects available, and their distinctive markings aid in identification. However, as soon as possible use other means to confirm (verify) any LOP or fix so determined. (Note: Conservative or traditional navigators *categorically reject* the use of floating ATONs for determination of LOPs or fixes. A less extreme point of view is adopted here, but caution should be the watchword if floating ATONs are used for LOPs.)

Fifth, ranges make for the most accurate LOPs, so these should be used whenever possible. This is partially a consequence of the precision with which small deviations can be seen on a range. But, it is also important to recall that no conversion of bearings from compass or magnetic are necessary before LOPs can be plotted from ranges. Thus, any errors due to compass deviation, local magnetic anomalies, or failure to apply properly the corrections for deviation or variation are eliminated. Look for "natural" as well as man-made ranges. (Remember, though, that many other vessels could also be using ranges as ATONs, and keep a sharp lookout for traffic when using these.)

Sixth, it takes some practice before accurate compass bearings can be reliably obtained from the deck of a wave-tossed boat. If in doubt, take the average of several bearings rather than a single number. Learn to hold a hand-bearing compass as level as possible to minimize observation errors.

Finally, take the time to plot LOPs carefully. Parallel rules or paraline plotters can slip when transferring lines--particularly on a crowded and pitching navigator's desk aboard a vessel. Check plotted bearings (including the conversion from compass to true) at least twice.

WHAT IS THE WORTH OF A SINGLE LOP?

It is well known, and discussed at length later in this chapter, that two LOPs determine a fix, and that three or more LOPs enable a determination of the accuracy of a fix. But, it is also important to note that even a single LOP can be useful.

One LOP may not enable you to determine "where you are," but it can be useful to determine "where you are not." In other words, a single LOP can enable the mariner to rule out possible locations. And, as shown below, a single LOP has many other uses.

In certain situations, objects can be selected for a visual (or electronic) LOP that are more or less directly in line with the vessel's course, either ahead or astern. A single LOP from such an object can be used to determine whether or not the vessel is making good the intended course, even though a fix is not obtained. Such an LOP is sometimes said to be a *course* or *trackline LOP*. Such opportunities can happen by chance, or alternatively, can be part of the voyage plan itself. In other words, a course can be laid out in such a way that several objects can be used for trackline LOPs along the intended course.

Course turnpoints can often be conveniently identified and selected by means of a single LOP. That is, the vessel proceeds along one course until the bearing of a preidentified (preferably fixed rather than floating) object reaches a predetermined bearing. For example, a portion of the voyage plan might be to proceed on a course of 090 degrees until a particular lighthouse bears 045 degrees, then come left to 045 and track inbound. If sufficient safe water existed on either side of the intended track, a single LOP would be sufficient to determine the turnpoint.

Alternatively, objects can be selected for determination of an LOP that are more or less directly abeam of the vessel. Here, an LOP can be used to compare the vessel's speed made good (SMG) with the vessel's speed through the water (STW). Such LOPs are sometimes termed *speed LOPs,* and can be preplanned in the same manner as course LOPs. Speed LOPs are particularly useful if the vessel is operating in a narrow channel or river where the margin for lateral error is small. In fact, many river mariners don't go to the trouble of determining fixes in the conventional sense at all, they simply use speed LOPs for position determination by noting the time when an identifiable and charted object passes abeam.

Finally, single LOPs can be used to determine an Estimated Position (EP) when used in conjunction with a DR position. (Estimated positions allowing for current are considered in a subsequent chapter.) Figure 6-4 illustrates the idea. This first shows a conventional DR plot for a voyage in the waters covered by the 1210-Tr chart. At 1000 the vessel takes departure from buoy N "8" and heads towards Mattapoisett Harbor at 4.0 knots. At 1030 an LOP from the tower on West Island is determined, and (following the instructions given in Chapter 5) a 1030 DR position is immediately plotted. Now consider the problem posed by this information. By hypothesis, the vessel is somewhere along the 1030 LOP (subject, of course, to the error provisos discussed above). But, absent the LOP, the best estimate of the vessel's position is the 1030 DR position. The generally recommended solution to this dilemma (see some of the references for an alternative procedure) is to *locate the vessel's EP along the LOP, but as close to the DR position as possible.* It is easy to show from the principles of plane geometry that the shortest distance between a point and a line is formed by a perpendicular drawn from the point to that line. In other words, the EP is that point along the LOP where a perpendicular line drawn from the DR position touches the LOP. Figure 6-4

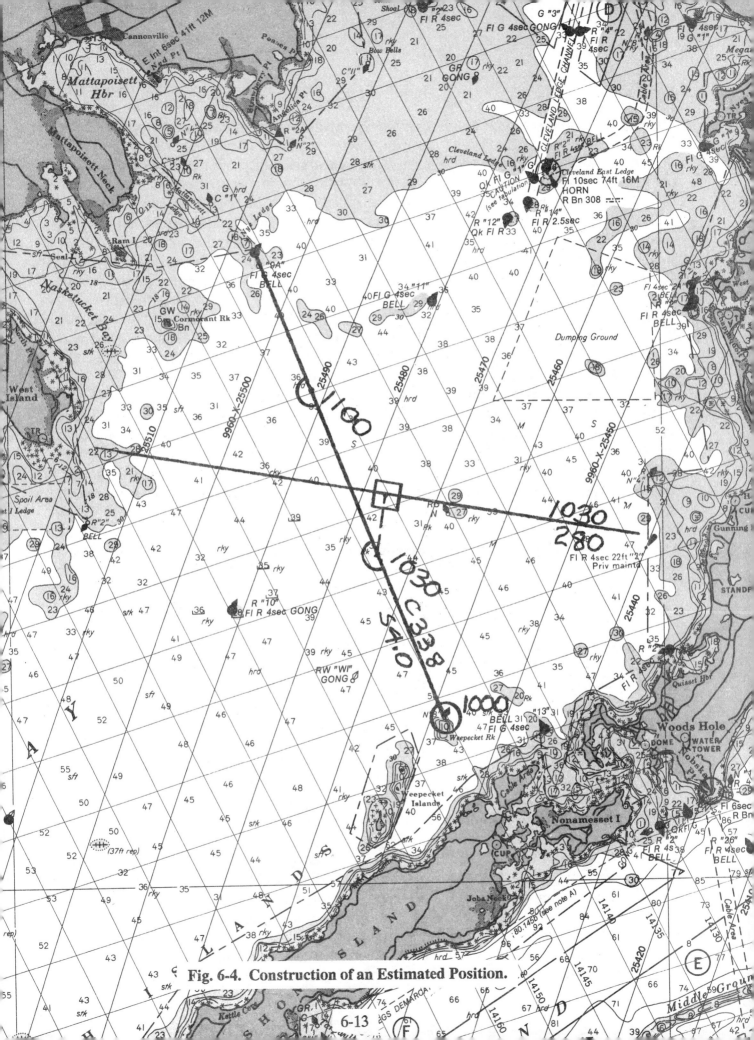

Fig. 6-4. Construction of an Estimated Position.

illustrates this construction. *The EP is denoted with a square around a dot.* If the time of the EP is clear from the construction, it may be omitted to reduce chart clutter. Otherwise, it is recommended that the time be written at an angle to the chart axis, in much the same manner as the DR position. (Note that this recommendation, unlike others in this text, is inconsistent with the notation recommended in Bowditch and other sources. The reason for this recommended departure from accepted convention is to more realistically capture the notion of an EP as approximate, in the same way as a DR position. "Traditionalists" may wish to write the EP time parallel to one of the chart axes.) Although some would argue otherwise (see some of the references at the end of this chapter), *conventional practice is not to renew the DR plot at the EP--only at a fix, or running fix* (see below). This is because the EP so determined lacks the precision of a fix. The only circumstance where it is recommended that a new DR track should be started from an EP (rather than continued from the DR position) is if the EP were closer to hazards to navigation and prospects for a prompt fix were poor. The reason for this procedure is that, in this case, where the vessel's position is uncertain, it would be prudent to assume that the vessel is located at the more hazardous of the two locations (DR and EP) and a course be set to remain well clear of the hazards. This situation arises more commonly in areas that do not have the abundance of ATONs shown on the 1210-Tr chart. In the exercises given in the Student Study Guide, therefore, assume that a new DR track is started only from a fix or running fix. (Note: one of the common student plotting errors is to draw the EP at the intersection of the DR course and the LOP. Except for the case where the course line is exactly perpendicular to the LOP to begin with, this incorrect procedure will result in a position that is farther away from the DR position than if a perpendicular had been drawn.)

To distinguish the construction line used to determine the EP from the ship's course, it is recommended that the perpendicular line be dashed rather than solid. The true bearing of the construction line is easily seen to be the true bearing of the LOP plus or minus 90 degrees, or 010 degrees in the example shown in Figure 6-4. (As with all bearings, 360 degrees may have to be added to, or subtracted from, the result.) It is much easier to calculate the bearing and plot this exactly with parallel rules or a paraline plotter than to attempt to estimate the perpendicular by eye alone. (It is not necessary to label the bearing of the dashed line.) Any discrepancy between the EP and the DR position is a result of the factors discussed in Chapter 7 on currents and whatever lack of precision is entailed in the determination of the LOP.

To summarize, even a single LOP can be useful. If reference objects are selected so as to be along the course line, a single LOP enables the navigator to determine whether or not the vessel is making good the intended course. If reference objects are selected so as to pass abeam, the single LOP can be used to check the vessel's SMG. Additionally, the single LOP can be used to determine an EP, which incorporates both the DR position and the LOP. Absent an allowance for current, the EP is determined by drawing a dashed perpendicular line from the DR position to the LOP and is denoted by a square surrounding the point. Finally, a single LOP can later be advanced (or retired) to determine a running fix, as discussed later in this chapter.

THE FIX

The *fix* is an accurate position established by simultaneous, or nearly simultaneous, intersection (crossing) of two or more lines of position. Such combinations resulting in a fix include:

-- cross bearing--intersection of two or more LOPs determined from bearings
-- a range and a bearing--intersection
-- two ranges--intersection of the LOPs
-- two distances--intersection of circular LOPs
-- distance and bearing of object(s)
-- passing close to a fixed aid to navigation.

Fig. 6-5. FIX Determined By Intersection of Range With Visual Bearing.

6-15

To assure maximum accuracy of the fix, it is important that the intersection angle of any *two* LOPs be as close to 90° as possible. If there are *three* LOPs, these should intersect at angles as close to 60° or 120° as possible. Although following these criteria should result in minimizing errors in measurement, reasonable deviations of a few degrees (10 - 20) from the optimum should still provide an accurate fix (and as such, should not be discarded), but the accuracy will be degraded from the maximum possible. Intersection angles of less than 40° should be avoided for fixes unless they are all that are available. Then, the rule of using all available information would prevail. *Remember, a dead reckoning plot is always started over at a fix.*

CROSS BEARINGS

Crossing two or more lines of position based on bearings is a common means of establishing a fix. Figure 6-5 illustrates crossing two bearing LOPs, one from a range consisting of the two towers on Beavertail Pt and the other a visual LOP on the Point Judith Light sighted on a true bearing of 248 degrees from the vessel. The resulting fix is plotted with a circle around the point of intersection and the time (1015) written horizontally. Should the navigator be running a DR plot at this time (not shown in Figure 6-5), as is recommended, a new plot would be initiated using the 1015 fix as its beginning.

RANGE AND BEARING

Establishing a fix by the intersection of a range LOP and that provided by a bearing LOP is a convenient way to determine a turning point while following the range down a channel at night. While the two objects (lights) are in range, the boat is known to be on this LOP. By taking frequent bearings on another object (light) to

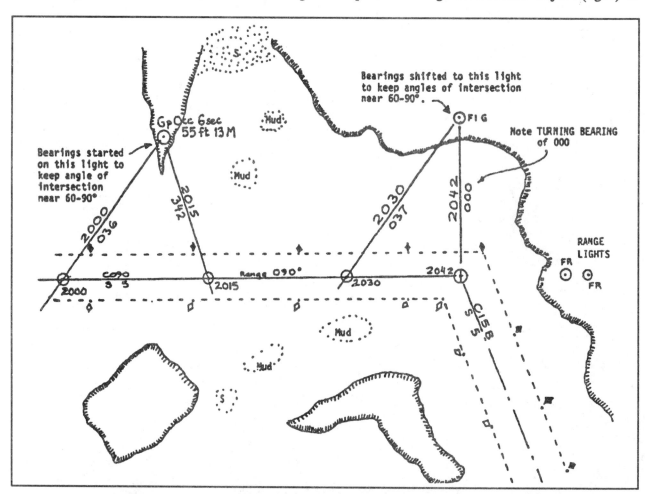

Fig. 6-6. Fixes Determined By Intersection of Bearings With Range and Illustration of Turning Bearing of 000 for Course Change to C158. All Directions Indicated are True.

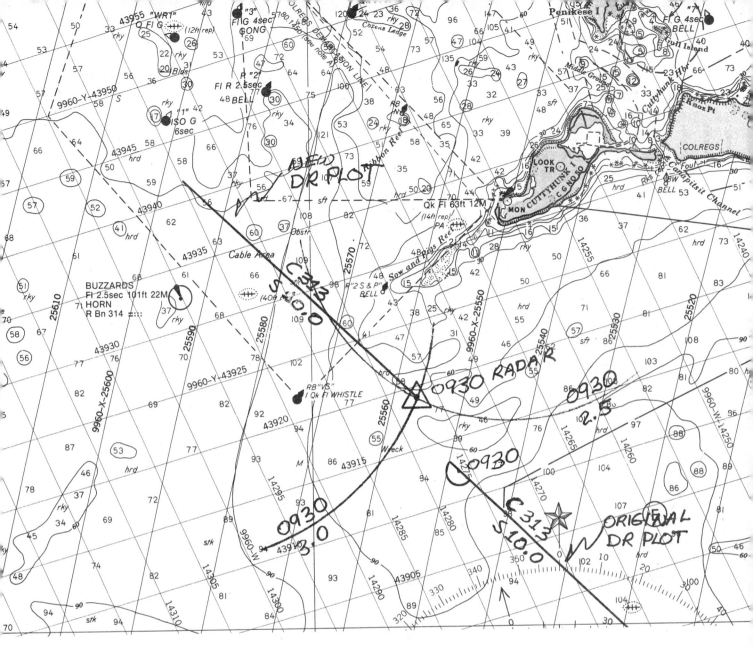

Fig. 6-7. Circular LOPs Determine Radar Fix, DR Track is Restarted.

one side, a series of fixes are determined and the progress of the vessel can be tracked. When the bearing reaches that marking the turning point, the navigator notes the location and recommends a change to the new course. It is essential that some other object (or method of fixing position) be used in conjunction with the range, else the vessel runs the risk of running into dangerous waters. Well-marked rivers where range lights are used, such as the Delaware, often employ a sequence of ranges to aid navigation. One range is followed until the next in

sequence is aligned (ranges are distinguished by the colors and flashing characteristics of the lights), whereupon the vessel turns and comes to the new course. Of course, it is important to maintain a sharp lookout for other vessels using the same range!

This process is illustrated in Figure 6-6, where the range of 090 is followed, with successive bearings taken first on the light on the point at 2000 (036), and 2015 (342), and then shifted to the flashing green light at 2030 (037), and finally, to the *turning bearing* (000) at 2042, at which time the boat changes to its new course of 158, to stay in the next channel. Fixes were obtained at 2000, 2015, 2030, and 2042, and were labeled accordingly with a circle around the point of intersection and the time, horizontally with the base of the chart.

TWO RANGES

Perhaps the easiest fix is obtained at the intersection of two ranges. The only label required upon obtaining this condition is a circle around the point of intersection and the time of the fix. Each range is an LOP, and the intersection constitutes a fix.

TWO DISTANCES

The intersection of two circular LOPs also establishes a fix, although there is a possibility of ambiguity since circles can intersect at two points. Unless the correct intersection is known, say by a rough bearing on some other reference, two "fixes" are possible, but only one is correct. Circular LOPs are often developed by radar observations. This fix is indicated in Figure 6-7 with radar range determinations of 3.0 M from Buzzards Bay Light and 2.5 M from the SW tip on Cuttyhunk Island. The point of intersection would be labeled with a *circle* and the time if the LOPs were determined by *visual* means (i.e., sextant angle or stadimeter reading) but with a *triangle* and the time if *either or both* of the LOPs were determined by electronic means. The word RADAR would also be added after the time if the LOP was determined by radar. As with any other fix, a new DR track is initiated after the fix as shown in Figure 6-7. (Note also in Figure 6-7 that the time is written above, and distance written below, the LOP regardless of whether these are within or outside the arc. This is easier to read.)

The reason that a special symbol (the triangle) is used for electronic fixes is that these may be less accurate (RDF bearing uncertainties, as discussed in Chapter 9, are generally considered to be less accurate than visual bear-

ings) and the use of a special symbol reminds the navigator that "some fixes may be more equal than others." (Some responsible navigators would go even further, at least with respect to RDF fixes and represent these as an EP rather than a fix.)

Figure 6-7 shows both the DR position and the fix. This provides a useful opportunity for a brief digression to cover some practical aspects of the navigator's job. Perhaps most important, the navigator should not be content with simply following rote procedures, such as immediately starting a new DR plot from the fix, without pausing to check the plausibility and implications of the information just developed. The navigator should attempt to rationalize the apparent facts. For example, is the discrepancy between the DR position and the fix plausible? In this example, the two positions are quite close, so there is probably no reason to look further, except to note that there appears to be a current (or wind/current combination) setting the vessel north and slightly west of the DR position. File this information away and see if this trend is continued at the next fix--perhaps this current should be compensated for in planning the next course using the methods discussed in Chapter 7 on current sailing. But, suppose that the DR position and the fix were farther apart. Rather than simply accepting this conclusion as fact, the navigator should use the opportunity to check the accuracy of the DR plot, the fix, or both. The fix might be checked, for example, by taking another range or bearing, or by measuring the depth of water and consulting the chart to see if this information is consistent with the fix. If there is any doubt of the validity of the "fix," a simple expedient would be to label as an EP.

This example serves to illustrate another relevant point. That is, information should be plotted and analyzed as soon as possible after it is gathered. If the fix information is simply recorded for later analysis, the opportunity of checking the fix by additional measurements will be lost forever. A good navigator should not "get behind" the vessel; new information should be analyzed as it is developed. If this cannot be done, the navigator may wish to slow down (see Chapter 12).

Finally, the navigator should always be alert to the possibility that his/her vessel is "standing into danger." In this example, the vessel is likely to pass closer to the "sow and pigs reef" than originally planned. A glance at this portion of the chart shows that the western edge of this reef is marked by a buoy (R "2S & P" bell). Perhaps the lookouts should be alerted to watch for this buoy, or the radar should be adjusted to a smaller range setting to help ensure safe passage. Alternatively, perhaps the vessel's course should be altered more towards the Buzzards Bay entrance light to ensure that the reef is left a safe distance to starboard. Which (if any) of these choices are prudent would depend upon numerous factors, such as the prevailing visibility, draft of the vessel, and the navigator's familiarity with the local waters. But the key lesson to draw from this example is that plotting and fix taking are not simply passive activities done according to rote, but rather should provide the foundation for considered action.

DISTANCE AND BEARING TO OBJECT

This fix is often used with radar where the PPI gives both bearing and distance. Caution should be used, however, with radar *bearings,* the precision of which is about 1°-2° in azimuth at best (see Chapter 9) and could be worse if the vessel is yawing appreciably. The precision of the distance measurement is usually better. Here the intersection of the circular distance LOP and the straight line bearing LOP determines the fix.

BEARING AND LINE OF SOUNDINGS

A vessel coasting--running offshore, essentially parallel with the coast--may make use of this fix while taking soundings and a bearing when the opportunity presents itself. As the course is run, the soundings are plotted at intervals, according to the speed and course of the

vessel, on a piece of drafting parchment or vellum (a smooth heavy tracing paper) using the same scale as on the chart. When the bearing is taken, the distance from the object is determined by aligning the soundings along the course and the bearing, and moving the sounding trace toward or away from the object (on the bearing line) until close agreement with the charted soundings is obtained. This determines a fix. However, this fix is not very precise unless the soundings change abruptly or offer some other, unique feature which distinguishes the specific area from others. A navigator may be more comfortable terming this an estimated position and labeling this position with a square to denote an EP.

In circumstances of reduced visibility (e.g., in fog) it is often convenient to navigate by following a depth contour, rather than laying out straight line courses. Although the computation of DR positions along a curved course are more tedious, the actual course can be approximated by a series of straight lines and, with practice, quite accurate DR plots can be made. If the sea bottom is well shaped, it is surprisingly easy to follow a depth contour.

PASSING CLOSE TO A FIXED CHARTED AID TO NAVIGATION

Every time the vessel passes a fixed charted aid to navigation which is expected to be on station--such as a light tower--a fix is obtained. It is a matter of judgment whether or not to label it a fix if a *floating* aid is passed close aboard. In Figure 6-4, for example, passing close to buoy N 8 was judged equivalent to a fix and so denoted with a circle. The factors contributing to this judgment included depth soundings indicating a shoal and the close proximity to identifiable objects on the shore.

RUNNING FIX (R FIX)

It is not always possible to obtain two LOPs at nearly the same time. For example, poor visibility may limit the number of objects that can be seen. In this case, a running fix may some-

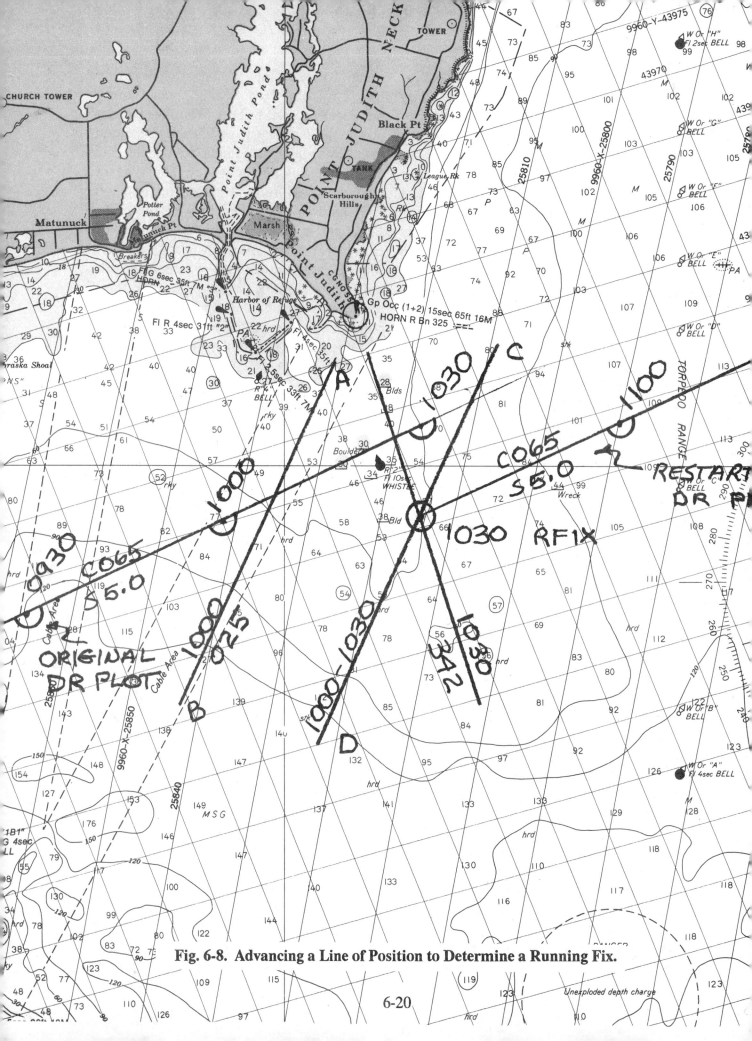

Fig. 6-8. Advancing a Line of Position to Determine a Running Fix.

times be used. A running fix uses an instant LOP on one object, with a previous (or subsequent) LOP *on the same or another object,* which is "time corrected" (advanced or retired) by dead reckoning calculation of the vessel's direction and distance traveled during the interval between observations of the LOPs. This section considers the running fix without any allowance for current. Chapter 7 discusses the running fix with current.

To plot a running fix, follow the steps below, which are also illustrated in Figure 6-8.

1. Allow for the time lapse between the first and second bearing. This is done by advancing (or retiring) the first LOP along the vessel's dead reckoning course as if it were advancing (or retiring) at the same speed and in the same direction as the vessel's *course* and *speed.*

2. The first LOP is advanced (retired) by moving it parallel to itself, forward (backward) *along the course line* for the distance the vessel traveled to the second LOP. The intersection of the advanced (or retired) LOP at the time of taking the second bearing represents the best estimate of position and is called a running fix (abbreviated R Fix).

3. A new dead reckoning plot is started at the position of the running fix.

4. Avoid advancing (or retiring) an LOP for more than 30 minutes, especially if you are in near-shore waters where currents are extremely variable, unpredictable, and/or uncertain.

The scenario behind this example is as follows. Vessel *Perdida* is southwest of Point Judith on a course of C065 maintaining 5.0 knots in intermittent showers and 4 ft. seas. A portion of the DR plot for this segment (labeled "original DR plot") is shown in Figure 6-8, along with DR positions at 1000 and 1030. At 1000 a visual

bearing (converted to 025 degrees true) is taken on the light at the tip of Point Judith, and the LOP is plotted (correctly labeled and denoted "AB" in Figure 6-8). The 1000 LOP crosses ahead of the 1000 DR position, suggesting that the SMG is greater than 5 knots and/or that *Perdida* is farther south than the DR position would indicate. *Perdida*'s navigator monitors the depth sounder and alerts the lookout to watch for buoy R "2" as a check on the vessel's position. But, R "2" is not able to be seen (possibly because of the seas) or heard. In any event, at 1030 Point Judith Light is again seen, bearing 342 degrees true. This second LOP is drawn and the navigator decides to plot a running fix. The steps are detailed below.

1. Obtain the time interval and distance that the vessel traveled since the 1000 LOP.

$$\frac{\begin{array}{r} 10 \text{ hr } 30 \text{ min} \\ -10 \text{ hr} \end{array}}{30 \text{ min time interval}}$$

2. Apply the equation for distance (a nautical slide rule may be used).

$$D = ST/60$$
$$D = 5 \times 30/60$$
$$D = 150/60 = 2.5 \text{ nautical miles}$$

3. Using a pair of dividers, measure the distance (2.5 M) off the latitude or nautical mile scale along the 065 course line in the direction traveled from the point where the 1000 LOP crosses the course line.

4. Advance the first LOP, *ensuring it is moved parallel to itself forward along the true course line for the distance traveled (2.5 M).* Draw the advanced LOP, labeling the new line (1000-1030) to indicate that it is an advanced LOP over the period from 1000 to 1030. This advanced LOP is denoted "CD" in Figure 6-8.

5. Plot the second bearing. The running fix is located at the point of intersection with the advanced LOP. Label this point with a circle, and horizontally with 1030 R Fix, clear of the course line. A new DR plot is started at this running fix.

The above example focuses on the mechanics of plotting a running fix. Were this an actual situation, the navigator would actively explore other means to determine *Perdida*'s position. The crossing angle of the advanced LOP and the 1030 LOP is much smaller than the ideal 90 degrees, and the failure to observe or hear buoy R "2" are factors that would be of concern. Depth information could rule out the possibility that *Perdida* is too close to Point Judith but is not of much help in deciding between the 1030 DR position and the running fix (both lie nearly along the 60 ft. depth contour). This might be a good time to stop imitating Christopher Columbus and look at the loran!

In the illustration in Figure 6-8, the running fix was determined using nonsimultaneous observations of *the same object*. A running fix can also be determined from two nonsimultaneous observations of *two different objects*. In this case, the procedure is identical to that described above, except that the second LOP is taken from another object.

In essence, the running fix assumes that the vessel's SMG and CMG are equal to the STW and course, respectively. In other words, the procedure assumes that the DR plot over the time interval between the two observations is without error. To the extent that this assumption is valid, the running fix is likewise error free. However, current and wind conspire to undermine the validity of this assumption. Other things being equal, therefore, a conventional fix is superior to a running fix.

In the illustration in Figure 6-8 the vessel was assumed to maintain a constant course and speed. A running fix can also be determined if the vessel changes course and/or speed. All that is necessary is to find the *resultant* course and speed over the interval. The resultant course and speed can be determined by drawing a single line between the DR positions at the time that the original bearing is taken and the time that the second LOP is taken and treating this as the overall course and speed line. Consult the references given in the bibliography for details.

ANGLE ON THE BOW

(This section is more technical, and can be omitted without any loss of continuity.) Running fixes on the same object can also be treated mathematically, without reference to the charts. Figure 6-9 provides an illustration of the running fix, and symbols used in this discussion. Here the vessel takes a first bearing on an object (e.g., a lighthouse), and converts this to an angle on the bow. (Also referred to as an angle off the bow.) This angle, shown as angle Y in Figure 6-9, is measured from 0 through 180 degrees. (For this purpose, it is not necessary to distinguish right from left, as it is assumed that the object remains on one or the other side of the vessel.)

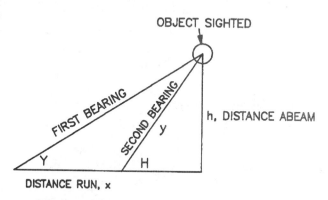

Fig. 6-9. Two Bearing Problem Illustrated.

After taking the first bearing, the vessel maintains course and speed, until a second bearing is taken. The second bearing is likewise converted to an angle on the bow, and is shown as angle H in Figure 6-9. The distance run between the bearings, denoted x, can be calculated from the usual TSD formula discussed in Chapter 5 as $x = ST/60$.

F1

TABLE 6-3. ABBREVIATED TABLE OF VALUES OF FACTOR F1 FOR "ANGLE ON THE BOW" COMPUTATIONS.

FIRST ANGLE (DEGREES)	SECOND ANGLE (DEGREES)																
	10	15	20	25	30	35	40	45	50	55	60	65	70	75	80	85	90
5	1.000	0.502	0.337	0.255	0.206	0.174	0.152	0.136	0.123	0.114	0.106	0.101	0.096	0.093	0.090	0.089	0.087
10		1.992	1.000	0.671	0.508	0.411	0.347	0.303	0.270	0.246	0.227	0.212	0.201	0.192	0.185	0.180	0.176
15			2.970	1.490	1.000	0.757	0.612	0.518	0.451	0.403	0.366	0.338	0.316	0.299	0.286	0.275	0.268
20				3.924	1.970	1.321	1.000	0.809	0.684	0.596	0.532	0.484	0.446	0.418	0.395	0.377	0.364
25					4.849	2.434	1.633	1.236	1.000	0.845	0.737	0.657	0.598	0.552	0.516	0.488	0.466
30						5.737	2.879	1.932	1.462	1.183	1.000	0.872	0.778	0.707	0.653	0.610	0.577
35							6.581	3.303	2.216	1.677	1.357	1.147	1.000	0.892	0.811	0.749	0.700
40								7.375	3.702	2.484	1.879	1.521	1.286	1.121	1.000	0.909	0.839
45									8.113	4.072	2.732	2.067	1.673	1.414	1.233	1.100	1.000
50										8.789	4.411	2.960	2.240	1.813	1.532	1.336	1.192
55											9.399	4.717	3.165	2.395	1.938	1.638	1.428
60												9.937	4.987	3.346	2.532	2.049	1.732
65													10.399	5.219	3.502	2.650	2.145
70														10.782	5.411	3.631	2.747
75															11.083	5.563	3.732
80																11.299	5.671
85																	11.430

NOTE: MORE COMPLETE TABLE CAN BE FOUND IN BOWDITCH.

F2

TABLE 6-4. ABBREVIATED TABLE OF VALUES OF FACTOR F2 FOR "ANGLE ON THE BOW" COMPUTATIONS.

FIRST ANGLE (DEGREES)	SECOND ANGLE (DEGREES)																
	10	15	20	25	30	35	40	45	50	55	60	65	70	75	80	85	90
5	0.174	0.130	0.115	0.108	0.103	0.100	0.098	0.096	0.094	0.093	0.092	0.091	0.090	0.090	0.089	0.088	0.087
10		0.516	0.342	0.284	0.254	0.236	0.223	0.214	0.207	0.201	0.196	0.192	0.188	0.185	0.182	0.179	0.176
15			1.016	0.630	0.500	0.434	0.394	0.366	0.346	0.330	0.317	0.306	0.297	0.289	0.281	0.274	0.268
20				1.658	0.985	0.758	0.643	0.572	0.524	0.488	0.461	0.438	0.420	0.403	0.389	0.376	0.364
25					2.425	1.396	1.050	0.874	0.766	0.692	0.638	0.596	0.562	0.533	0.508	0.486	0.466
30						3.291	1.851	1.366	1.120	0.969	0.866	0.790	0.731	0.683	0.643	0.608	0.577
35							4.230	2.336	1.698	1.374	1.175	1.040	0.940	0.862	0.799	0.746	0.700
40								5.215	2.836	2.034	1.628	1.378	1.208	1.082	0.985	0.906	0.839
45									6.215	3.336	2.366	1.874	1.572	1.366	1.214	1.096	1.000
50										7.200	3.820	2.682	2.105	1.751	1.509	1.330	1.192
55											8.140	4.275	2.974	2.313	1.909	1.632	1.428
60												9.006	4.686	3.232	2.494	2.041	1.732
65													9.772	5.041	3.449	2.640	2.145
70														10.414	5.329	3.617	2.747
75															10.914	5.541	3.732
80																11.256	5.671
85																	11.430

NOTE: MORE COMPLETE TABLE CAN BE FOUND IN BOWDITCH.

Now if angle H is exactly twice angle Y--for example, if Y = 20 and H = 40, or Y = 45 and H = 90, then it follows that the triangle formed by the distance run and the two bearings is an isosceles triangle, with the distance-off at the second bearing, denoted y in Figure 6-9, exactly equal to the distance run between the fixes. Because no mathematics is involved in figuring this out, it is a common method of figuring distance-off. Choosing such a pair of angles and calculating distance-off is termed "doubling the angle on the bow."

Although the computations are particularly simple if the angle on the bow is doubled, the method can be employed for any pair of angles (ideally not too closely spaced for maximum accuracy) on the bow, Y and H. In particular, it can be shown (using the law of sines from elementary trigonometry) that the distance-off at the second bearing, y, is given by the equation, $y = (ST/60)\sin Y/\sin(H-Y)$, and that the distance-off when directly abeam, denoted by the symbol h in Figure 6-9, is $h = (ST/60)(\sin Y)(\cos[90-H])$ divided by $\sin(H-Y)$. (This distance, h, is sometimes called the distance at the closest point of approach (CPA) and is discussed at greater length in Chapter 9.) An electronic calculator, equipped with trigonometric functions, can be used to calculate the distances y and h. This is the most convenient method.

Alternatively, special purpose tables can be used to find the multiplying coefficients in the above equations. To illusrate, let F1 be equal to $\sin Y/\sin(H-Y)$. Table 6-3 gives values for F1 as a function of the angles Y and H. Simply enter the table at the row corresponding to the angle on the bow at the first bearing and the column corresponding to the angle on the bow at the second bearing. The value read from the table, F1, is then multiplied by the distance traveled, ST/60, to calculate y.

Likewise, let F2 be defined as $(\sin Y)(\cos[90-H])/\sin(H-Y)$. Table 6-4 shows F2 as a function of the angles Y and H. F2 is read from the table and multiplied by the distance between bearings, ST/60, to determine the distance-off when abeam, or the CPA. (A more comprehensive set of tables can be found in Bowditch.)

The calculations go faster if a worksheet, such as that shown in Table 6-5, is used to organize the calculations. As a specific numerical illustration, suppose that Auxiliary vessel 273007 is maintaining a true course of 090, and speed of 6 knots, in an area where the magnetic variation is 015W. At 1200, a magnetic bearing of 090 is taken on a lighthouse using a hand-bearing compass assumed here to be free of deviation. The true bearing is, therefore, 090 - 015W = 075. The angle on the bow is the absolute difference (i.e., difference without regard to sign) between the true bearing 075 and the vessel's course (090) or 015 in this example. Now suppose that at 1230, vessel 273007 again takes a bearing on the light, 060M or 045 true. The second angle on the bow is, using the absolute value, equal to 045. In the time interval between the bearings, the vessel moved a distance, x, of (6)(30)/60, or 3.0 nautical miles. From Table 6-3, factor F1 is 0.518, and, from Table 6-4, F2 is 0.366. The vessel's distance-off at the second bearing is 0.518(3.0) or 1.6 nautical miles (rounded to one decimal place), and the distance of the CPA is 0.366(3.0) or 1.1 nautical miles. Table 6-6 shows the completed worksheet for this example.

This procedure is exactly equivalent to plotting the running fix. As discussed here, no allowance for current is included. Although the computations may appear tedious, with practice these can be done rapidly and reliably, particularly if a worksheet is employed. Bear in mind also, that no calculations are required in the event that the angle on the bow is doubled.

DANGER BEARINGS

Before summarizing the material presented in this chapter one last topic, danger bearings, is noted. To make the discussion concrete, refer to Figure 6-10. This shows an extract from a vessel's DR plot. The vessel is steering a course generally east, and intends to round a point of

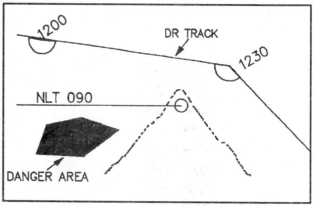

Fig. 6-10. Danger Bearing Illustrated.

TABLE 6-5. WORKSHEET FOR ANGLE ON THE BOW COMPUTATIONS

Item No.	Item	Value	Units	Remarks
1.	Course	_____	degrees	Entered in degrees true.
2.	Speed	_____	knots	From speedometer or speed curve.
3.	Variation	_____	degrees (E, W)	From nautical chart.
4.	Time of first bearing	_____	HH:MM	Read from watch.
5.	First bearing to object	_____	degrees	From hand-bearing compass.
6.	First bearing of object (true)	_____	degrees	Line 5 + Line 3 (if east) or -Line 3 (if west).
7.	Angle off bow at first bearing	_____	degrees	Absolute value of [Line 6 -Line 1].
8.	Time of second bearing	_____	HH:MM	Read from watch.
9.	Second bearing to object	_____	degrees	From hand-bearing compass.
10.	Second bearing of object (true)	_____	degrees	Line 9 + Line 3 (if east) or -Line 3 (if west).
11.	Angle off bow at second bearing	_____	degrees	Absolute value of [Line 10 -Line 1].
12.	Time between bearings	_____	minutes	Line 8 -Line 4 converted to minutes.
13.	Distance run between bearings	_____	M	D = (Line 2)(Line 12)/60.
14.	Factor 1	_____	NA	From Table 6-3, or sin (Line 7)/sin(Line 11 -Line 7).
15.	Factor 2	_____	NA	From Table 6-4, or (Line 14) x Cos (90 -Line 1).
16.	Distance off at second bearing	_____	M	(Line 13) x (Line 14).
17.	Distance off abeam (CPA)	_____	M	(Line 13) x (Line 15).

TABLE 6-6. WORKSHEET FOR ANGLE ON THE BOW COMPUTATIONS

Item No.	Item	Value	Units	Remarks
1.	Course	090	degrees	Entered in degrees true.
2.	Speed	6	knots	From speedometer or speed curve.
3.	Variation	015 W	degrees (E, W)	From nautical chart.
4.	Time of first bearing	1200	HH:MM	Read from watch.
5.	First bearing to object	090	degrees	From hand-bearing compass.
6.	First bearing of object (true)	075	degrees	Line 5 + Line 3 (if east) or -Line 3 (if west).
7.	Angle off bow at first bearing	015	degrees	Absolute value of [Line 6 -Line 1].
8.	Time of second bearing	1230	HH:MM	Read from watch.
9.	Second bearing to object	060	degrees	From hand-bearing compass.
10.	Second bearing of object (true)	045	degrees	Line 9 + Line 3 (if east) or -Line 3 (if west).
11.	Angle off bow at second bearing	045	degrees	Absolute value of [Line 10 -Line 1].
12.	Time between bearings	30	minutes	Line 8 -Line 4 converted to minutes.
13.	Distance run between bearings	3.0	M	D = (Line 2)(Line 12)/60.
14.	Factor 1	0.518	NA	From Table 6-3, or sin (Line 7)/sin(Line 11 -Line 7).
15.	Factor 2	0.366	NA	From Table 6-4, or (Line 14) x Cos (90 -Line 1).
16.	Distance off at second bearing	1.6	M	(Line 13) x (Line 14).
17.	Distance off abeam (CPA)	1.1	M	(Line 13) x (Line 15).

ITEM	DIAGRAM	DESCRIPTION
DR plot	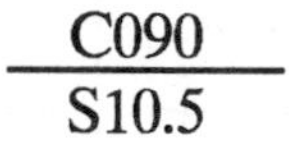 C090 / S10.5	Course (090 true) written above line, speed (10.5 knots) written below line.
DR position	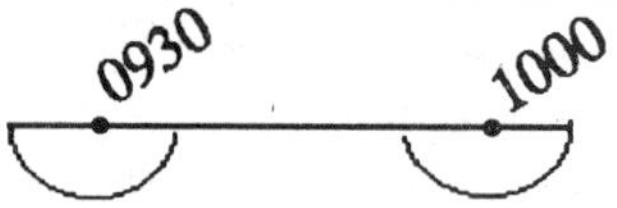 0930 1000	Time (24 hour) written at angle to semicircle denoting DR position.
Departure	 0730 ⊙—	Departure time (24-hour) written horizontal to chart axis denoted by circle with dot inside.
LOP	 1030 / 045	Lightly drawn line with time (24-hour) above LOP and true bearing beneath.
Estimated Position	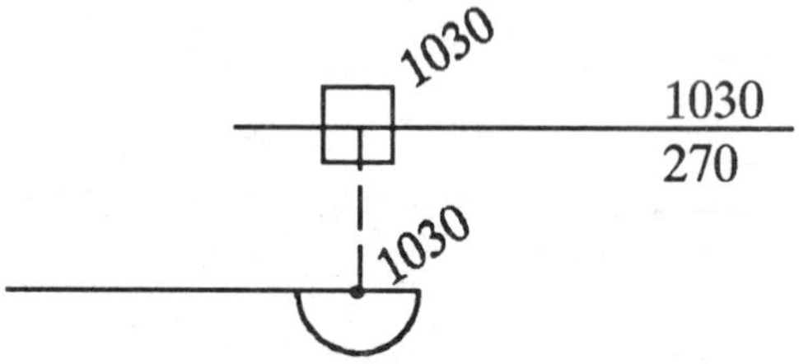 1030 ▢ 1030 / 270 / 1030	Square located where dashed perpendicular line from DR position touches LOP.
Visual Fix	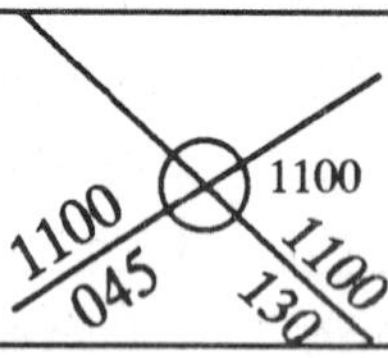 ⊗ 1100 / 1100 / 045 / 1100 / 130	Circle where two or more LOPs cross. Time written parallel to chart axis.
Electronic Fix	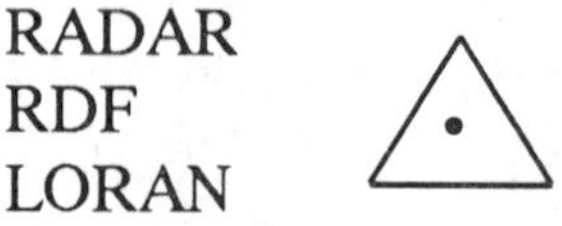 RADAR RDF LORAN △	Triangle used when one or more electronic LOPs shown cross. Time and method (if relevant).
Running Fix	 1030 ⊙ R FIX	Circle with time written horizontally and abbreviation R FIX.

Fig. 6-11. A Concise Summary of Navigation Drafting Symbols.

land with a lighthouse before turning southeast enroute to its destination. Suppose, however, that there is an unmarked danger area (e.g., fish traps, shoals, coral, etc.) just west of the light, and denoted by the shaded area in Figure 6-10. A prudent mariner might wish to ensure that a wide berth was given to this area. One simple procedure would be to lay off a line (shown in Figure 6-10) well north of the area, and to note the bearing of this line (here 090 true). Provided that the actual true bearing to the light was never less than 090 true, the mariner could be sure that the vessel would not enter the danger area. The bearing, 090 in this example, is termed a *danger bearing* and labeled NLT (for Not Less Than) above the danger bearing. (As a practical matter, this is one of the areas where it would also be prudent to write the magnetic bearing on the chart as well, since a hand-bearing compass is likely to be used as a check. Obviously, if the hazard to navigation were on the other side, NMT, for not more than, would be used. Conventional practice would be to draw "whiskers" or hatch marks, not shown in Figure 6-10, on the side of the danger bearing facing the hazard.

In order to use danger bearings to advantage it is necessary that there be a charted object (here the lighthouse) on which bearings can be taken. Obviously, danger bearings only make sense if the hazard is not otherwise well marked. However, even if a buoy were shown on the chart it might be worthwhile to lay off a danger bearing as a precaution in the event that the buoy is off station. (This advice is particularly helpful in areas of the world and seasons where buoys are less frequently on station.) Readers interested in additional detail on danger bearings should consult the references at the end of this chapter.

SUMMARY OF SYMBOLS

Figure 6-11 presents a summary and brief description of the drafting symbols used for DR and piloting in this text. The notation is broadly consistent with modern U.S. and Canadian usage. However, it differs substantially from that employed in other parts of the world. Aside from some additional notation introduced in Chapter 7, this comprises the entire set of symbols used.

THE MOST PROBABLE POSITION (MPP)

Because there are always errors associated with all measurements, it is almost impossible to establish the *exact* position of the vessel on the chart relative to the earth. However, when the information is fully sufficient, such as three reliable lines of position crossing at a point (or,

more typically, within a very small triangle), little judgment is necessary to establish a satisfactory estimate of the vessel's position.

But, there are also circumstances when the navigator has uncertain or conflicting information regarding the vessel's position. Three LOPs, for example, may not cross at a single point or be located within a small triangle, or the apparent fix may be located an implausible distance away from the vessel's DR position. Situations such as these require a careful weighing of the information at hand and intelligent and cautious rejection of suspicious information. The resulting position, adjusted for such discrepancies, is termed the *most probable position* (MPP). Many mariners equate a MPP with an EP. Although an MPP could be an EP in certain circumstances, the MPP is a more general concept than an EP. In principle, a MPP could be a fix, running fix, EP, DR position or some combination of these. In the example given in Figure 6-8, some navigators would, no doubt, decide that the running fix determined was a MPP or EP rather than a fix. There is no generally agreed upon symbol or label to denote a MPP, however, the letters MPP written next to the position would be clear enough. Likewise, there is no clear consensus among navigators on whether or not to start a new DR plot at a MPP. The more "conservative" navigators would certainly not renew a DR plot at a MPP, waiting instead until a "proper" fix was determined. Other equally competent practitioners would have a more flexible attitude on this question.

Many of the "judgment" issues, such as whether or not to use floating aids for fixes, how much faith to put in a running fix, whether or not to start a new DR plot from a MPP or EP, serve to remind us that navigation is both an *art* and a *science*.

REFERENCES

Same as Chapter 5 with the additions shown below. Note that some of these references present alternative notation or express different points of view than taken in this text.

Anon, "Celestial Navigation, the Basics (Part VII) This Segment Offshore Plotting," *Ocean Navigator,* No. 13, May/June 1987, pp. 49, *et seq.*

Bright, C. "Celestial Navigation, The Basics: Celestial Draftsmanship," *Ocean Navigator,* Jan/Feb 1989, pp. 53, *et seq.*

Campbell, S. *The Yachting Book of Practical Navigation,* Dodd, Mead & Company, New York, 1985, especially pp. 81 - 101.

Fraser, B. *Weekend Navigator,* John de Graff, Inc., Clinton Corners, NY, 1981.

Graves, F. *Piloting,* International Marine Publishing Co., Camden, ME, 1981, pp. 108, *et seq.*

Groth, L. "Sticking With the DR Position," *Ocean Navigator,* Nov/Dec 1988, pp. 15, *et seq.*

Kielhorn, W. V. *A Piloting Primer,* privately published, Naples, FL, 1988.

Sexton, J. "Interpreting the Single LOP, What to Do When Your DR Position is Several Miles From a New LOP?," *Ocean Navigator,* No. 11, Jan/Feb 1987, pp. 48, *et seq.*

Vesey, T. "Dead Reckoning in Fog," *Cruising World,* Vol. 15, No. 10, October 1989, pp. 33, *et seq.*

Walsh, G. "Coastal Navigation, The Basics, Building on DR: The Line of Position," *Ocean Navigator,* No. 19, May/June 1988, pp. 55, *et seq.*

Williams, J. R. "Starting A Fresh DR Track, A Navigator Makes the Case For Using EPs and Running Fixes," *Ocean Navigator,* No. 20, July/August 1988, pp. 68, *et seq.*

Chapter 7

Current Sailing

This chapter covers the important topic of current sailing for the mariner. It builds upon the material presented in Chapters 5 and 6, to include consideration of current in voyage planning. It is important reading for sailors and power boaters alike.

Sailors are long accustomed to dealing with wind and current in voyage planning. Winds affect the vessel's speed through the water (STW) and determine the necessity to tack rather than run direct courses to a destination. Current, likewise, affects the speed of advance (SOA) and the required course to achieve a desired track. These truths are obvious to sailors.

Power vessel operators, in contrast, often regard wind or current as minor annoyances except when either assumes extreme proportions. Currents are thought to present more of a challenge for powerboat *seamanship* than powerboat *navigation*. This view is overly simplistic and misleading. As shown in this chapter and later in Chapter 11, current can be very important to power vessels--particularly in terms of fuel efficiency and range. Operators of commercial vessels pay a great deal of attention to current in selecting the advantageous time to enter a harbor or navigate a river. But power vessels are also affected by current in less subtle ways; ask any navigator why DR positions are not exact!

This chapter has three principal objectives: first, to introduce the final notation necessary for plotting; second, to enable the navigator to determine the actual current affecting his/her vessel; and finally, to enable the navigator to determine the course necessary to compensate for estimated currents and to calculate the resulting SOA. To accomplish these objectives requires some elementary knowledge of vectors which are introduced early in this chapter from a mechanical, rather than a mathematical, perspective. Steps to solution are clearly described and illustrated with numerical examples. Additionally, the Maneuvering Board (M Board) is introduced in this chapter as a tool for rapid and accurate analysis of current sailing problems. Use of M boards for other applications (e.g., radar plotting) is deferred until Chapter 9. Finally, a more complete voyage-planning form is introduced to simplify and organize current sailing calculations.

This chapter is slightly shorter than Chapters 5 or 6, but teaching experience suggests that it requires fully as much time to master as the earlier chapters on DR and piloting. It is suggested that the student reread the DR chapter, particularly the definitions contained therein, before studying this chapter.

CURRENT

The process of allowing for current in determining the predicted course made good, or in determining the effect of a current on the direction of motion of a vessel, is termed *current sailing*. For the purposes of this discussion, the term *current* as used in current sailing includes:

1. The horizontal motion of water over the ground, including ocean current, tidal, and river currents,
2. the effect of wind and seas, and
3. the effects of steering due to the helmsman, compass error, speed curve error, tachometer or other engine error, log or speedometer error, fouled bottom, or unusual trim.

APPLICATIONS

Current sailing may also be used to correct course and speed for the effects of known (measured or calculated) or suspected current in order to arrive at the intended destination at the intended time. Current sailing may be applied directly to a DR plot to correct a DR position into an EP, or it may be applied before the DR plot to adjust a course prior to its running.

CURRENT SAILING TERMS

The following terms are used in current sailing:

Estimated Current. The current developed from evaluation of known or predicted forces using calculations, current tables, diagrams, and/or charts. These methods are presented in Chapter 8.

Actual Current. This is the current measured as the difference between the vessel's actual position (fix) and that predicted without taking into account the effects of current (i.e., the DR position). The actual current incorporates all of the effects of current described above.

Set. Set is the direction *toward* which a current flows, or the *direction* toward which the vessel has been moved as a result of the current. SET is expressed in degrees, true. (This convention is exactly opposite to that for wind. The wind direction is the direction *from* which the wind is blowing.)

Drift. Drift is the *magnitude* or *speed* of the current. DRIFT is expressed in knots or statute miles per hour depending on the units used in the area.

THE CURRENT TRIANGLE

Graphical calculation of current effects involves the use of the *current triangle,* which is a simple vector diagram. The components of the current triangle have both *magnitude* and *direction.* The current triangle can be constructed on a separate piece of blank paper, or directly on the chart using the compass rose as a convenient means of measuring direction, and the latitude scale as a means of determining magnitude in units of speed (knots or mph). Additionally, current problems can be solved on an M board, the approach recommended here.

MANEUVERING BOARD (M Board)

The M board is a special-purpose plotting aid that is published by the Defense Mapping Agency (DMA). It is sold in pads of 50 sheets and comes in two sizes, a 10-inch diameter (DMA number 5090), and a 20-inch diameter (DMA number 5091). The 5090 is more convenient aboard small vessels and can be purchased at authorized agents for DMA publications and many dealers in navigation supplies. It is reproduced in the Student Study Guide and in Figure 7-1. The M board is a so-called *polar diagram,* consisting of ten equally spaced concentric rings, termed *distance circles,* around an origin (denoted by the symbol "e," drawn by hand in Figure 7-1) graduated with the numbers 2 through 10 (1 is not shown but is implicit). These distance circles can be used to represent either distance (e.g., in yards, statute, or nautical miles) or speed (e.g., in knots or statute miles per hour). The M board also contains 36 equally spaced bearing lines, one for every 10 degrees in azimuth (written on the outermost ring), originating at the center and radiating towards the outer rings. Along the outermost ring are smaller degree degradations, enabling azimuths to be drawn every 1 degree from 0 through 359 degrees. Just

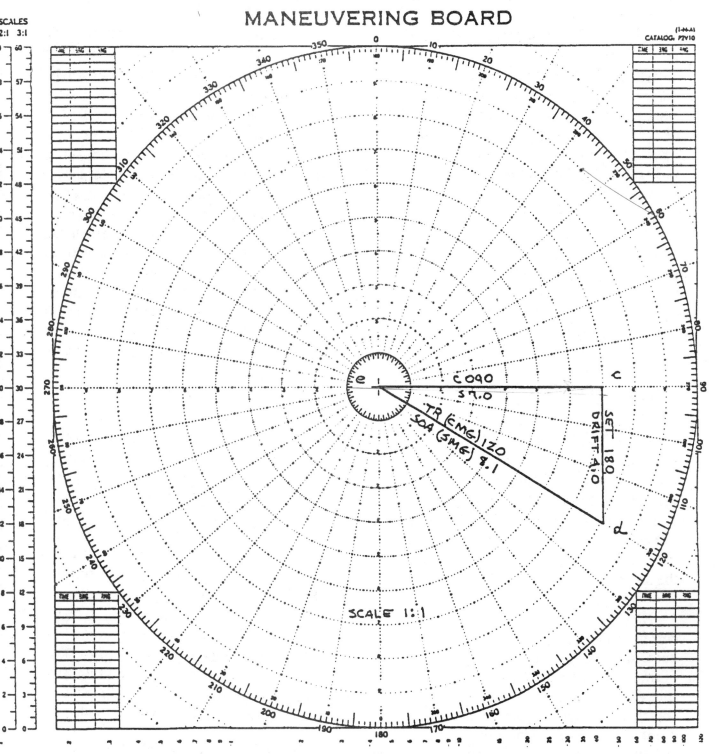

Fig. 7-1. Maneuvering Board with Example Problem.

beneath the outer bearing scale is an inner bearing scale, shown in smaller print, that presents the reciprocals of the principal bearings (e.g., the reciprocal of 10 degrees is 190 degrees, and this is shown beneath the 10 degree mark). At the bottom (not shown in Figure 7-1 because of space limitations) is a self-explanatory nomogram that can be used to solve time-speed-distance (TSD) problems. On each side of the sheet are two auxiliary scales, four in total (representing alternative scales of 2:1, 3:1, 4:1, and 5:1) that can be used in lieu of the principal distance scale. There are also inset tables for recording time, bearing, and range, a feature that is useful for radar plotting but is not relevant here. The use of the M board is explained below.

VECTORS TO DETERMINE THE EFFECTS OF A KNOWN OR ESTIMATED CURRENT

The effects of current on a vessel are easily determined with an M board. As a first example, assume that a vessel is steering a course of 090 degrees and maintaining a speed of 7 knots. The *course* or *velocity vector* for the ship is diagrammed in Figure 7-1, and denoted "ec." It is drawn outward from the origin (e) a distance of 7 units along a bearing of 090 degrees. In vector terminology, the "tail" of the vector is at the origin, and the "head" of the vector is located at the point (090 degrees, 7 knots). For this example, a distance scale of 1:1 is used, so the "range rings" can be read in knots directly. If an alternate scale were used, all that would be necessary is to set the dividers using the auxiliary scales to the right or left. (It is good practice to record the scale used somewhere on the diagram for later reference.) To draw the ec vector, simply use a paraline plotter or parallel rules, align the origin and the 090 mark on the outer bearing ring, and draw a solid line of length 7 units. (If a bearing were intermediate between the outer graduations, it would be convenient to use a divider preset to a 7-unit length to locate the head of the vector.) Label this first vector with the course and speed in the same manner as for a DR: course above the line and speed beneath the line.

Now suppose that there is an estimated current with a set of 180 degrees and drift of 4 knots affecting the progress of the vessel. Obviously, the overall effect of this current will be to shift (set) the vessel to the right (south) of its course. In other words, the estimated course of advance (COA) or course made good (CMG) will be greater than 090. Likewise, the SOA or speed made good (SMG) may differ from the speed through the water (STW, or more simply, speed, S). (SOA and SMG are virtually--but not exactly--interchangeable terms. The distinction is discussed later.) The operative question is, by how much?

To answer this question it is first necessary to draw another vector, the *current* or *drift vector,* to represent the effects of the current. In this case, the current vector is drawn from the *head* of the course vector, c, in the direction of the set of 180 degrees, a length of 4 units, and labeled SET 180, DRIFT 4, as is also shown in Figure 7-1. DRIFT is sometimes written Dft or simply "D" to save space. (Some navigators, however, use the symbol "D" for distance and, therefore, to avoid possible ambiguity try not to use "D" for drift.) To draw this vector, the parallel rule, or paraline plotter, is first aligned with the origin along a bearing of 180 degrees and then walked or rolled until aligned with the head of the course vector. A pair of dividers preset to length 4 (the drift in this example) is used to determine the length of the current vector. The tail or the drift vector is at point c, and the head is labeled d.

Finally, the resultant vector, ed, which denotes either the track (TR)/SOA or CMG/SMG can be determined. It is drawn from the origin (e), to the head of the current vector (d). The TR or CMG can be read from the outer bearing ring and is approximately equal to 120 degrees, some 30 degrees to the right of the course steered. The SOA or SMG is given by the length of the vector just drawn in, approximately 8.1 knots in this example, 16% more than the STW. (Any current for which the SMG is *greater* than the STW is termed a *fair current*. If the SOA/SMG is *less* than the STW the current is termed *foul*.) This vector is labeled with the TR or CMG above the line and SOA or SMG beneath the line. This completes the analysis of the problem. The effect of the current is easily seen and determined quantitatively by use of the M board.

In this example, the difference between the course steered and estimated track, which might be termed the *current drift angle* (CDA), is quite substantial. In general, the CDA is a function of the relative orientation of the course and drift vectors and of the vessel's STW compared to the drift. CDA's are largest when the current is abeam (90 degrees to the vessel's course), and when the drift is large compared to the vessel's speed, as shown in Table 7-1, for a "beam" cur-

TABLE 7-1. CURRENT DRIFT ANGLES (DEGREES OFF COURSE) AS A FUNCTION OF VESSEL STW AND CURRENT DRIFT FOR BEAM CURRENT.

VESSEL STW (KNOTS)	DRIFT OF BEAM CURRENT (KNOTS)							
	1.00	1.50	2.00	2.50	3.00	4.00	4.50	5.00
1.0	45.0	56.3	63.4	68.2	71.6	76.0	77.5	78.7
2.0	26.6	36.9	45.0	51.3	56.3	63.4	66.0	68.2
3.0	18.4	26.6	33.7	39.8	45.0	53.1	56.3	59.0
4.0	14.0	20.6	26.6	32.0	36.9	45.0	48.4	51.3
5.0	11.3	16.7	21.8	26.6	31.0	38.7	42.0	45.0
6.0	9.5	14.0	18.4	22.6	26.6	33.7	36.9	39.8
7.0	8.1	12.1	15.9	19.7	23.2	29.7	32.7	35.5
8.0	7.1	10.6	14.0	17.4	20.6	26.6	29.4	32.0
9.0	6.3	9.5	12.5	15.5	18.4	24.0	26.6	29.1
10.0	5.7	8.5	11.3	14.0	16.7	21.8	24.2	26.6
14.0	4.1	6.1	8.1	10.1	12.1	15.9	17.8	19.7
16.0	3.6	5.4	7.1	8.9	10.6	14.0	15.7	17.4
18.0	3.2	4.8	6.3	7.9	9.5	12.5	14.0	15.5
20.0	2.9	4.3	5.7	7.1	8.5	11.3	12.7	14.0
25.0	2.3	3.4	4.6	5.7	6.8	9.1	10.2	11.3
30.0	1.9	2.9	3.8	4.8	5.7	7.6	8.5	9.5
35.0	1.6	2.5	3.3	4.1	4.9	6.5	7.3	8.1
40.0	1.4	2.1	2.9	3.6	4.3	5.7	6.4	7.1

rent. Inspection of Table 7-1 (produced by computer) shows why power vessels with planing hulls capable of high speeds are likely to be less affected than slower sailboats. But, it also shows that CDAs are significant, nonetheless, and should not be disregarded. Assuming a 4-knot drift, for example, the CDA would be nearly 6 degrees, even if the vessel's STW were 40 knots, hardly a negligible effect.

The effect of current on the vessel's progress in the original example can also be shown in a more familiar manner, by use of the DR plot, shown in Figure 7-2. The DR course and DR positions are now shown beginning with a fix or departure assumed to take place at 1000. Remember, the DR positions do not include the effect of current, so the DR course line is plotted in a conventional manner. Instead, the effects of the estimated current are shown in a series of estimated positions (EPs), or DR positions,

corrected for drift. The vector diagram on the M board was for a time period of one hour, so the drift vector, cd, is drawn from the 1100 DR position to determine the 1100 EP. The drift vector is drawn with a dashed line and appropriately labeled as shown. EPs for times other than 1100 are easily drawn from the corresponding DR positions parallel to the drift vector a length sufficient to touch the line drawn from departure to the 1100 EP.

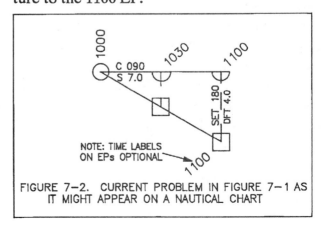

FIGURE 7-2. CURRENT PROBLEM IN FIGURE 7-1 AS IT MIGHT APPEAR ON A NAUTICAL CHART

7-5

Arguably, the line connecting the EPs is a more realistic estimate of the vessel's actual path with respect to the ground, so the student may wonder again why the DR plot is not abandoned in favor of the EP plot. Although there is some merit to this idea, remember that the drift vector is merely an estimate and may later be proven wrong with fixes. All that is known with (near) certainty is that the vessel steered 090 and maintained 7 knots. Thus, it is recommended in situations where there is a predictable current that *both* DR and EPs be drawn.

The above method for estimating the effects of a known current on the vessel's position is also used in correcting a running fix for current. In the conventional running fix calculation, the first LOP is advanced along the course steered a distance equal to the DR distance over the time period that the first LOP is advanced. In the presence of a known current, the above procedure is used to determine the resultant CMG/SMG, and the LOP is advanced along the CMG (rather than the course) a distance calculated using the SMG (rather than the speed) over the time interval that the first LOP is being advanced. The position so determined might be termed a running fix corrected for drift, or an estimated position, depending upon the likely accuracy of the drift estimate. In following this procedure, make sure that you properly take into account the time between LOPs and do not, for example, arbitrarily assume that the current is affecting the progress of the vessel for one hour, when the interval between LOPs is only 20 minutes.

DISTINCTIONS BETWEEN TR/CMG AND SOA/SMG

It was noted above that the terms TR and CMG (likewise SOA and SMG) were virtually, but not exactly, interchangeable. The distinctions were not central to the first example but become more important for discussion of the other current problems. As used in current sailing, the track (TR) refers to an *intended* or *expected* direction of travel with respect to the ground (course of advance (COA) is a synonym), whereas course made good (CMG) refers to the *actual* direction of travel with respect to the ground. Likewise, SOA refers to an *intended* or *expected* average ground speed, whereas speed made good (SMG) refers to an *actual* average ground speed.

The next current problem, discussed below, refers to the determination of the actual current, from knowledge of the course steered and speed maintained, as compared to the actual average ground speed and direction. In other words, for determination of the actual current, the vessel's course and speed vector is compared to the CMG/SMG. (Whatever the vessel's intentions or expectations were is beside the point.)

Alternatively, for planning purposes, it is necessary to decide what course and speed to run in order to maintain an intended track (TR) and, possibly intended average ground speed as well. Solutions to this problem are also discussed in this chapter. But here the TR and SOA are relevant. Put somewhat differently, TR and SOA refer to before-the-fact estimates, whereas CMG and SMG refer to actual, rather than planned, courses and speeds.

These differences are subtle and are often ignored by mariners. Indeed, if the before-the-fact estimates of current are accurate, then the TR is almost exactly equal to the CMG, and the COA is likewise equal to the SMG.

DETERMINATION OF SET AND DRIFT

Set and drift are usually determined from an analysis of the DR plot when a fix is obtained, by simply reversing the procedure described above. Briefly stated, current set and drift serve as the link between a fix and a DR position. The procedure is carried out in the following four steps and is illustrated with a numerical example from a portion of a cruise in the waters covered by the 1210-Tr chart. Although an M board could be used for estimation of the current vector, it is more common to solve this problem directly on a chart, so this technique will be illustrated.

First, prepare a DR plot in the conventional manner, noting either departure or the vessel's earlier fix, together with course(s) steered and speed(s) maintained. (Note that it is not necessary that the vessel steer only one course and/or maintain only one speed for the procedure to produce correct answers! This point is made clear in a later example.) An illustrative DR plot is provided in Figure 7-3, and shows that the vessel takes departure from the green lighted buoy near Quick's Hole on the east side of Nashawena Island at time 1330, the course (213 degrees true) and speed (5 knots) maintained, and the appropriate DR positions plotted every 30 minutes on the hour and half hour.

Second, plot a fix whenever it is obtained. In this example, a cross bearing fix is obtained (355 degrees true to the light on the SW tip of Cuttyhunk Island and 301 degrees true to the Buzzards Bay entrance light) at 1450. (If desired, a CMG/SMG vector can be drawn in by connecting the initial fix and the newly acquired fix with a straight line, measuring the CMG, and calculating the SMG by the time-speed-distance (TSD) formula.) Immediately plot the DR position corresponding to the fix time, as is illustrated in Figure 7-3.

Third, draw a dashed line, the drift vector, from the DR position just plotted to the fix taken at the same time. Measure the bearing of this drift vector *(from the DR position to the fix)* using a paraline plotter or parallel rule. This bearing (320 degrees true in the example) is the set. Label the drift vector appropriately with the set written above the dashed line representing the drift vector.

Finally, measure the length of the drift vector--1.6 nautical miles in this example. This is the distance that the vessel drifted *over the time period between the two fixes.* Remember that drift is the distance covered in one hour (it is measured in knots or statute miles per hour), and, therefore, it is necessary to divide by the time period (either in decimal hours or using $S = 60D/T$ in minutes) to calculate the rate. In this example, the time period between fixes was 1 hour and 20 minutes (80 minutes), so the drift = 60 (1.6)/80, or 1.2 knots. (**A common error is to forget this step.**) Add the label to the drift vector directly beneath the set notation. The drift vector just determined is termed the *actual current,* because it is based on actual data rather than an estimate derived from current tables, charts, or diagrams (see Chapter 8). But, because there are possible errors of measurement in this calculation, it is more technically accurate to term this an estimate of the actual current.

It was noted above that there is no requirement that the vessel maintain a constant course or speed for the calculations to be accurate. Any combination of course and speed changes can be accommodated, provided that these are recorded and reflected in the DR plot. Figure 7-4 illustrates this slightly more complex case. Here the vessel takes departure from the Harbor of Refuge near Point Judith at 0900 and makes several course and/or speed changes as shown on the DR plot. At 1030 a fix is obtained from a range line consisting of the two towers located on Beavertail Point and the tank (bearing 272 degrees true) located on Point Judith Neck. This 1030 fix is plotted, together with the 1030 DR position. The drift vector is drawn in and the bearing (set = 226 degrees) and length (0.9 nautical miles) determined. The time between departure and the first fix was 1.5 hours, so the estimated drift is 0.9/1.5 or 0.6 knots. The set and drift are labeled appropriately. As can be seen, the procedure incorporating course and/or speed changes is only slightly more complicated (because the DR plot is more complex) but is otherwise identical to the sim-

CURRENT SET AND DRIFT LINK A FIX WITH A DR POSITION

DR POSITION

FIX

pler case. Incidentally, this example is a nice illustration of the fact that the CMG and SMG vector is, to some degree, an abstraction. The CMG/SMG vector is determined by connecting the two fixes with a straight line. In this case, the straight line would carry the vessel over a portion of Point Judith! Do not think of this as an error; it follows directly from the definition of the CMG as a resultant.

These two examples show that the procedure for calculation of the actual current is quite simple and quick to do. Common errors include drawing the drift vector from the fix to the DR position (thus obtaining the reciprocal of the set), failure to take into account the time between fixes, and failing to plot a DR position corresponding to the time that the fix was taken. Remember also to renew the DR plot at the fix.

It was noted earlier that an M board could be used as well as the chart. For cases where a constant course and speed have been maintained, the problem is particularly simple and amounts to reversing the logic used in constructing Figure 7-1. That is, the course and speed vector, ec, is first drawn. Next, the CMG/SMG vector, ed, is drawn based on the vessel's actual positions at the time of the two fixes. Finally, the current vector, cd, is drawn from the course/speed vector to the CMG/SMG vector. The orientation and length of this vector give the set and drift, respectively. *(Remember to draw the vector from c to d, and not from d to c, else the set will be off by 180 degrees!)*

ADDITIONAL REMARKS ON DETERMINATION OF CURRENT

In the preceding examples it was shown how to estimate the actual current by comparing the DR position with a fix. It is also possible to estimate a current by comparing a DR position with an EP derived from a single LOP neglecting any allowance for current. All that is necessary is to substitute the word EP for the word fix in the above discussion. However, because the EP derived from a single LOP is likely to be less

accurate than a fix, the estimated actual current is likewise less accurate.

Even if a fix, rather than an EP, is used for estimation of actual current, it is important to realize the limitations of this estimate. First, the "actual current" so determined reflects all of the factors listed under the definition of current, e.g., helmsman's errors, errors in the speed curve, wind effects, and other factors that have little or nothing to do with the horizontal movement of water. Additionally, absent this consideration, the estimated actual current should be termed an "historical estimate" relevant to a particular time and expanse of water. Conventional practice is to use this historical estimate as an indication of the future, but it must be borne in mind that what is needed is a forecast of future current in the area where the vessel will be cruising, rather than of past currents for areas already traveled. It requires some judgment to decide whether or not to use the actual current determined on one leg of a trip as an estimate for the next leg of the voyage. Current diagrams and related material, discussed in Chapter 8, provide an indication of the spatial distribution of current, and hence the possible differences between the current in one area and that in another. If these differences are small, the mariner may use the historical estimate with more confidence. Local knowledge is also useful in forming enlightened judgments.

To return to the topic of the accuracy of the actual current estimate, it is important to note that the overall accuracy is a function of the fix accuracy and the time period over which the estimate was developed. If the time period is "short," the fix will be "close" to the DR position and any errors in the fix or the DR plot will have a substantial effect on the error in the resulting current estimate. However, if too long a time period is used, the current estimate is less proximate and, therefore, less relevant. As a practical matter, a time period of at least 30 minutes and as much as 1 hour or more is often used for current determination. An exception to this rule

Fig. 7-3. Determination of Actual Current by Comparison of a Fix with a DR Position.

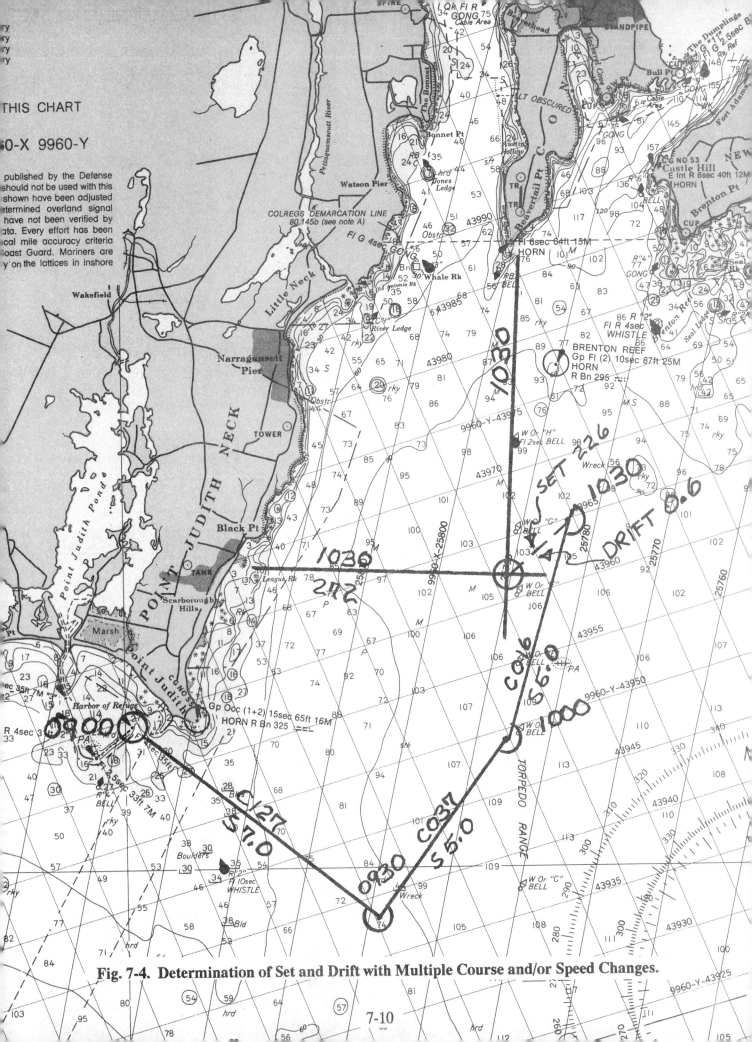

Fig. 7-4. Determination of Set and Drift with Multiple Course and/or Speed Changes.

should probably be made in the case of loran fixes, which are normally quite accurate. Additionally, most modern loran units are interfaced with the vessel's helm and speed measuring equipment (if installed). This interface, coupled with the incredible miniaturization of computers, makes it possible for the loran to automatically compute actual current set and drift. These computations (and others such as a continuous calculation of CMG and SMG) are done in "real time" and can be substituted for the more laborious procedures given here. (This topic is explored in more detail in Chapter 9.)

DETERMINATION OF A COURSE TO STEER (CURRENT GIVEN)

A common problem in current sailing is to determine the appropriate course to steer (C) in order to make good an intended track (TR) assuming that the current set and drift are known (either because these are estimated in advance using the methods of Chapter 8 or determined by a comparison of the vessel's DR position with a fix as discussed above), as well as the vessel's speed (S). This problem is easily solved on an M board in the following five steps.

To make the discussion concrete, assume that the vessel wishes to make good a track of 050 degrees, and that the current set and drift are 130 degrees and 2 knots respectively. The vessel's speed is 8 knots. The M board solution is shown on Figure 7-5 and is discussed below.

First, lightly draw a line of arbitrary length in the direction of the intended track (050 degrees). When completed, this line will represent the vessel's track (TR) and Speed of Advance (SOA). However, the length (SOA) cannot yet be determined. The vector begins at the origin, e, of the M board.

Second, draw the current vector from the origin, e, and label the set and drift. The head of the current vector, located in this example at the point (130 degrees, 2 knots), is designated with the letter "g" in Figure 7-5. As in the earlier M

board example, a scale of 1:1 is convenient and is also noted.

Third, set the drafting compass to a length equal to the speed, S, of the vessel using the distance or auxiliary scales as appropriate. Place the metal point of the compass on the *head* of the current vector (at g), and "swing" an arc of length S (8.0 units in this example) until it intersects the track line lightly drawn in the first step. Note and darken this intersection point, labeled "f" in Figure 7-5.

Fourth, draw a solid line from point g to point f. This line is the course/speed vector for the vessel. Using a parallel rule or paraline plotter, measure the bearing of this line. This angle, 036 degrees in this example, is the course that needs to be steered at 8.0 knots to make good the intended track. Label the course (C 036) and speed (S 8.0) as on a DR plot.

Fifth, darken and measure the length of the TR/SOA vector ef. This length (approximately 8.1 units in the example) is the estimated SOA along the track. Label the track (TR 050) and SOA (SOA 8.1) on the vector ef as shown.

This completes the procedure. The answer is interpreted as follows. To make good an intended track of 050 degrees in a current with drift 2.0 knots, and set 130 degrees, it is necessary to steer a course of 036 degrees if the vessel's speed is 8.0 knots. The estimated SOA is approximately 8.1 knots. It is good practice to check the plausibility of the results before setting off on the calculated course. In this example, the current set is to the right of the intended track. That is, the current is tending to push the vessel to the right of the intended track. It makes sense, therefore, that the course to compensate for this current should be to the left of track. And, indeed, 036 degrees (the course) is to the left of 050 degrees (the intended track). The difference between the course steered and track (036-050 = 014 degrees) is termed the *current correction angle* (CCA). This result is plausible. Next, con-

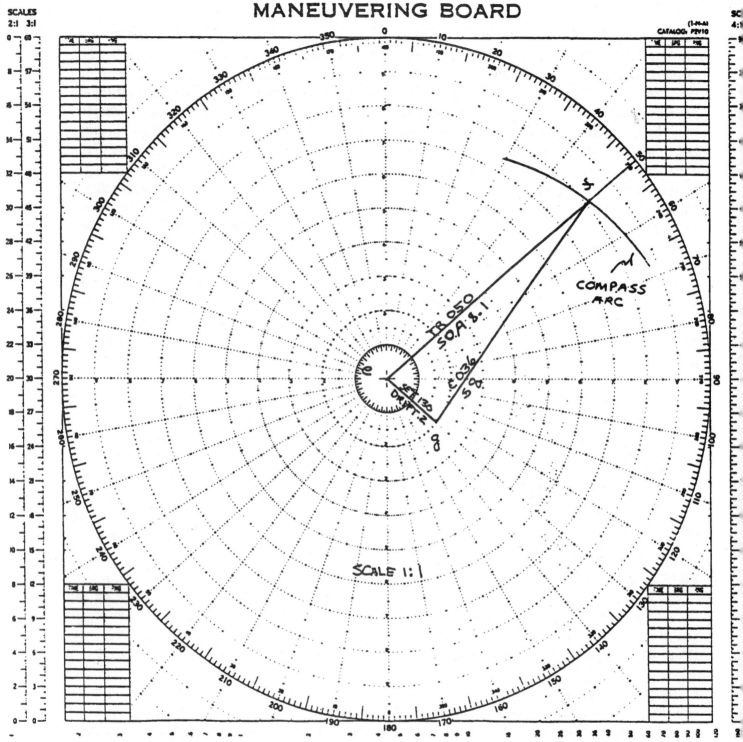

Fig. 7-5. Determination of Course to Make Intended Track with Current Given.

sider the SOA estimate. Because the current set is forward of the beam, albeit only slightly, the SOA should be (slightly) greater than the vessel's speed. In other words, the current in this example is (slightly) fair. This, too, checks, as the calculated SOA (8.1 knots) is slightly greater than S (8.0 knots).

The current correction angle can be determined mathematically and is a function of the relative bearing of the set compared to the vessel's course and the ratio of the drift to the vessel's speed. Current correction angles are largest when the current is abeam the intended track and when the drift is large in relation to the vessel's speed. This point is illustrated in Table 7-2, which shows computer calculated values of the current correction angle in degrees as a function of the relative bearing of the set in relation to the track (the rows in the table) and the ratio of the drift to speed (the columns). In this example, the relative bearing of the set is 80 degrees, and the ratio of drift to speed (2/8) is 0.25. Reading along the row corresponding to the relative bearing (080) and down the column corresponding to the speed ratio (0.25), the table entry, -14 degrees, is shown. Thus, to maintain a track of 050 the vessel would need to steer 050-014 or 036 degrees, exactly the value determined by use of the M board.

CURRENT COMPENSATION WHEN THE SOA IS PRESPECIFIED

The technique described above is applicable to calculation of the course to steer to compensate for known or estimated currents in the conventional case where the vessel's speed is specified. This is the usual situation in current sailing. The speed is either estimated (in the case of sailing vessels) or "known" as in the case of powerboats maintaining a specified engine throttle (RPM) setting. In either case the vessel's speed is assumed to be fixed in advance rather than a decision variable of the problem.

It is also sometimes of interest to solve current problems where the SOA, rather than the speed, is specified (e.g., in "log" races or in an attempt to rendezvous at a specified time, reaching an inlet at slack current, crossing a shoal during high tide, passing under a bridge at low tide, etc.), and the vessel's speed is assumed to be a decision variable, rather than fixed in advance. In this case, it is also assumed that the current is known (or able to be estimated) as are the intended track and SOA. The problem is to determine the course to steer and speed to maintain in order to make good the intended track and SOA. Solution of this problem is a minor variant--a simplification, in fact--of the technique discussed above. It, too, is solved on an M board, using the sequence of three steps

noted below. As an example, assume that the estimated time of departure (ETD) is 1015, and that an estimated time of arrival (ETA) of 1045 at a locating bearing 280 degrees true and 4.15 miles distant is desired. The estimated current sets 150 degrees at 3.0 knots. What are the course to steer and speed to maintain? A TSD calculation readily shows that the SOA must be 9.0 knots to attain the ETA, so the problem givens are: SOA 9.0 knots, set 150 degrees, drift 3.0 knots, and intended track 280 degrees. The M board solution is shown in Figure 7-6.

First, draw the TR/SOA vector from the origin, e, out along the intended track (280 degrees) a length equal to the SOA (9.0 knots) to the point f. (Unlike the case where the speed, rather than the SOA is specified, this vector can be drawn completely in the first step.) A scale of 1:1 is used here.

Second, draw the current vector from the origin, e, to point g, as in the earlier case and label the set (150 degrees) and drift (3.0 knots).

Third, draw the course/speed vector from the head of the current vector (point g) to the head of the TR/SOA vector (point f). Measure the length of this vector (11.2 units); this is the required speed (11.2 knots) to make good the SOA. Next, measure the bearing (using a parallel rule or paraline plotter), 292 degrees in this example. This is the course required to compensate for the current.

The answer is interpreted as follows. To make good as intended track of 280 degrees and SOA of 9.0 knots in a current with set of 150 degrees and drift 3.0 knots it is necessary to steer 292 degrees and maintain 11.2 knots. The answer is plausible; the current is setting the ship to the left of track, so the CCA should be to the right. Additionally, the current is foul, so the speed will have to exceed the intended SOA.

All current problems can be broken down into one of four categories: determination of the EP from course steered and speed maintained,

TABLE 7-2.   CURRENT CORRECTION ANGLE AS A FUNTION OF RELATIVE BEARING OF SET AND RATIO OF DRIFT TO STW.

RELATIVE BEARING OF SET (DEGREES)	RATIO OF CURRENT DRIFT TO VESSEL'S SPEED THROUGH THE WATER (STW)															
	0.00	0.05	0.10	0.15	0.20	0.25	0.30	0.35	0.40	0.45	0.50	0.60	0.70	0.80	0.90	1.00
0	0	0	0	0	0	0	0	0	0	0	0	0	0	0	0	0
10	0	0	-1	-1	-2	-2	-3	-3	-4	-4	-5	-6	-7	-8	-9	-10
20	0	-1	-2	-3	-4	-5	-6	-7	-8	-9	-10	-12	-14	-16	-18	-20
30	0	-1	-3	-4	-6	-7	-9	-10	-12	-13	-14	-17	-20	-24	-27	-30
40	0	-2	-4	-6	-7	-9	-11	-13	-15	-17	-19	-23	-27	-31	-35	-40
50	0	-2	-4	-7	-9	-11	-13	-16	-18	-20	-23	-27	-32	-38	-44	-50
60	0	-2	-5	-7	-10	-13	-15	-18	-20	-23	-26	-31	-37	-44	-51	-60
70	0	-3	-5	-8	-11	-14	-16	-19	-22	-25	-28	-34	-41	-49	-58	-70
80	0	-3	-6	-8	-11	-14	-17	-20	-23	-26	-29	-36	-44	-52	-62	-80
90	0	-3	-6	-9	-12	-14	-17	-20	-24	-27	-30	-37	-44	-53	-64	-90
100	0	-3	-6	-8	-11	-14	-17	-20	-23	-26	-29	-36	-44	-52	-62	-80
110	0	-3	-5	-8	-11	-14	-16	-19	-22	-25	-28	-34	-41	-49	-58	-70
120	0	-2	-5	-7	-10	-13	-15	-18	-20	-23	-26	-31	-37	-44	-51	-60
130	0	-2	-4	-7	-9	-11	-13	-16	-18	-20	-23	-27	-32	-38	-44	-50
140	0	-2	-4	-6	-7	-9	-11	-13	-15	-17	-19	-23	-27	-31	-35	-40
150	0	-1	-3	-4	-6	-7	-9	-10	-12	-13	-14	-17	-20	-24	-27	-30
160	0	-1	-2	-3	-4	-5	-6	-7	-8	-9	-10	-12	-14	-16	-18	-20
170	0	0	-1	-1	-2	-2	-3	-3	-4	-4	-5	-6	-7	-8	-9	-10
180	0	0	0	0	0	0	0	0	0	0	0	0	0	0	0	0
190	0	0	1	1	2	2	3	3	4	4	5	6	7	8	9	10
200	0	1	2	3	4	5	6	7	8	9	10	12	14	16	18	20
210	0	1	3	4	6	7	9	10	12	13	14	17	20	24	27	30
220	0	2	4	6	7	9	11	13	15	17	19	23	27	31	35	40
230	0	2	4	7	9	11	13	16	18	20	23	27	32	38	44	50
240	0	2	5	7	10	13	15	18	20	23	26	31	37	44	51	60
250	0	3	5	8	11	14	16	19	22	25	28	34	41	49	58	70
260	0	3	6	8	11	14	17	20	23	26	29	36	44	52	62	80
270	0	3	6	9	12	14	17	20	24	27	30	37	44	53	64	90
280	0	3	6	8	11	14	17	20	23	26	29	36	44	52	62	80
290	0	3	5	8	11	14	16	19	22	25	28	34	41	49	58	70
300	0	2	5	7	10	13	15	18	20	23	26	31	37	44	51	60
310	0	2	4	7	9	11	13	16	18	20	23	27	32	38	44	50
320	0	2	4	6	7	9	11	13	15	17	19	23	27	31	35	40
330	0	1	3	4	6	7	9	10	12	13	14	17	20	24	27	30
340	0	1	2	3	4	5	6	7	8	9	10	12	14	16	18	20
350	0	0	1	1	2	2	3	3	4	4	5	6	7	8	9	10

determination of the actual current from knowledge of the course steered and maintained compared to the CMG/SMG, determination of the course to steer to compensate for known currents in order to make good an intended track given either the speed or SOA. Review the steps for solution of each of these problem types and practice plotting these on both a chart and an M board. Pay particular attention to what is being plotted as well as to the steps. For example, suppose you estimate a current and use this estimate to calculate a course to compensate so as to make good an intended track. Later, you determine a fix and wish to calculate the actual current. Remember to compare the DR track with the CMG/SMG--*neither the TR nor the SOA enter into this calculation*. Practice alone prevents these blunders.

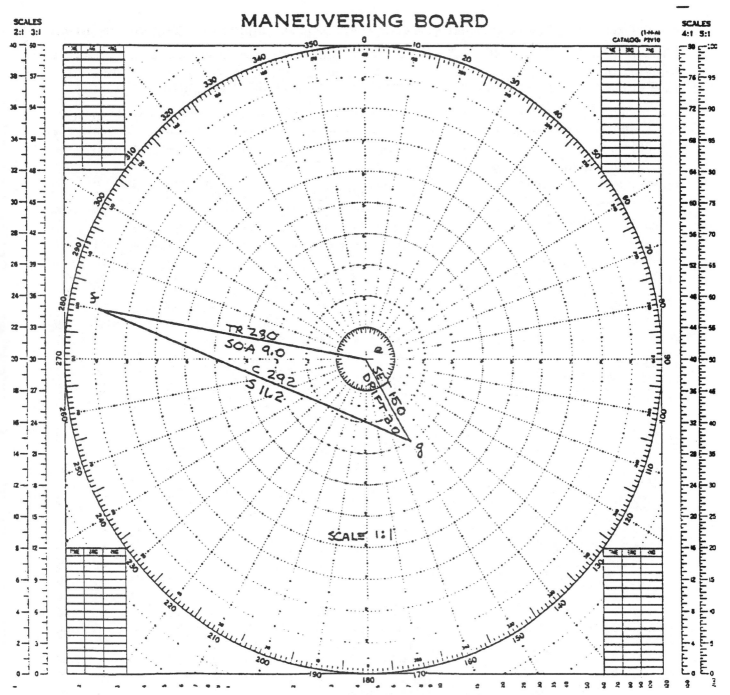

**Fig. 7-6. Determination of the Course and Speed
to Achieve a Specified Track and SOA, with Known Current**

EPs WITH CURRENT AND LOPs

Earlier in this chapter it is shown how to determine an estimated position (EP) using the course steered, speed maintained, and actual or estimated set and drift of the current. This amounts to nothing more than drawing in the DR plot, and adding a dashed line to represent the current vector. The current vector is drawn from the vessel's DR position a distance equal to the calculated drift, at an angle equal to the set of the current, as illustrated in Figure 7-2. This EP should properly be termed the "EP considering current alone."

In Chapter 6, EPs are discussed in the context of a DR position and a single LOP. There it is noted that the EP (neglecting current) could be plotted by simply drawing a perpendicular dashed line from the vessel's DR position at the time of the LOP to the LOP. This EP should properly be termed the "EP considering the LOP alone."

It sometimes happens that both actual (or estimated) current and an LOP are available. Figure 7-7 illustrates this situation. The vessel's position is fixed at 1400 and thereafter it maintains a course of 090 (true) at a speed of 6.0 knots. The DR plot is shown over the time interval from 1400 to 1500, as is the 1500 DR position. Assume that the estimated set and drift of the current are 180 degrees and 4.0 knots, respectively. This estimate enables an EP to be drawn considering this current alone. This EP is shown in Figure 7-7, drawn as the square. (Normally, the time corresponding to this EP would also be shown, but this is omitted here to save chart clutter.) Now, suppose that at 1500 a

lighthouse is sighted bearing 045 true. This LOP is drawn and properly labeled in Figure 7-7. This raises the question: how can both current and LOP information be considered? To develop the answer, note first that, absent current, the EP would be drawn at the intersection of the perpendicular line from the DR position to the LOP. This line is drawn in Figure 7-7, and represents the best estimate of the vessel's position considering only the DR information and the LOP. This point is denoted "EP LOP only" in Figure 7-7. However, compared to the DR position used to draw this EP, an improved estimate of position is available which reflects the estimated current. Logically, it follows that a yet improved estimate of the vessel's position is available, obtained by simply drawing a perpendicular line from the EP (current only) to the LOP, rather than from the DR position. This improved position estimate is denoted the "EP

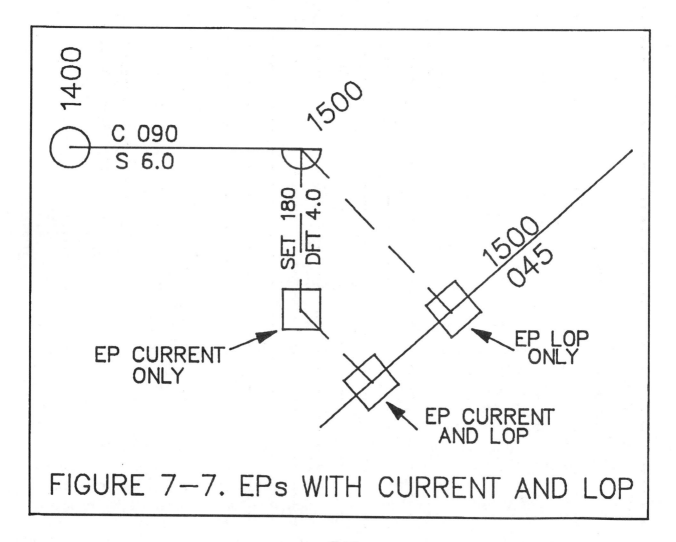

FIGURE 7-7. EPs WITH CURRENT AND LOP

REMARKS ON VOYAGE PLAN:

BLOCK ISLAND TO WOOD'S HOLE

GENERAL INFORMATION:

DATE: _6-9-89_
NAVIGATOR: _LDM_
VESSEL: _PERDIDA_

CHECK ITEMS
CHARTS REQD: ✓   CURRENT TABLES: ✓
COAST PILOT: ✓   DEVIATION TABLE: ✓
LIGHT LIST: ___   FUEL/RPM TABLE: ✓
TIDE TABLES: ✓   PILOT CHARTS: ___

NAV. GEAR: ✓
TIMEPIECE: ✓

TIME START: _1030_   FOB (GAL): _____

DETAILED LEG PLAN:

LEG	FROM	TO	INTENDED TRACK (TRUE)	LEG DISTANCE (N.M.)	POWER SETTING (RPM)	ESTIMATED STW (KNOTS)	CURRENT SET	CURRENT DRIFT	TRUE COURSE	VARIATION	MAGNETIC COURSE	DEVIATION	COMPASS COURSE	ESTIMATED SOA (KNOTS)	ETE HH:MM	ETA HH:MM	EST. FUEL CONSUMPTION (GAL)	EST. FUEL REMAINING (GAL)
1	"1A"	WOR "A"	050	9.2	1250	5.3	130	2	028	15W	043	3E	040	5.2	1:46	1216		

Fig. 7-8. Illustrative Voyage Planning Worksheet with
First Leg of Voyage Entered.

considering current and LOP," and is shown on Figure 7-7. Its construction is quick and simple. First, draw the current vector on the chart from the DR position. Next, draw a perpendicular line from the position just determined (EP considering current only) to the LOP. (The numbers chosen in the example depicted in Figure 7-7 are exaggerated for graphic clarity.) To finish the diagram, a square is drawn around this position, and the time written at an angle alongside.

VOYAGE PLANNING--PUTTING IT ALL TOGETHER

As discussed above, current sailing techniques are useful for two purposes. First, these are used for prevoyage planning to estimate the requisite courses and SOAs based on forecasted currents (see Chapter 8 for details), and second, in a more or less "real time" mode where a comparison of the vessel's DR plot with positions enables calculation of actual currents and necessary course adjustments.

Normally, current problems are solved sequentially. For example, a preliminary estimate of set and drift is used to calculate a course and estimate an SOA. This course is steered until a subsequent fix is obtained. The fix is compared to the DR position, and a revised estimate of current set and drift is made. This revised set and drift is compared to known information (see Chapter 8) and adjusted (if necessary) based upon the vessel's future intended track. The revised set and drift are used to determine a new course and SOA, and so on in an iterative manner.

Prevoyage planning is an important activity in itself. From the point of view of the ACN course, it provides an opportunity to integrate the various topics covered thus far, e.g., charts, the ship's compass, DR, piloting, and current sailing. The essence of prevoyage planning is to select the appropriate route and timing of the voyage (from inspection of relevant charts and other reference materials), lay out the voyage legs (including the identification of suitable objects for fixes, turnpoints, etc.), precalculate courses, SOAs, fuel consumption, and other tasks.

There is no one "best" approach to this planning process, but it is helpful to have a worksheet, or checklist, to structure the process. One "trip planning worksheet" is shown in Figure 7-8. It contains checklist information and entries for such items as track, leg distance, engine RPM, STW, current set and drift, course to steer (true), the TVMDC calculations, estimated SOA, estimated time enroute (ETE), estimated time of arrival (ETA), and fuel planning data (discussed in Chapter 11). These entries are arranged in the order in which they would normally be calculated for planning purposes. The first (handwritten) line describes one leg of a voyage from Block Island to Wood's Hole on the 1210-Tr Chart. Follow through the calculations and ensure that you are able to understand how these are developed.

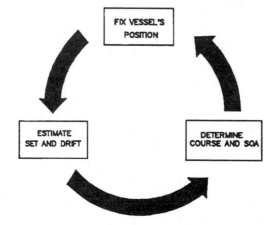

NORMALLY, CURRENT PROBLEMS ARE SOLVED SEQUENTIALLY

FIX VESSEL'S POSITION

ESTIMATE SET AND DRIFT

DETERMINE COURSE AND SOA

REFERENCES

For additional material on current sailing, please refer to the some references as given at the end of Chapters 5 and 6. Note that books published in Great Britain use a different set of drafting symbols than are employed here.

On the topic of determining running fixes corrected for current, the following additional texts are particularly useful:

Ministry of Defense, (Navy) BR45(1) *Admiralty Manual of Navigation,* Volume 1, D/DNW/102/3/14/2, Her Majesty's Stationary Office (HMSO), London, UK, 1987, pp 204 *et seq.*

Coolen, E. *Nicholls's Concise Guide to Navigation,* Volume 1, Brown, Son & Ferguson Ltd, Glasgow, Scotland, 1987, pp 314 *et seq.*

Chapter 8

Tides and Tidal Currents

his chapter provides a discussion of two important phenomena to the mariner: tides and tidal currents. Tides and tidal currents are of great interest to the oceanographer as well, but the focus of this chapter is on items of interest to the mariner.

Estimating the height of tides is very important for such purposes as identifying safe water, knowing how much anchor line to deploy when anchoring, and estimating the vertical clearance under bridges. Knowledge of how to estimate tidal currents is equally important, but for different reasons. Tidal current information is essential for voyage planning generally, and specifically for such purposes as selecting a time to enter inlets, rivers, or bays to maximize safety and/or minimize travel time, and estimating the speed made good (SMG) and fuel consumption for voyages in areas affected by tidal currents.

Prediction and estimation of tides or tidal currents is facilitated by use of the *Tide Tables,* or *Tidal Current Tables,* published annually by the National Ocean Service. The bulk of this chapter is devoted to a discussion of how to use these tables. To facilitate these computations, three separate worksheets are included, along with directions for their use. The computations are not difficult, amounting to nothing more than addition, multiplication, and extracting information from tables, but experience in teaching the ACN course indicates that students often make careless errors in these computations, so it is important to pay careful attention to detail to ensure that the answers are correct.

TIDES AND TIDAL PATTERNS

At the outset, it is important to distinguish between two related but distinct terms. *Tide* refers to the *vertical* motion of the water, *tidal current* (called *tidal stream* by the British) to the *horizontal* motion of the water. Both tides and tidal currents have the same origin and vary with the same factors including the gravitational effects of the moon and sun, and runoff from rain or snowfall. But these are logically very different concepts.

As noted, tides result from the gravitational effects of the moon and sun, and experience (and theory) indicate that tides are periodic. There are predictable variations in tidal heights, hour-by-hour, day-by-day, season-by-season, and year-by-year. All tidal heights are measured from a datum or reference plane. In the United States, and certain other parts of the world, this reference plane is what is termed mean lower low water (MLLW). The term *high water* denotes the maximum height reached by each rising tide, and *low water* the minimum height reached by each falling tide. The *tidal range* is the difference between consecutive high and low waters.

Figures 8-1 and 8-2, taken from the *Tidal Tables,* show the hourly and daily patterns of tide heights (measured relative to datum) for several locations on the east, gulf, and west coasts of the United States. This small sample is sufficient to indicate the most important patterns (discussed below) and some typical tidal heights and ranges.

As can be seen from the patterns in Figures 8-1 and 8-2, there are often two high and two low

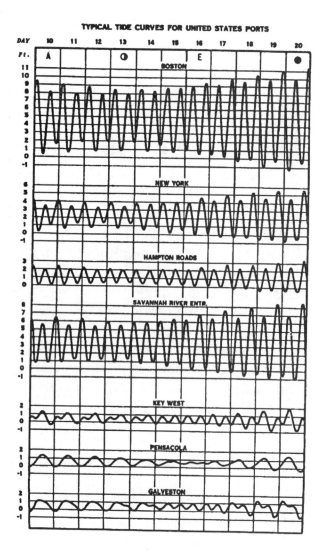

Fig. 8-1. Typical Tide Curves for United States Ports.

tide will have one high and one low tide each day, a *semidiurnal* tide has a period of approximately one-half of a tidal day (see, for example, the patterns for Boston, and New York in Figure 8-1), that is, there are typically two times of high water and two times of low water in each day. A *mixed* pattern (see, for example, Seattle, WA, or San Francisco, CA, as shown in Figure 8-2) is a type of tide with a large inequality in the high and/or low water heights, with two high waters and two low waters usually occurring each tidal day.

In addition to the daily patterns evident in the illustrations in Figure 8-1 and 8-2, there are more subtle patterns with a longer period. Tides have *decreased* range when the moon is in *apogee* (farthest from the earth, denoted with the symbol "A" in Figures 8-1 and 8-2), and *increased* range when the moon is in perigee (closest to the earth).

When the moon and the sun are in line and "pulling together" (i.e., at a new or full moon a phenomenon termed *syzygy* and pronounced "siz-zigee"), larger tidal ranges, termed *spring tides* occur. (The term spring has nothing to do with the season.) Alternatively, when the gravitational forces of the sun and the moon are at right angles (i.e., the moon is said to be in *quadrature*), tides with smaller ranges, termed *neap tides*, occur.

Tidal range varies with location on the earth, as well as with the positions of the sun and moon. Examination of the patterns shown in Figures 8-1 and 8-2, show that there are substantial differences in the tidal ranges among US ports. At Anchorage, Alaska, for example, the tidal range is 30 feet or more, whereas at Key West or Pensacola, Florida, the tidal range is considerably smaller (only 2 or 3 feet). Other locations with large tidal ranges include the Bay of Fundy (adjoining the provinces of Nova Scotia and New Brunswick in Canada) where mean tidal ranges of 40 feet or more are observed, some locations on the coast of Maine (20 feet or

waters in a day, but other patterns occur (see below). Tides follow the moon more closely than the sun (although the sun is much larger, the moon is very much closer to the earth, more than compensating for the mass difference in the gravitation equation), and so the period evident in these figures tends to match that of the lunar day--approximately 24 hours and 50 minutes. Because the lunar day is slightly longer than the solar day, the times for high and low tides occur later on each succeeding calendar day.

There are three principal daily patterns observed for tides: *diurnal, semidiurnal,* and *mixed.* A *diurnal* tide has a period or cycle of approximately one tidal (lunar) day--that is, a diurnal more), and near the southern tip of South America. Locations with relatively small tidal ranges include Barnegat Bay, New Jersey (less than 1 foot), and portions of the Chesapeake Bay. The area covered by the 1210-Tr chart includes some locations with small ranges (e.g., Little Harbor near Woods Hole with a range of 1.4 ft.), and others (e.g., several locations in Buzzards Bay) where the tidal range is larger (4 to 5 ft.).

This brief sample of tidal data indicates that the practical importance of tidal phenomena varies from region to region, and even location-to-location within regions. Mariners from some locations in New Jersey, for example, may worry little about tides, while tides are a central fact of life for boaters in Maine or other areas with large tidal range.

PRACTICAL REASONS WHY TIDES ARE IMPORTANT

Before discussing how tidal heights are estimated, it is useful to review briefly why knowledge of tides is important to the mariner. (Anyone who has run aground, had to replace or straighten a bent prop or shaft, had their anchor drag, or trimmed the top few feet off the mast of their sailboat by crossing under a bridge with insufficient clearance can skip this section--such experience provides more than ample motivation for careful study of this chapter!)

In Chapter 3, it was noted that the charted depth of water is based on a datum of mean lower low water (MLLW, the average of the lower of the low tides each day). Actual water depths vary with the tide, so in order to calculate these depths--and thus, whether or not safe water exists--it is necessary to calculate tidal heights. Knowledge of water depths is obviously important to the *safety* of the voyage--after all, who wants to run aground, or have to wait days until high tides are sufficient to clear a harbor? (Vessels imprisoned in harbors with shallow entrances awaiting favorable tides were often said to be "neaped.")

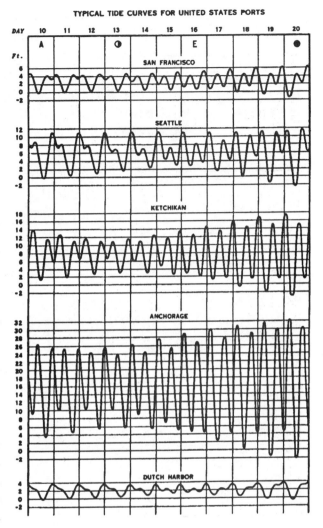

Fig. 8-2. Typical Tide Curves for United States Ports.

Knowledge of water depths can also be important to the *efficiency* of a voyage as well as its safety. It often happens, for example, that you have a choice of alternate routes to your final destination--a deep but indirect channel, or a shorter, more direct route that takes you over the shallows. Knowledge of tidal heights may enable you to take shortcuts--perfectly safely--that save substantial distance and (therefore) time. All that might be necessary is to plan the voyage at a time when the tides are relatively high. (Seamen in days gone by were taught to enter an unfamiliar harbor cautiously at "half tide and rising." Half tide ensured that there would be water under the vessel, and a rising tide meant that the vessel could be promptly re-

Table 8-1. Actual Scope of Anchorline at High Tide as a Function of Low Water Depth and Intended Scope for Various Values of Tidal Range Assuming that Vessel is Anchored at Low Tide.

Intended Scope	Water Depth When Anchoring (Ft.)	Tidal Range (Feet)						
		1	2	3	4	5	7	10
6	3	5.0	4.3	3.8	3.3	3.0	2.5	2.0
6	4	5.1	4.5	4.0	3.6	3.3	2.8	2.3
6	5	5.3	4.7	4.2	3.8	3.5	3.0	2.5
6	6	5.3	4.8	4.4	4.0	3.7	3.2	2.7
6	7	5.4	4.9	4.5	4.2	3.9	3.4	2.8
6	8	5.5	5.0	4.6	4.3	4.0	3.5	3.0
6	9	5.5	5.1	4.7	4.4	4.1	3.7	3.1
6	10	5.5	5.1	4.8	4.5	4.2	3.8	3.3
6	12	5.6	5.3	4.9	4.7	4.4	4.0	3.5
7	3	5.8	5.0	4.4	3.9	3.5	2.9	2.3
7	4	6.0	5.3	4.7	4.2	3.8	3.2	2.6
7	5	6.1	5.4	4.9	4.5	4.1	3.5	2.9
7	6	6.2	5.6	5.1	4.7	4.3	3.7	3.1
7	7	6.3	5.7	5.3	4.8	4.5	3.9	3.3
7	8	6.4	5.8	5.4	5.0	4.7	4.1	3.5
7	9	6.4	5.9	5.5	5.1	4.8	4.3	3.7
7	10	6.5	6.0	5.6	5.3	4.9	4.4	3.8
7	12	6.5	6.1	5.8	5.4	5.2	4.7	4.1
8	3	6.7	5.7	5.0	4.4	4.0	3.3	2.7
8	4	6.9	6.0	5.3	4.8	4.4	3.7	3.0
8	5	7.0	6.2	5.6	5.1	4.7	4.0	3.3
8	6	7.1	6.4	5.8	5.3	4.9	4.3	3.6
8	7	7.2	6.5	6.0	5.5	5.1	4.5	3.8
8	8	7.3	6.7	6.2	5.7	5.3	4.7	4.0
8	9	7.3	6.8	6.3	5.9	5.5	4.9	4.2
8	10	7.4	6.9	6.4	6.0	5.6	5.1	4.4
8	12	7.5	7.0	6.6	6.2	5.9	5.3	4.7

floated--assuming a soft bottom--in the event of miscalculation.)

Knowledge of tidal heights is also very important when *anchoring* or *mooring*. Suppose, for example, that you anchor in 3 feet of water, and that the distance from the bow to the water-line for your vessel is 2 feet. Following recommended procedures, you elect to deploy 40 feet of anchor line, figuring that this will give you a "safe" scope of 8 to 1 (40/ (3 + 2) = 8). But suppose that the tide were low when you anchored, and that the tidal range were 5 feet. At high tide, when the water depth would be 8 feet

(5 + 3), the effective scope would be reduced to only 4 to 1 (40/ (3 + 5 + 2) = 4), not nearly enough. (Table 8-1 shows how the actual scope of anchor line at high tide varies with the scope at low tide and the tidal range.) The point of these simple calculations is that you should plan to put out enough line to ensure a sufficient scope at high tide--which means that you need to know the state of the tide at anchoring, and the depth of water at high tide. These calculations can be really dramatic for areas, such as Anchorage, Alaska (a misnomer to be sure), or the Bay of Fundy, where (as discussed above) the tidal range can be 30 or 40 feet! (At some of these locations it may not even be possible to deploy sufficient anchor line to ensure a safe scope at high tide. The only alternative is to maintain a constant anchor watch.)

Anchoring at low tide risks deploying an insufficient scope if the tidal range is not considered. But, anchoring at high tide also has risks, if tidal heights are ignored. This is because the radius of the *swing circle* (the distance from the anchor to the stern of the vessel) increases for a fixed anchor line length as the tide height decreases. If this effect is not considered, you run the risk of becoming on intimate terms with other vessels in a crowded anchorage!

Finally, knowledge of tidal heights is important to determine whether or not there is sufficient clearance between the vessel's mast(s) and overhead obstructions, such as bridges. In some critical cases, it may be necessary to pass under a bridge at low tide to ensure that sufficient clearance exists.

For these and other reasons it is important for the mariner to know how to estimate tide heights.

SOURCES OF TIDAL INFORMATION

There are several sources of tidal information. Many newspapers, for example, routinely publish information on the time and height of tides at several locations. Television weather broadcasts, particularly those oriented towards mariners, often contain tidal information, as do scheduled government weather broadcasts. Several private companies publish almanacs or other guides that contain tidal information. Increasingly, computer software is coming on the market that automates the calculation of tidal heights. All that is required is one of the many "laptop" computers to run this software.

But, the most important source of tidal information (and, indeed, the source of the reference data republished by other firms) are the *Tide Tables,* published by the US Department of Commerce, National Oceanic and Atmospheric Administration (NOAA), National Ocean Service (NOS). These tidal tables are published *annually* in four volumes, as follows: Europe and West Coast of Africa (including the Mediterranean Sea); East Coast of North and South America (including Greenland); West Coast, North and South America (including the Hawaiian Islands); Central and Western Pacific Ocean and Indian Ocean. Together, these four volumes contain daily predictions for 198 so-called *reference* ports (discussed below), and differences and other constants (necessary for calculation) for about 6,000 other ports/locations. Several other countries (e.g., Great Britain, Canada, Brazil, Argentina) also publish accurate and useful tables, but these are not discussed in this chapter.

USE OF THE TIDE TABLES

The publication *Tide Tables* consists of seven separate sets of tables. Of these, Tables 1, 2, and 3 are required for estimation of tidal heights, and are discussed here. The remaining four tables relate to estimation of the time for sunrise/sunset, moonrise/moonset, and some units conversion (ft. to meters and reduction of local mean time to standard time).

Locations for which tidal predictions can be made with the aid of the *Tide Tables* are subdivided into two classes: *reference stations,* and *subordinate stations* (substations). Reference stations (called *standard ports* by the British)

Table 8-2. Excerpt from Table 1 of *Tide tables*.

40

NEWPORT, R.I., 1989

Times and Heights of High and Low Waters

JANUARY

Day	Time h m	Height ft	Height m	Day	Time h m	Height ft	Height m
1 Su	0210	3.0	0.9	16 M	0240	3.8	1.2
	0730	0.8	0.2		0904	0.3	0.1
	1429	2.6	0.8		1507	2.9	0.9
	1931	0.5	0.2		2049	0.1	0.0
2 M	0303	3.1	0.9	17 Tu	0341	3.8	1.2
	0835	0.7	0.2		1023	0.2	0.1
	1522	2.6	0.8		1607	2.9	0.9
	2030	0.4	0.1		2159	0.1	0.0
3 Tu	0354	3.3	1.0	18 W	0439	3.9	1.2
	0941	0.6	0.2		1127	0.1	0.0
	1618	2.7	0.8		1703	3.0	0.9
	2128	0.3	0.1		2304	0.0	0.0
4 W	0445	3.5	1.1	19 Th	0532	4.0	1.2
	1040	0.4	0.1		1217	0.0	0.0
	1708	2.9	0.9		1755	3.2	1.0
	2223	0.1	0.0		2359	-0.1	0.0
5 Th	0532	3.8	1.2	20 F	0622	4.0	1.2
	1132	0.1	0.0		1255	-0.1	0.0
	1756	3.1	0.9		1841	3.3	1.0
	2317	-0.1	0.0				
6 F	0618	4.0	1.2	21 Sa	0044	-0.2	-0.1
	1217	-0.1	0.0		0707	4.0	1.2
	1842	3.3	1.0		1332	-0.1	0.0
					1927	3.5	1.1
7 Sa	0009	-0.3	-0.1	22 Su	0123	-0.3	-0.1
	0705	4.2	1.3		0750	4.0	1.2
	1303	-0.3	-0.1		1403	-0.1	0.0
	1929	3.5	1.1		2009	3.5	1.1
8 Su	0058	-0.5	-0.2	23 M	0159	-0.2	-0.1
	0751	4.3	1.3		0831	3.8	1.2
	1345	-0.5	-0.2		1427	-0.1	0.0
	2015	3.6	1.1		2050	3.5	1.1
9 M	0148	-0.6	-0.2	24 Tu	0233	-0.1	0.0
	0838	4.3	1.3		0911	3.7	1.1
	1429	-0.6	-0.2		1454	-0.1	0.0
	2103	3.8	1.2		2132	3.5	1.1
10 Tu	0237	-0.6	-0.2	25 W	0306	0.0	0.0
	0926	4.2	1.3		0948	3.4	1.0
	1513	-0.6	-0.2		1523	0.0	0.0
	2151	3.8	1.2		2212	3.4	1.0
11 W	0327	-0.6	-0.2	26 Th	0339	0.1	0.0
	1015	4.0	1.2		1028	3.2	1.0
	1558	-0.5	-0.2		1553	0.1	0.0
	2243	3.9	1.2		2254	3.2	1.0
12 Th	0422	-0.4	-0.1	27 F	0414	0.3	0.1
	1105	3.8	1.2		1110	2.9	0.9
	1646	-0.4	-0.1		1625	0.2	0.1
	2337	3.8	1.2		2336	3.1	0.9
13 F	0518	-0.2	-0.1	28 Sa	0451	0.4	0.1
	1203	3.5	1.1		1152	2.7	0.8
	1736	-0.3	-0.1		1702	0.2	0.1
14 Sa	0035	3.8	1.2	29 Su	0024	3.0	0.9
	0624	0.0	0.0		0536	0.6	0.2
	1302	3.2	1.0		1243	2.5	0.8
	1832	-0.1	0.0		1746	0.3	0.1
15 Su	0136	3.7	1.1	30 M	0120	2.9	0.9
	0739	0.2	0.1		0632	0.7	0.2
	1403	3.0	0.9		1342	2.4	0.7
	1936	0.0	0.0		1837	0.4	0.1
				31 Tu	0217	3.0	0.9
					0734	0.7	0.2
					1443	2.4	0.7
					1939	0.4	0.1

FEBRUARY

Day	Time h m	Height ft	Height m	Day	Time h m	Height ft	Height m
1 W	0317	3.1	0.9	16 Th	0423	3.5	1.1
	0851	0.6	0.2		1124	0.3	0.1
	1542	2.5	0.8		1648	3.0	0.9
	2046	0.3	0.1		2311	0.1	0.0
2 Th	0415	3.4	1.0	17 F	0516	3.6	1.1
	1005	0.4	0.1		1207	0.1	0.0
	1639	2.8	0.9		1738	3.2	1.0
	2157	0.1	0.0				
3 F	0506	3.7	1.1	18 Sa	0001	0.0	0.0
	1103	0.1	0.0		0604	3.7	1.1
	1730	3.1	0.9		1239	0.0	0.0
	2301	-0.2	-0.1		1823	3.4	1.0
4 Sa	0557	4.0	1.2	19 Su	0039	-0.1	0.0
	1153	-0.2	-0.1		0648	3.7	1.1
	1820	3.5	1.1		1307	0.0	0.0
	2356	-0.5	-0.2		1905	3.5	1.1
5 Su	0644	4.2	1.3	20 M	0111	-0.2	-0.1
	1241	-0.5	-0.2		0727	3.8	1.2
	1907	3.8	1.2		1332	-0.1	0.0
					1944	3.7	1.1
6 M	0048	-0.7	-0.2	21 Tu	0141	-0.2	-0.1
	0731	4.4	1.3		0806	3.7	1.1
	1324	-0.7	-0.2		1355	-0.2	-0.1
	1954	4.1	1.2		2022	3.7	1.1
7 Tu	0138	-0.9	-0.3	22 W	0210	-0.2	-0.1
	0817	4.4	1.3		0842	3.6	1.1
	1407	-0.9	-0.3		1420	-0.1	0.0
	2041	4.2	1.3		2100	3.7	1.1
8 W	0228	-0.9	-0.3	23 Th	0238	-0.1	0.0
	0906	4.3	1.3		0919	3.4	1.0
	1451	-0.9	-0.3		1446	-0.1	0.0
	2129	4.3	1.3		2137	3.5	1.1
9 Th	0318	-0.8	-0.2	24 F	0308	0.0	0.0
	0953	4.1	1.2		0955	3.2	1.0
	1535	-0.8	-0.2		1513	-0.1	0.0
	2220	4.3	1.3		2214	3.4	1.0
10 F	0409	-0.6	-0.2	25 Sa	0342	0.1	0.0
	1043	3.7	1.1		1033	2.9	0.9
	1620	-0.6	-0.2		1548	0.0	0.0
	2313	4.1	1.2		2254	3.2	1.0
11 Sa	0502	-0.3	-0.1	26 Su	0417	0.2	0.1
	1138	3.4	1.0		1113	2.7	0.8
	1709	-0.3	-0.1		1622	0.1	0.0
					2340	3.1	0.9
12 Su	0011	3.9	1.2	27 M	0502	0.4	0.1
	0605	0.0	0.0		1200	2.5	0.8
	1237	3.1	0.9		1705	0.3	0.1
	1805	0.0	0.0				
13 M	0112	3.7	1.1	28 Tu	0035	3.0	0.9
	0719	0.4	0.1		0553	0.5	0.2
	1341	2.8	0.9		1300	2.3	0.7
	1909	0.2	0.1		1758	0.4	0.1
14 Tu	0218	3.5	1.1				
	0859	0.4	0.1				
	1448	2.7	0.8				
	2033	0.3	0.1				
15 W	0323	3.5	1.1				
	1024	0.4	0.1				
	1550	2.8	0.9				
	2206	0.3	0.1				

MARCH

Day	Time h m	Height ft	Height m	Day	Time h m	Height ft	Height m
1 W	0135	3.0	0.9	16 Th	0301	3.3	1.0
	0653	0.6	0.2		1005	0.5	0.2
	1408	2.4	0.7		1531	2.8	0.9
	1903	0.4	0.1		2207	0.4	0.1
2 Th	0240	3.1	0.9	17 F	0400	3.3	1.0
	0810	0.6	0.2		1100	0.4	0.1
	1513	2.6	0.8		1626	3.0	0.9
	2017	0.4	0.1		2308	0.3	0.1
3 F	0341	3.3	1.0	18 Sa	0453	3.3	1.0
	0926	0.4	0.1		1140	0.3	0.1
	1613	2.9	0.9		1714	3.3	1.0
	2136	0.1	0.0		2351	0.1	0.0
4 Sa	0439	3.6	1.1	19 Su	0538	3.4	1.0
	1031	0.0	0.0		1209	0.2	0.1
	1706	3.1	1.0		1757	3.5	1.1
	2244	-0.2	-0.1				
5 Su	0532	3.9	1.2	20 M	0023	0.0	0.0
	1127	-0.3	-0.1		0619	3.5	1.1
	1756	3.8	1.2		1231	0.1	0.0
	2343	-0.6	-0.2		1836	3.7	1.1
6 M	0620	4.2	1.3	21 Tu	0051	-0.1	0.0
	1214	-0.6	-0.2		0659	3.6	1.1
	1843	4.2	1.3		1254	0.0	0.0
					1915	3.8	1.2
7 Tu	0036	-0.9	-0.3	22 W	0118	-0.2	-0.1
	0709	4.3	1.3		0735	3.6	1.1
	1259	-0.9	-0.3		1318	-0.1	0.0
	1931	4.5	1.4		1952	3.9	1.2
8 W	0126	-1.1	-0.3	23 Th	0143	-0.2	-0.1
	0756	4.4	1.3		0812	3.5	1.1
	1343	-1.0	-0.3		1343	-0.1	0.0
	2017	4.7	1.4		2028	3.8	1.2
9 Th	0215	-1.1	-0.3	24 F	0211	-0.2	-0.1
	0844	4.2	1.3		0847	3.3	1.0
	1426	-1.0	-0.3		1410	-0.1	0.0
	2106	4.7	1.4		2105	3.7	1.1
10 F	0303	-0.9	-0.3	25 Sa	0242	-0.1	0.0
	0932	4.0	1.2		0924	3.1	0.9
	1511	-0.8	-0.2		1442	-0.1	0.0
	2154	4.5	1.4		2142	3.6	1.1
11 Sa	0353	-0.7	-0.2	26 Su	0315	0.0	0.0
	1022	3.7	1.1		1004	2.9	0.9
	1555	-0.6	-0.2		1514	0.0	0.0
	2249	4.2	1.3		2222	3.4	1.0
12 Su	0445	-0.3	-0.1	27 M	0351	0.2	0.1
	1117	3.3	1.0		1043	2.7	0.8
	1645	-0.2	-0.1		1551	0.2	0.1
	2347	3.9	1.2		2305	3.2	1.0
13 M	0547	0.1	0.0	28 Tu	0433	0.3	0.1
	1216	3.0	0.9		1134	2.5	0.8
	1740	0.1	0.0		1637	0.3	0.1
					2357	3.1	0.9
14 Tu	0048	3.6	1.1	29 W	0526	0.4	0.1
	0703	0.4	0.1		1233	2.5	0.8
	1320	2.8	0.9		1732	0.4	0.1
	1852	0.4	0.1				
15 W	0155	3.4	1.0	30 Th	0102	3.1	0.9
	0845	0.5	0.2		0626	0.5	0.2
	1427	2.7	0.8		1339	2.6	0.8
	2035	0.5	0.2		1839	0.5	0.2
				31 F	0211	3.1	0.9
					0738	0.5	0.2
					1445	2.8	0.9
					1958	0.4	0.1

Time meridian 75° W. 0000 is midnight. 1200 is noon.
Heights are referred to mean lower low water which is the chart datum of soundings.

generally include commercially important ports and locations for which a generally long series of tidal observations are available. Tidal predictions are generally most accurate for reference stations. Subordinate stations (called *secondary ports* by the British) are locations from which a relatively short series of observations is reduced by comparison with simultaneous observations at reference stations, as discussed below.

Tide prediction for reference stations is made using Table 1 of the *Tide Tables,* which presents daily tide predictions for high and low water. Table 8-2 of this text, for example, contains an excerpt from Table 1 of the *Tide Tables* for the reference station Newport, RI, over the months of January, February, and March 1989. This table contains the predicted time and height (in feet and meters) of the high and low tides for each day in the year. Reference to Table 8-2, for example, shows that on 1 January, high tides are expected at 0210 and 1429 (tidal heights of 3.0 and 2.6 ft., respectively), and low tides are expected at 0730 and 1931 (tide heights of 0.8 and 0.5 ft., respectively). All times given in the *Tide Tables* are in standard time (in the 24-hour system). *Therefore, during periods when daylight savings time is in effect, it is necessary to convert either to or from standard time.*

It occasionally happens (even in areas with semidiurnal tides) that there will only be two highs and a low, or two lows and a high in a given day. This occurs because the tides follow the slightly longer lunar day. This can be seen on 27 February 1989, for example, when there are low tides at 0502 and 1705, and a single high tide at 1200.

Examination of the daily predictions for Newport shown in Table 8-2 indicates that, although the majority of the tidal heights are positive (i.e., above datum), low tides are occasionally beneath datum (a negative entry). At these times, the actual water depths will be less than the charted values.

Tide predictions are now made by computers, using algorithms based upon the predictable motions of the sun and moon, measurements of past tide heights, and reflect an allowance for seasonal variation representing average *freshet* (heavy rains or snow) and *drought* (dry) conditions. Unusual conditions (higher or lower than average snow or rainfall, etc.), however, will cause the tides to be higher or lower than predicted from the tables. Likewise, changes in winds or barometric conditions cause variations in sea level. Typically, an onshore wind or a low barometer will increase the heights of both the high and low waters compared to predictions based on average values. Likewise, offshore winds or a high barometer will decrease high and low waters relative to predictions. (Consult Bowditch for equations that can be used to correct for these meteorological conditions.) Therefore, the tide height predictions should not be regarded as without error. It is a matter of judgment coupled with local knowledge how much of a safety margin to apply to these predictions.

SUBORDINATE STATIONS

Table 2 of the *Tide Tables* (excerpted in Table 8-3 of this text) shows what are termed "tidal differences and other constants." The entries of this table include:

1. A station or substation identification number. For example, Penikese Island is substation number 1101.

2. A place name corresponding to each location for which predictions are available. In this example, *Penikese Island,* is the name given to substation number 1101.

3. The approximate latitude and longitude of the locations for which predictions are available. For accurate work, take the time and trouble to plot this position on the nautical chart, rather than simply rely on the place name. Occasionally, these plots will put you on dry land, but the exercise is instructive in any event.

Table 8-3. Excerpt from Table 2 of *Tide Tables*.

TABLE 2. – TIDAL DIFFERENCES AND OTHER CONSTANTS

NO.	PLACE	POSITION		DIFFERENCES				RANGES		Mean Tide Level
		Lat.	Long.	Time		Height		Mean	Spring	
				High water	Low water	High water	Low water			
		° ′ N	° ′ W	h. m.	h. m.	ft	ft	ft	ft	ft
	Nantucket Island-Cont. Time meridian, 75°W			on BOSTON, p.36						
1041	Nantucket..........................	41 17	70 06	+1 07	+0 52	*0.31	*0.31	3.0	3.6	1.6
1043	Eel Point.........................	41 17	70 12	+0 39	+0 07	*0.24	*0.24	2.3	2.7	1.2
1045	Tuckernuck Island, East Pond.......	41 18	70 15	+0 48	+0 29	*0.27	*0.27	2.6	3.1	1.4
1047	Muskeget Island, north side........	41 20	70 18	+0 25	+0 15	*0.21	*0.21	2.0	2.4	1.1
1049	Smith Point, north side............	41 17	70 14	+0 48	-0 30	*0.16	*0.16	1.5	1.9	0.9
				on NEWPORT, p.40						
1051	Miacomet Rip.......................	41 14	70 06	+0 15	+0 50	*0.49	*0.49	1.7	2.0	0.9
	Martha's Vineyard									
1053	Wasque Point, Chappaquiddick Island.....	41 22	70 27	+2 02	+3 20	*0.31	*0.31	1.1	1.4	0.6
1055	Off Jobs Neck Pond.................	41 21	70 35	+0 01	+0 22	*0.77	*0.77	2.7	3.2	1.4
1057	Off Chilmark Pond..................	41 20	70 43	-0 16	+0 04	*0.82	*0.82	2.9	3.5	1.5
1059	Squibnocket Point.................	41 19	70 46	-0 45	-0 02	*0.82	*0.82	2.9	3.7	1.6
1061	Nomans Land........................	41 16	70 49	-0 19	+0 18	*0.85	*0.85	3.0	3.6	1.6
1063	Gay Head...........................	41 21	70 50	-0 06	+0 45	*0.82	*0.82	2.9	3.5	1.5
1065	Menemsha Bight.....................	41 21	70 46	+0 02	+0 37	*0.77	*0.77	2.7	3.4	1.4
1067	Cedar Tree Neck....................	41 26	70 42	+0 10	+1 32	*0.62	*0.62	2.2	2.8	1.2
1069	Off Lake Tashmoo...................	41 28	70 38	+1 08	+2 11	*0.60	*0.60	2.1	2.5	1.1
				on BOSTON, p.36						
1071	West Chop..........................	41 29	70 36	+0 18	-0 29	*0.15	*0.15	1.4	1.7	0.7
1073	Vineyard Haven.....................	41 27	70 36	+0 27	+0 01	*0.18	*0.18	1.7	2.0	0.9
1075	East Chop..........................	41 28	70 34	+0 29	-0 12	*0.18	*0.18	1.7	2.0	0.8
1077	Oak Bluffs.........................	41 27	70 33	+0 32	-0 12	*0.18	*0.18	1.7	2.0	0.9
1079	Edgartown..........................	41 23	70 31	+0 57	+0 18	*0.20	*0.20	1.9	2.3	1.0
1081	Cape Poge, Chappaquiddick Island........	41 25	70 27	+0 46	+0 04	*0.23	*0.23	2.2	2.6	1.2
	Vineyard Sound			on NEWPORT, p.40						
1083	Nobska Point.......................	41 31	70 39	+0 41	+2 05	*0.43	*0.43	1.5	1.9	0.8
	Woods Hole									
1085	Little Harbor..................	41 31	70 40	+0 32	+2 21	*0.40	*0.40	1.4	1.8	0.8
1087	Oceanographic Institution.....	41 32	70 40	+0 22	+1 59	*0.52	*0.50	1.8	2.3	1.0
1089	Uncatena Island (south side)........	41 31	70 42	+0 17	+0 22	*1.02	*1.02	3.6	4.5	1.9
1091	Tarpaulin Cove....................	41 28	70 46	+0 11	+1 23	*0.54	*0.54	1.9	2.4	1.0
	Quicks Hole									
1093	South side....................	41 26	70 51	-0 10	+0 09	*0.71	*0.71	2.5	3.1	1.3
1095	Middle........................	41 27	70 51	0 00	+0 10	*0.85	*0.85	3.0	3.7	1.6
1097	North side....................	41 27	70 51	-0 08	-0 08	*0.99	*0.99	3.5	4.4	1.8
	Buzzards Bay									
1099	Cuttyhunk Pond entrance............	41 25	70 55	+0 01	+0 01	*0.97	*0.97	3.4	4.2	1.8
1101	Penikese Island....................	41 27	70 55	-0 17	-0 16	*0.97	*0.97	3.4	4.2	1.8
1103	Kettle Cove........................	41 29	70 47	+0 09	+0 02	*1.08	*1.08	3.8	4.7	2.1
1105	West Falmouth Harbor...............	41 36	70 39	+0 21	+0 18	*1.14	*1.14	4.0	5.0	2.2
1107	Barlows Landing, Pocasset Harbor...	41 41	70 38	+0 24	+0 18	*1.14	*1.14	4.0	5.0	2.2
1109	Abiels Ledge.......................	41 42	70 40	+0 11	+0 16	*1.11	*1.11	3.9	4.9	2.2
1111	Monument Beach.....................	41 43	70 37	+0 23	+0 18	*1.14	*1.14	4.0	5.0	2.2
1113	Cape Cod Canal, RR. bridge <6>.....	41 44	70 37	+1 15	- - -	*0.99	*0.99	3.5	4.4	1.9
1115	Great Hill.........................	41 43	70 43	+0 17	+0 15	*1.16	*1.16	4.1	5.1	2.2
1117	Wareham, Wareham River.............	41 45	70 43	+0 22	+0 16	*1.16	*1.16	4.1	5.1	2.2
1119	Bird Island........................	41 40	70 43	+0 05	-0 02	*1.19	*1.19	4.2	5.2	2.3
1121	Marion.............................	41 42	70 46	+0 09	+0 10	*1.14	*1.14	4.0	5.0	2.2
1123	Mattapoisett.......................	41 39	70 49	+0 10	+0 05	*1.11	*1.11	3.9	4.9	2.2
1125	West Island (west side)............	41 36	70 50	+0 09	+0 08	*1.05	*1.05	3.7	4.6	1.9
1127	Clarks Point.......................	41 36	70 54	+0 03	+0 03	*1.05	*1.05	3.7	4.6	1.9
1129	New Bedford........................	41 38	70 55	+0 07	+0 07	*1.05	*1.05	3.7	4.6	1.9
1131	Belleville, Acushnet River.........	41 40	70 55	+0 07	+0 09	*1.08	*1.08	3.8	4.7	2.1
1133	South Dartmouth, Apponagansett Bay......	41 35	70 57	+0 25	+0 33	*1.05	*1.05	3.7	4.6	1.9
1135	Dumpling Rocks.....................	41 32	70 55	+0 01	-0 02	*1.05	*1.05	3.7	4.6	1.9
	Westport River									
1137	Westport Harbor...............	41 30	71 06	+0 09	+0 33	*0.85	*0.85	3.0	3.7	1.6
1139	Hix Bridge, East Branch.......	41 34	71 04	+1 40	+2 30	*0.77	*0.77	2.7	3.4	1.4
	RHODE ISLAND, Narragansett Bay									
1141	Sakonnet...........................	41 28	71 12	-0 13	-0 01	*0.88	*0.86	3.1	3.9	1.7
1143	Anthony Point, Sakonnet River......	41 38	71 13	-0 02	-0 02	*1.09	*1.07	3.8	4.8	2.1
1145	Beavertail Point...................	41 27	71 24	-0 05	+0 04	*0.99	*1.00	3.5	4.3	1.9
1147	Castle Hill........................	41 28	71 22	-0 05	+0 12	*0.94	*0.93	3.3	4.1	1.8
1149	NEWPORT............................	41 30	71 20	Daily predictions				3.5	4.4	1.9
1151	Conanicut Point....................	41 34	71 22	+0 07	-0 06	*1.07	*1.07	3.8	4.7	2.0
1153	Prudence Island, (south end).......	41 35	71 19	+0 08	-0 04	*1.08	*1.07	3.8	4.8	2.0
1155	Bristol Point......................	41 39	71 19	+0 18	+0 07	*1.14	*1.14	4.0	5.0	2.1
1157	Bristol Highlands..................	41 42	71 18	+0 08	-0 07	*1.18	*1.21	4.2	5.2	2.2
1159	Bristol Ferry......................	41 38	71 15	+0 16	+0 01	*1.16	*1.14	4.1	5.1	2.2
1161	Fall River, State Pier.............	41 42	71 10	+0 19	-0 01	*1.25	*1.25	4.4	5.5	2.4

Endnotes can be found at the end of table 2.

4. Time and height difference data. To illustrate how these data are used, please refer to substation 1101, Penikese Island, in Buzzards Bay in Table 8-3. The first two numbers shown in the differences columns are the *time differences* (in hours and minutes) for high water and low water at this substation, compared to a designated reference station. A glance over the differences columns indicates that all substations after 1083 in numerical sequence shown on this page are keyed to the reference station, "Newport." (Reference stations are selected in an attempt to match the tidal characteristics of the substation. Often these are quite close to the substation, but occasionally these are far removed. A number of substations in Antarctica, for example, are keyed to Galveston, Texas.) These time differences are to be added to the times (algebraic sign important) at the reference station to estimate the times of the corresponding high and low water at the subordinate station. For example, the time differences shown for Penikese Island are: -0 hrs, 17 minutes for high water, and -0 hrs, 16 minutes for low water. The significance of the minus signs in this table entry is that both high and low water occur earlier at Penikese Island, than at Newport. (Had the signs been positive, the times would have been later.) It was noted above, for example, that high water would occur at Newport on 1 January 1989 at 0210, and later at 1429. The tide time differences for Penikese Island applied to these times mean that high water will occur 17 minutes earlier, or at 0153, and 1412. (In making this subtraction or addition, it is also necessary to keep track of the day, as well as the time. for example, if the time difference for high tide had been -3 hours, then the 0153 high tide at Newport 1 January 1989, would occur at Penikese Island at 2253 on 31 December 1988.)

The next set of differences shown in Table 8-3 are *height differences* at high and low water. Height difference information in the *Tide Tables* can be expressed in any of three ways. **First,** the table entry may be a number with either a plus or minus sign in front. This is to be interpreted as the quantity to be added or subtracted from the height of the corresponding tide height at the reference station to calculate the height at the subordinate station. The significance of a table entry of -0.2 at high water, for example, is that the height of the high tide at the subordinate station is 0.2 feet lower than the high tide at the corresponding reference station. **Second,** the table entries may be prefixed with an asterisk, as is the case for Penikese Island. The asterisk is used to denote a multiplicative (rather than additive) correction factor. So, for example, the factors given in Table 8-3 for the high tide and the low tide are both 0.97 (this is a numerical coincidence) for Penikese Island. Thus, the height of the 0153 high tide at Penikese, is the height of the corresponding tide at Newport, 3.0 ft., multiplied by 0.97, or approximately 2.9 ft. Likewise, the height of the 1412 high tide at Penikese Island, is the height of the corresponding tide at Newport, 2.6 ft., multiplied by 0.97, or approximately 2.5 ft. **Third,** table entries may consist of both an asterisk and an algebraic sign, such as (*0.4 + 1.5). In this case the height of the tide at the reference station is to be multiplied by the number denoted with an asterisk, and then added to the next number. A reference height of 5 ft. would then translate to 0.4 (5.0) + 1.5 = 3.5 ft. The reason for these different formats in the tide height difference column is that several relationships are considered for correlation of reference stations and substations; the best (most accurate) relationship is chosen for inclusion in the *Tide Tables,* but this "best predictor" varies from station to station.

5. *Tide ranges* are shown in the next two columns of Table 2 of the *Tide Tables,* reproduced in Table 8-3 in this text. Typically two

ranges are given: *mean range,* and *spring range. The mean range is the difference in height between mean high water and mean low water.* At Penikese Island, the mean range is 3.4 ft., as shown in Table 8-3. *The spring range is the average semidiurnal range occurring semimonthly as the result of the moon being new or full* (syzygy again). Numerically it is equal to 4.2 ft. in this example. In general, the spring range is larger than the mean range where the type of tide is either semidiurnal or mixed, and is of no practical significance where the type of tide is diurnal. For locations where the tide type is diurnal, the table gives the diurnal range, which is the difference in height between mean higher high water and mean lower low water.

6. Finally, Table 2 of the *Tide Tables* (reproduced in Table 8-3 of this text) shows the *mean tide level -- 1.8 ft. in the case of Penikese Island. The mean tide level (also termed half tide level) is a plane midway between mean low water and mean high water, measured from chart datum.* If it is desired to estimate the level of *mean high water* (MHW), all that is necessary is to add one-half of the mean tidal range to the mean tide level. Thus, for example, MHW at Penikese Island would be 1.8 + 0.5 (3.4) = 3.5 ft.

USE OF A TIDE WORKSHEET

Thus far, the *Tide Tables* have been used to estimate the time and height of high and low water at either a reference or subordinate station. These same tables can be used to estimate *the height of the tide at any desired time.*

The computations of tide heights are conveniently done using a tide table worksheet, one version of which is illustrated in Table 8-4. It contains space to write down the relevant entries from the *Tide Tables,* and directions for making the required computations. Table 8-5 contains a worked-out example of a tide height calculation for 0900 on 1 January 1989, at Penikese Island. This example is used to illustrate the calcula-

tions. Follow through these calculations to ensure familiarity with the procedure.

The worksheet given in Table 8-4 has three sections. The top section is used to record the relevant inputs to the problem, the middle section to calculate the times and heights of high and low tides at the reference station (and if necessary the substation), and the bottom section to calculate the height of the tide at any time. Completion of the top and middle sections is simple, and has been illustrated above. One or two additional comments are appropriate, however. First, take the time to copy correctly the high water and low water time differences and height differences. A common error made by students and experienced mariners alike is to apply the low water time difference, for example, to the high water time at the reference station. Second, ensure that you use the correct formula for calculating tide heights at subordinate stations from reference stations. The asterisk in the tide difference for this station means that the tide heights are to be multiplied, rather than added.

The use of the bottom part of the worksheet is discussed here. The purpose of this section is to facilitate the calculation of the tide heights at any time, from knowledge of the daily highs and lows calculated in the middle section of the worksheet.

To simplify these calculations, the *Tide Tables* contain Table 3, reproduced in this text as Table 8-6. It consists of a series of factors, to be added or subtracted from the nearest high or low tide to estimate the height of the tide at any time. Its use is illustrated as follows:

1. Enter the desired time and date of tide height prediction in the bottom of the worksheet, 0900, 1 January 1989. (In the event that daylight savings time is in use on the date, ensure that either this time is converted to standard time, or that the calculations in the middle of the worksheet are expressed in daylight savings time.)

TABLE 8 - 4. COMPLETE TIDE TABLE WORKSHEET

Substation: _____	Date: _____	Look up these values from Table 2., "Tidal Differences and Other Constants." This section can be omitted if the desired location can be found in Table 1 "Daily Tide Predictions" of the *Tide Tables*. Height differences denoted with an asterisk are to be multiplied rather than added to reference station height.
Ref. Station: _____	.Substation #: _____	
HW Time Diff: _____	Diff. of Hgt. At HW: ____	
LW Time Diff: _____	Diff of Hgt. at LW: _____	

Calculations:		Look up heights and times for reference stations in Table 1., Daily Tide Predictions. Add or subtract time differences for substations to Table 1 times for reference Stations. Calculate the height at the substation from the height of the tide at the reference station plus or minus the height difference tabulated above, unless denoted with an asterisk -- in which case the tabulated factors should be multiplied by the heights of the corresponding tides at the reference station. Keep in mind that the time differences may place the required reference tide on the day before or after the date in question for the substation. Remember, times given in tables are standard zone time, not daylight savings time. Subtract 1 hour from daylight savings time to calculate zone time.
Ref. Station: _____	Substation: _____	
Condition Time Height	Condition Time Height	
LW _____	LW _____	
HW _____	HW _____	
LW _____	LW _____	
HW _____	HW _____	
LW _____	LW _____	
HW _____	HW _____	

Height of Tide at Any Time:

Location: _____	Time: _____	Date: _____

Duration of Rise or Fall: _____	Length of time between high and low tides that bracket desired time
Time from Nearest Tide: _____	Use the lesser of the times from the last tide, or time until the next tide
Range of Tide: _____	Difference in height between tides on either side of desired time: remember that subtracting a negative number is logically equivalent to addition
Height of Nearest Tide: _____	Height of tide closest to desired time
Tabled Correction: _____	From Table 3
Height of Tide at Time: _____	Add above correction if nearest tide is low water, subtract otherwise
Charted Depth: _____	Determined from chart
Depth of Water at Time: _____	Add tide height to charted depth to calculate depth at required time

2. Compute the duration of rise or fall. Referring to the subordinate station calculations for Penikese Island in Table 8-5, for example, note that 0900 falls between the low water at 0714 and the high water at 1412. The difference between these times (remember that there are 60, not 100 minutes in an hour) is 6 hours and 58 minutes.

3. Compute the time from the nearest tide. In this case, there are two adjacent tides to be compared, the low water which occurs at

TABLE 8 - 5. COMPLETE TIDE TABLE WORKSHEET

Substation: Penikese	Date: 1 January 1989	Look up these values from Table 2., "Tidal Differences and Other Constants." This section can be omitted if the desired location can be found in Table 1 "Daily Tide Predictions" of the *Tide Tables*. Height differences denoted with an asterisk are to be multiplied rather than added to reference station height.
Ref. Station: Newport	Substation #: 1101	
HW Time Diff: -0:17	Diff. of Hgt. At HW: *0.97	
LW Time Diff: -0:16	Diff. of Hgt. at LW: *0.97	

Calculations:

Ref. Station: Newport   Substation: Penikese

Condition	Time	Height		Condition	Time	Height
LW	_____			LW	_____	
HW	0210	3.0		HW	0153	2.9
LW	0730	0.8		LW	0714	0.8
HW	1429	2.6		HW	1412	2.5
LW	1931	0.5		LW	1915	0.5
HW	_____			HW	_____	

Look up heights and times for reference stations in Table 1., Daily Tide Predictions. Add or subtract time differences for substations to Table 1 times for reference Stations. Calculate the height at the substation from the height of the tide at the reference station plus or minus the height difference tabulated above, unless denoted with an asterisk -- in which case the tabulated factors should be multiplied by the heights of the corresponding tides at the reference station. Keep in mind that the time differences may place the required reference tide on the day before or after the date in question for the substation. Remember, times given in tables are standard zone time, not daylight savings time. Subtract 1 hour from daylight savings time to calculate zone time.

Height of Tide at Any Time:

Location: Penikese   Time: 0900   Date: 1 January 1989

Duration of Rise or Fall: ____6:58____ Length of time between high and low tides that bracket desired time

Time from Nearest Tide: ____1:46____ Use the lesser of the times from the last tide, or time until the next tide

Range of Tide: ____1.7____ Difference in height between tides on either side of desired time: remember that subtracting a negative number is logically equivalent to addition

Height of Nearest Tide: ____0.8____ Height of tide closest to desired time

Tabled Correction: ____0.2____ From Table 3

Height of Tide at Time: ____1.0____ Add above correction if nearest tide is low water, subtract otherwise

Charted Depth: _____ Determined from chart

Depth of Water at Time: _____ Add tide height to charted depth to calculate depth at required time

---

0714, and the high water which occurs at 1412. The time in question, 0900, is closer to the low water at 0714. The time difference (0900 - 0714) is 1 hour 46 minutes.

4. Compute the range of the tide. The range is the difference between the high water (2.5

ft.), and the adjacent low water (0.8 ft.), or 1.7 ft. in this example.

5. Enter the height of the nearest tide in the worksheet. Since the nearest tide is the low water at 0714, the number, 0.8 ft., corresponding to this tide is entered.

6. Read Table 3 of the *Tide Tables* (Table 8-6 of this text) to determine the factor to be added or subtracted from the height of the nearest tide. Enter the top section of Table 8-3 at the row *closest* to the duration of rise or fall just determined in step 2. (No interpolation is required.) In this example, the nearest entry is 7 hours. Read *across* this row to find the number closest to the time from the nearest high water or low water, which is 1 hour 46 minutes in this example. The closest time to 1:46 is 1 hour 52 minutes. Now, read *down* the column that has the entry 1 hour 52 minutes to the lower table and stop at the table entry in the row that is closest to the range of the tide (1.7 ft. in this example, so 1.5 ft. is the closest row). This entry, termed the *correction to heights*, is 0.2 in this example, and is entered in the worksheet in Table 8-5.

7. Compute the height of the tide at the desired time as the height of the nearest tide plus or minus the tabled entry. If the nearest tide is *low water* (as in this example), *the table entry is added*, and therefore, the height of the tide at 0900 is 0.8 + 0.2 = 1.0 ft. *If the nearest tide were high tide, the correction determined in step 6 would be subtracted*, rather than added.

8. If it is desired to estimate the depth of water at a particular location, the height of the tide calculated in step 7 is added to the charted depth to determine the depth of water at the desired time.

These eight steps are all that are required to estimate tide heights at any time--and also water depths at any time. Although it takes some time to read through and complete a calculation for the first time, with practice comes familiarity and speed. Be careful to avoid the common errors shown in Table 8-7. These same errors occur in making tidal current calculations. (Practice soon convinces you of the desirability of using a computer for the calculations!) The worksheet helps to ensure accuracy in the event that manual calculations are made. There is nothing more irritating than writing these entries on a piece of scratch paper, losing your place (from some minor distraction such as a large ship bearing down on your vessel), and having to reconstruct calculations from these paper scraps now wet from a wake.

Finally, tide height calculations are useful to estimate the vertical clearance under obstructions. The worksheet given in Table 8-8 structures the calculations. The directions for use are reproduced on the worksheet and are clear enough not to require an example. The only judgmental input to the calculations detailed in Table 8-8 is the required *safety margin. A safety margin is appropriate to allow for the inaccuracies in the tide height estimation and the possibility that waves caused by wind or wakes will reduce clearance.* There are no hard-and-fast rules for selection of an appropriate margin, but many mariners would want at least a 3 ft. margin.

TIDAL CURRENT

Accompanying the periodic rise and fall of the tide is a horizontal flow of the water, known as the tidal current. The relevance of current information to voyage planning is explored in some detail in Chapters 7 and 11, and therefore, not repeated here.

The set (direction towards which the current is flowing) and drift (speed) of a current can be estimated in several ways. **First,** currents can often be observed directly from the movement of the water around stationary objects, such as bridge pilings, lobster traps, or buoys. This phenomenon is commonly termed the "current wake." With practice, the mariner can learn to judge the speed of the current from the size and other characteristics of the current wake. Rules of thumb developed from experience indicate that a one-knot current causes a definite ripple, a three-knot current will cause swirls and eddies for several yards, and a five-knot current will cause a boiling wake to stretch out "down current" for perhaps 50 yards. The angle of lean of the harbor buoys is another indication of the

Table 8-6. Heights of Tide at Any Time (Table 3 of *Tide Tables*)

Time from the nearest high water or low water

Duration of rise or fall, see footnote h.m.	h.m.	h.m.	h.m.	h.m.	h.m.	h.m.	h.m.	h.m.	h.m.	h.m.	h.m.	h.m.	h.m.	h.m.	h.m.
4 00	0 08	0 16	0 24	0 32	0 40	0 48	0 56	1 04	1 12	1 20	1 28	1 36	1 44	1 52	2 00
4 20	0 09	0 17	0 26	0 35	0 43	0 52	1 01	1 09	1 18	1 27	1 35	1 44	1 53	2 01	2 10
4 40	0 09	0 19	0 28	0 37	0 47	0 56	1 05	1 15	1 24	1 33	1 43	1 52	2 01	2 11	2 20
5 00	0 10	0 20	0 30	0 40	0 50	1 00	1 10	1 20	1 30	1 40	1 50	2 00	2 10	2 20	2 30
5 20	0 11	0 21	0 32	0 43	0 53	1 04	1 15	1 25	1 36	1 47	1 57	2 08	2 19	2 29	2 40
5 40	0 11	0 23	0 34	0 45	0 57	1 08	1 19	1 31	1 42	1 53	2 05	2 16	2 27	2 39	2 50
6 00	0 12	0 24	0 36	0 48	1 00	1 12	1 24	1 36	1 48	2 00	2 12	2 24	2 36	2 48	3 00
6 20	0 13	0 25	0 38	0 51	1 03	1 16	1 29	1 41	1 54	2 07	2 19	2 32	2 45	2 57	3 10
6 40	0 13	0 27	0 40	0·53	1 07	1 20	1 33	1 47	2 00	2 13	2 27	2 40	2 53	3 07	3 20
7 00	0 14	0 28	0 42	0 56	1 10	1 24	1 38	1 52	2 06	2 20	2 34	2 48	3 02	3 16	3 30
7 20	0 15	0 29	0 44	0 59	1 13	1 28	1 43	1 57	2 12	2 27	2 41	2 56	3 11	3 25	3 40
7 40	0 15	0 31	0 46	1 01	1 17	1 32	1 47	2 03	2 18	2 33	2 49	3'04	3 19	3 35	3 50
8 00	0 16	0 32	0 48	1 04	1 20	1 36	1 52	2 08	2 24	2 40	2 56	3 12	3 28	3 44	4 00
8 20	0 17	0 33	0 50	1 07	1 23	1 40	1 57	2 13	2 30	2 47	3 03	3 20	3 37	3 53	4 10
8 40	0 17	0 35	0 52	1 09	1 27	1 44	2 01	2 19	2 36	2 53	3 11	3 28	3 45	4 03	4 20
9 00	0 18	0 36	0 54	1 12	1 30	1 48	2 06	2 24	2 42	3 00	3 18	3 36	3 54	4 12	4 30
9 20	0 19	0 37	0 56	1 15	1 33	1 52	2 11	2 29	2 48	3 07	3 25	3 44	4 03	4 21	4 40
9 40	0 19	0 39	0 58	1 17	1 37	1 56	2 15	2 35	2 54	3 13	3 33	3 52	4 11	4 31	4 50
10 00	0 20	0 40	1 00	1 20	1 40	2 00	2 20	2 40	3 00	3 20	3 40	4 00	4 20	4 40	5 00
10 20	0 21	0 41	1 02	1 23	1 43	2 04	2 25	2 45	3 06	3 27	3 47	4 08	4 29	4 49	5 10
10 40	0 21	0 43	1 04	1 25	1 47	2 08	2 29	2 51	3 12	3 33	3 55	4 16	4 37	4 59	5 20

Correction to height

Range of tide, see footnote Ft.	Ft.	Ft.	Ft.	Ft.	Ft.	Ft.	Ft.	Ft.	Ft.	Ft.	Ft.	Ft.	Ft.	Ft.	Ft.
0.5	0.0	0.0	0.0	0.0	0.0	0.0	0.1	0.1	0.1	0.1	0.1	0.2	0.2	0.2	0.2
1.0	0.0	0.0	0.0	0.0	0.1	0.1	0.1	0.2	0.2	0.2	0.3	0.3	0.4	0.4	0.5
1.5	0.0	0.0	0.0	0.1	0.1	0.1	0.2	0.2	0.3	0.4	0.4	0.5	0.6	0.7	0.8
2.0	0.0	0.0	0.0	0.1	0.1	0.2	0.3	0.3	0.4	0.5	0.6	0.7	0.8	0.9	1.0
2.5	0.0	0.0	0.1	0.1	0.2	0.2	0.3	0.4	0.5	0.6	0.7	0.9	1.0	1.1	1.2
3.0	0.0	0.0	0.1	0.1	0.2	0.3	0.4	0.5	0.6	0.8	0.9	1.0	1.2	1.3	1.5
3.5	0.0	0.0	0.1	0.2	0.2	0.3	0.4	0.6	0.7	0.9	1.0	1.2	1.4	1.6	1.8
4.0	0.0	0.0	0.1	0.2	0.3	0.4	0.5	0.7	0.8	1.0	1.2	1.4	1.6	1.8	2.0
4.5	0.0	0.0	0.1	0.2	0.3	0.4	0.6	0.7	0.9	1.1	1.3	1.6	1.8	2.0	2.2
5.0	0.0	0.1	0.1	0.2	0.3	0.5	0.6	0.8	1.0	1.2	1.5	1.7	2.0	2.2	2.5
5.5	0.0	0.1	0.1	0.2	0.4	0.5	0.7	0.9	1.1	1.4	1.6	1.9	2.2	2.5	2.8
6.0	0.0	0.1	0.1	0.3	0.4	0.6	0.8	1.0	1.2	1.5	1.8	2.1	2.4	2.7	3.0
6.5	0.0	0.1	0.2	0.3	0.4	0.6	0.8	1.1	1.3	1.6	1.9	2.2	2.6	2.9	3.2
7.0	0.0	0.1	0.2	0.3	0.5	0.7	0.9	1.2	1.4	1.8	2.1	2.4	2.8	3.1	3.5
7.5	0.0	0.1	0.2	0.3	0.5	0.7	1.0	1.2	1.5	1.9	2.2	2.6	3.0	3.4	3.8
8.0	0.0	0.1	0.2	0.3	0.5	0.8	1.0	1.3	1.6	2.0	2.4	2.8	3.2	3.6	4.0
8.5	0.0	0.1	0.2	0.4	0.6	0.8	1.1	1.4	1.8	2.1	2.5	2.9	3.4	3.8	4.2
9.0	0.0	0.1	0.2	0.4	0.6	0.9	1.2	1.5	1.9	2.2	2.7	3.1	3.6	4.0	4.5
9.5	0.0	0.1	0.2	0.4	0.6	0.9	1.2	1.6	2.0	2.4	2.8	3.3	3.8	4.3	4.8
10.0	0.0	0.1	0.2	0.4	0.7	1.0	1.3	1.7	2.1	2.5	3.0	3.5	4.0	4.5	5.0
10.5	0.0	0.1	0.3	0.5	0.7	1.0	1.3	1.7	2.2	2.6	3.1	3.6	4.2	4.7	5.2
11.0	0.0	0.1	0.3	0.5	0.7	1.1	1.4	1.8	2.3	2.8	3.3	3.8	4.4	4.9	5.5
11.5	0.0	0.1	0.3	0.5	0.8	1.1	1.5	1.9	2.4	2.9	3.4	4.0	4.6	5.1	5.8
12.0	0.0	0.1	0.3	0.5	0.8	1.1	1.5	2.0	2.5	3.0	3.6	4.1	4.8	5.4	6.0
12.5	0.0	0.1	0.3	0.5	0.8	1.2	1.6	2.1	2.6	3.1	3.7	4.3	5.0	5.6	6.2
13.0	0.0	0.1	0.3	0.6	0.9	1.2	1.7	2.2	2.7	3.2	3.9	4.5	5.1	5.8	6.5
13.5	0.0	0.1	0.3	0.6	0.9	1.3	1.7	2.2	2.8	3.4	4.0	4.7	5.3	6.0	6.8
14.0	0.0	0.2	0.3	0.6	0.9	1.3	1.8	2.3	2.9	3.5	4.2	4.8	5.5	6.3	7.0
14.5	0.0	0.2	0.4	0.6	1.0	1.4	1.9	2.4	3.0	3.6	4.3	5.0	5.7	6.5	7.2
15.0	0.0	0.2	0.4	0.6	1.0	1.4	1.9	2.5	3.1	3.8	4.4	5.2	5.9	6.7	7.5
15.5	0.0	0.2	0.4	0.7	1.0	1.5	2.0	2.6	3.2	3.9	4.6	5.4	6.1	6.9	7.8
16.0	0.0	0.2	0.4	0.7	1.1	1.5	2.1	2.6	3.3	4.0	4.7	5.5	6.3	7.2	8.0
16.5	0.0	0.2	0.4	0.7	1.1	1.6	2.1	2.7	3.4	4.1	4.9	5.7	6.5	7.4	8.2
17.0	0.0	0.2	0.4	0.7	1.1	1.6	2.2	2.8	3.5	4.2	5.0	5.9	6.7	7.6	8.5
17.5	0.0	0.2	0.4	0.8	1.2	1.7	2.2	2.9	3.6	4.4	5.2	6.0	6.9	7.8	8.8
18.0	0.0	0.2	0.4	0.8	1.2	1.7	2.3	3.0	3.7	4.5	5.3	6.2	7.1	8.1	9.0
18.5	0.1	0.2	0.5	0.8	1.2	1.8	2.4	3.1	3.8	4.6	5.5	6.4	7.3	8.3	9.2
19.0	0.1	0.2	0.5	0.8	1.3	1.8	2.4	3.1	3.9	4.8	5.6	6.6	7.5	8.5	9.5
19.5	0.1	0.2	0.5	0.8	1.3	1.9	2.5	3.2	4.0	4.9	5.8	6.7	7.7	8.7	9.8
20.0	0.1	0.2	0.5	0.9	1.3	1.9	2.6	3.3	4.1	5.0	5.9	6.9	7.9	9.0	10.0

Obtain from the predictions the high water and low water, one of which is before and the other after the time for which the height is required. The difference between the times of occurrence of these tides is the duration of rise or fall, and the difference between their heights is the range of tide for the above table. Find the difference between the nearest high or low water and the time for which the height is required.

Enter the table with the duration of rise or fall, printed in heavy-faced type, which most nearly agrees with the actual value, and on that horizontal line find the time from the nearest high or low water which agrees most nearly with the corresponding actual difference. The correction sought is in the column directly below, on the line with the range of tide.

When the nearest tide is high water, subtract the correction.

When the nearest tide is low water, add the correction.

TABLE 8 - 7. COMMON ERRORS IN TIDE HEIGHT CALCULATIONS

- Neglecting to convert from daylight to standard times -- all tidal data are given in standard times in the *Tide Tables*.

- Not being alert to date changes when calculating tides for subordinate stations.

- Applying the high water time differences to low water or the converse.

- Failure to understand that factors denoted with an asterisk should be multiplied by rather than added or subtracted from reference station heights.

- Failure to select correct reference station for desired subordinate station.

- Arithmetic errors.

- (Less common) Failure to use the tables for the correct year.

direction and strength of the current, but here it is more difficult to provide useful rules of thumb. Some buoys are delicately balanced, and lean heavily to the side in light currents. Others require more substantial currents before a definite visual lean is evident. Take the time to study the buoys in your area and expand your store of local knowledge on your next voyage. An alternative procedure is to hold the vessel stationary in the current, relative to say a buoy or fixed structure, and drop a piece of wood over the side, timing how long it takes to move from the bow to the stern. If the wood requires t seconds to travel L feet, the current speed is approximately 0.59L/t. **Second,** currents can be calculated as-you-go, using the methods discussed in Chapter 7 for estimation. That is, current set and drift can be estimated from a comparison of the DR position with a fix. **Third,** currents can often be estimated or calculated from various published aids, including the *Tidal Current Tables, Tidal Current Charts,* or *Tidal Current Diagrams,* all published by NOS. Finally, publications such as the *U.S. Coast Pilot,* discussed in Chapter 10, provide useful data or information on currents.

The focus of this discussion is on the use of *Tidal Current Tables* although passing mention is made of the other sources. At the outset, it is important to make one point quite clear. The time of high and low water (discussed above) calculated for tides is not, in general, a reliable indication of the times of turning of the current or slack (slow) water. For some locations (e.g., those on the outer coast), the difference between the times of high or low water and the beginning of the ebb (flowing out of the river or bay) or flood (flowing into the river or bay) current may be small. But, for other locations, such as narrow channels, landlocked harbors, and certain tidal rivers, the time of slack may differ from the time of high or low water by as much as a matter of hours. Therefore, do not use the tide calculations as a surrogate for necessary current calculations. That, so to speak, is the "bad news." The "good news" is that the estimation of tidal currents from the published tables follows a very similar procedure to that employed for tide heights, so learning how to read and use the *Tidal Current Tables* is not such a chore.

TABLE 8 - 8. VERTICAL CLEARANCE WORKSHEET

Preliminary Information:

Vessel: _____ Date: _____ Location: _____

Navigator: _____ Time: _____ Object to be Cleared: _____

Clearance Computations:

Item	Value	Source/Remarks
1. Published Clearance:	_____	Read from applicable chart or other source.
2. Minimum Clearance:	_____	Masthead height.
3. Safety Margin:	_____	Judgment input (recommended as at least 3 ft.).
4. Required Clearance:	_____	Line 2 plus Line 3.
5. Height of Tide at Specified Time:	_____	From completed Tide Worksheet.
6. Mean Tide Level:	_____	From Table 2 (last column) of *Tide Tables* for appropriate station.
7. Mean Range:	_____	From Table 2 of *Tide Tables* for appropriate station.
8. Mean High Water:	_____	One half of Line 7 plus Line 6.
9. Clearance Increment:	_____	Line 8 minus Line 5 (may be negative quantity)
10. Predicted Clearance:	_____	Line 1 plus Line 9 (take note of sign)
11. Sufficient Clearance:	_____	Is predicted clearance (Line 10) greater than required clearance (Line 4)?

As with tides, tidal currents are periodic, and vary with both time and location. Figure 8-3, taken from the *Tidal Current Tables,* shows a time plot of tidal current data for several locations in the United States. As with tides, there is substantial variability in the strength (maximum drift) and temporal pattern of these currents. Average values for maximum currents at loca-

tions listed in the *Tidal Current Tables* vary from less than 1 knot to 5 knots or more. (At some other locations, such as Seymour Narrows in British Columbia, Canada, currents can be as strong as 14 knots.) Although these maximum values may not seem large on initial reflection, particularly to power boaters, a drift as small as 1 or 2 knots can have profound effects on fuel economy (see Chapter 11) and create challenges to seamanship. Anyone who has transited a tough inlet with an ebbing current matched against a stiff onshore wind has a healthy respect for the effects of even a "modest" current and can appreciate the utility of tidal current predictions for selecting the best time of transit. On long passages, small gains in efficiency by selecting the best routing, with due consideration for the effects of currents, translate into large cumulative gains.

Uncompensated currents can set the vessel off course (see Chapter 7), as well as affect the speed made good. Currents degrade the accuracy of the running fix unless these are considered in its construction. The mariner risks running into dangerous waters and/or becoming lost unless currents are considered and/or frequent fixes are taken in tidal waters (see chapters 5 and 6).

It is somewhat surprising but none the less true that there is little relation between the range of the tide and the strength of the maximum current, if comparisons are made among locations. Thus, for example, the maximum currents are relatively weak in areas off the coast of Maine, even though the tidal range is typically large in these areas. Conversely, the currents are relatively large in such areas as Nantucket Island and Nantucket Sound (near the area covered by the 1210-Tr chart), even though the tidal range is relatively small in these areas. However, *for a fixed location,* the speed of the maximum current (ebb or flood) is correlated with the tidal range. Thus, for example, during periods of the month when the tides at a station are largest (new or full moon, etc.) the maximum currents are also largest. The speed of the current is generally not constant across a body of water, but varies with location. It is generally greatest at mid-channel, and drops off near the shore. But, in winding rivers, the currents are generally largest towards the concave shore (along the "outside" curve). These statements have two important practical implications. **First,** it is very important to note

the exact location (latitude and longitude) for which a prediction is made in such publications as the *Tidal Current Tables.* **Second,** a careful mariner can (with due regard for shallows or other dangers to navigation) often select a course that reduce the strength of the foul currents encountered, or increases the strength of the fair current.

TIDAL CURRENT TABLES

These tables are published annually by NOS in the United States. Many other countries of the world also produce equivalent tables. Two volumes are published by NOS, one titled the At-

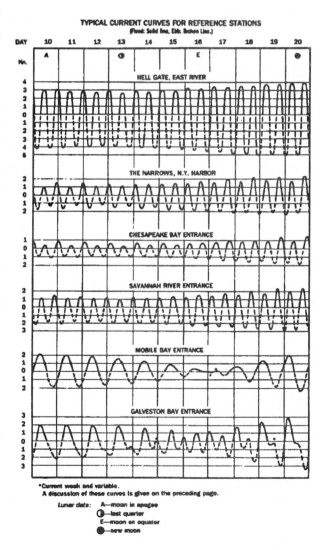

Fig. 8-3. Typical Current Curves for Reference Stations.

lantic Coast of North America, and the other the Pacific Coast of North America and Asia. The *Tidal Current Tables* are organized in a very similar format to the *Tide Tables*. For example, daily predictions are available for reference stations, and currents at subordinate stations are calculated from published tidal current differences. However, the number of reference stations and subordinate stations are far fewer than those given for the *Tide Tables*. For example, there are only 58 reference stations for tidal current predictions, compared to 198 reference stations for tide predictions. Additionally, the locations themselves may differ -- even if the name used to describe the station is the same. This is another reason to plot the latitude and longitude of the station as part of the planning process. Finally, the reference station for a particular substation may differ between the *Tide Tables* and the *Tidal Current Tables*. For example, there are actually two locations near Penikese Island (unusual, since fewer stations are given in the *Tidal Current Tables*) for which current predictions are available, neither of which corresponds in latitude or longitude to that used for Penikese Island in the *Tide Tables*. In this case, the difference in location is not great, but it is at other locations (e.g., near San Francisco, CA). Moreover, Penikese is referenced to the daily predictions for Newport, RI, in the *Tide Tables*, but to Pollack Rip Channel near the entrance to Nantucket Sound in the *Tidal Current Tables*, which is not even shown on the 1210-Tr chart!

USE OF THE *TIDAL CURRENT TABLES*

The publication, *Tidal Current Tables*, consists of five separate sets of tables. Of these, Tables 1, 2, and 3 are required for estimation of tidal currents at any time. Table 4 of the *Tidal Current Tables* is used for estimation of the duration of slack water (particularly important for divers) and Table 5 (Atlantic Coast only) presents data for rotary tidal currents. These latter two tables are discussed only briefly here, but are relatively easy to use from the directions included in the *Tidal Current Tables*.

The *Tidal Current Tables* also contain information on how currents are combined (vector addition) and on *Current Diagrams,* which graphically portray currents in several locations. Only a brief discussion of these tables and charts is included in this text, because of size and scope constraints, but clear directions are included in the *Tidal Current Tables*. (It almost goes without saying, that this publication is very important, and should be aboard any vessel.)

Tidal current prediction for *reference* stations is made using Table 1 of the *Tidal Current Tables,* which presents daily predictions of the times of slack water, and of maximum current (flood and ebb). Table 8-9 of this text, for example, contains an excerpt from Table 1 of the *Tidal Current Tables* for the reference station, Pollack Rip channel, over the months of January and February of 1989.

At the top of this table, the direction of the flood (035 degrees true) and the ebb (225 degrees true) is given for the reference station. Note that the flood and ebb directions are not necessarily reciprocal (180 degrees apart). The set of the current is given because general directions for flood and ebb are not always obvious, and moreover, the accurate direction is necessary to current sailing computations. Directions of flood and ebb at any subordinate station keyed to this reference station are *not* necessarily the same as those for the reference station and must be read from a separate table. For each day, three columns of data are provided; the times of slack water, and the time and velocity of maximum current. Refer, for example, to the table entry for 27 February 1989. Slack water times are estimated to occur at 0140, 0726, 1414, and 1952. (As with the *Tide Tables,* standard times in the 24-hour system are employed.) Times and strengths of maximum currents on this day are 0419 (when the current is 1.6 knots and ebbing, denoted by the letter **E** next to the current velocity), 1044 (when the current is flooding, denoted by the letter **F**, at a speed of 1.7 knots) 1645 (1.4 knot ebb), and 2303 (1.5 knot flood).

Table 8-9. Excerpt from Table 1 of *TIDAL CURRENT TABLES*, 1989.

POLLOCK RIP CHANNEL, MASSACHUSETTS, 1989

F-Flood, Dir. 035° True   E-Ebb, Dir. 225° True

JANUARY

Day	Slack Water Time h.m.	Maximum Current Time h.m.	Vel. knots	Day	Slack Water Time h.m.	Maximum Current Time h.m.	Vel. knots
1 Su		0050	1.7F	16 M		0051	1.8F
	0359	0642	1.5E		0403	0648	1.6E
	0955	1324	1.6F		1001	1334	1.9F
	1631	1907	1.3E		1645	1926	1.5E
	2212				2235		
2 M		0145	1.6F	17 Tu		0204	1.7F
	0450	0733	1.5E		0506	0755	1.6E
	1047	1421	1.7F		1106	1447	1.9F
	1727	2004	1.3E		1753	2040	1.4E
	2308				2344		
3 Tu		0241	1.6F	18 W		0313	1.7F
	0540	0827	1.5E		0607	0902	1.6E
	1137	1512	1.8F		1210	1553	2.0F
	1820	2057	1.3E		1858	2149	1.4E
4 W	0002	0332	1.6F	19 Th	0050	0418	1.7F
	0629	0916	1.5E		0706	1005	1.6E
	1225	1601	1.9F		1310	1652	2.1F
	1911	2149	1.4E		1957	2251	1.5E
5 Th	0053	0417	1.6F	20 F	0149	0514	1.7F
	0716	1001	1.6E		0801	1102	1.6E
	1311	1646	2.0F		1404	1743	2.2F
	1958	2237	1.5E		2049	2344	1.5E
6 F	0142	0501	1.7F	21 Sa	0241	0605	1.7F
	0800	1046	1.7E		0851	1151	1.7E
	1355	1728	2.1F		1452	1832	2.2F
	2043	2321	1.6E		2136		
7 Sa	0227	0540	1.7F	22 Su		0029	1.6E
	0843	1131	1.8E		0327	0650	1.8F
	1438	1808	2.2F		0936	1234	1.7E
	2126				1535	1913	2.2F
					2218		
8 Su		0004	1.7E	23 M		0108	1.6E
	0310	0621	1.8F		0409	0731	1.8F
	0926	1212	1.9E		1019	1312	1.7E
	1520	1846	2.3F		1616	1951	2.1F
	2209				2257		
9 M		0046	1.8E	24 Tu		0144	1.6E
	0353	0702	1.9F		0446	0808	1.8F
	1010	1257	2.0E		1100	1348	1.7E
	1604	1927	2.4F		1654	2030	2.1F
	2252				2335		
10 Tu		0131	1.9E	25 W		0217	1.6E
	0437	0744	2.0F		0523	0845	1.8F
	1055	1344	2.1E		1142	1425	1.7E
	1650	2013	2.4F		1732	2103	2.0F
	2337						
11 W		0216	2.0E	26 Th	0014	0252	1.6E
	0523	0831	2.0F		0601	0917	1.8F
	1144	1429	2.1E		1225	1506	1.6E
	1738	2058	2.4F		1812	2138	1.9F
12 Th	0024	0303	2.0E	27 F	0054	0333	1.6E
	0611	0918	2.1F		0642	1000	1.7F
	1236	1521	2.1E		1310	1547	1.6E
	1829	2147	2.3F		1854	2218	1.8F
13 F	0113	0354	2.0E	28 Sa	0136	0415	1.6E
	0702	1013	2.0F		0725	1041	1.7F
	1332	1614	1.9E		1359	1634	1.5E
	1923	2241	2.2F		1940	2301	1.7F
14 Sa	0206	0447	1.9E	29 Su	0223	0500	1.5E
	0758	1114	2.0F		0812	1133	1.6F
	1432	1713	1.8E		1452	1723	1.4E
	2022	2342	2.0F		2031	2352	1.6F
15 Su	0303	0545	1.8E	30 M	0312	0551	1.5E
	0857	1221	1.9F		0903	1228	1.6F
	1537	1816	1.6E		1549	1819	1.3E
	2126				2127		
				31 Tu		0049	1.5F
					0405	0644	1.4E
					0958	1330	1.6F
					1647	1920	1.2E
					2226		

FEBRUARY

Day	Slack Water Time h.m.	Maximum Current Time h.m.	Vel. knots	Day	Slack Water Time h.m.	Maximum Current Time h.m.	Vel. knots
1 W		0152	1.4F	16 Th		0307	1.6F
	0500	0743	1.4E		0552	0853	1.4E
	1053	1428	1.7F		1156	1542	1.9F
	1745	2019	1.3E		1845	2143	1.4E
	2326						
2 Th		0253	1.5F	17 F	0040	0408	1.6F
	0554	0837	1.4E		0654	0958	1.5E
	1148	1526	1.8F		1257	1637	2.1F
	1840	2116	1.3E		1943	2242	1.5E
3 F	0023	0348	1.5F	18 Sa	0138	0501	1.7F
	0645	0928	1.5E		0748	1052	1.6E
	1240	1617	1.9F		1350	1727	2.2F
	1930	2211	1.5E		2032	2331	1.5E
4 Sa	0115	0437	1.6F	19 Su	0226	0550	1.8F
	0734	1021	1.7E		0836	1139	1.7E
	1329	1703	2.1F		1437	1810	2.2F
	2017	2257	1.6E		2114		
5 Su	0202	0519	1.8F	20 M		0013	1.6E
	0820	1106	1.9E		0307	0631	1.9F
	1415	1746	2.3F		0919	1216	1.7E
	2101	2340	1.8E		1517	1851	2.2F
					2153		
6 M	0247	0602	1.9F	21 Tu		0046	1.6E
	0904	1153	2.0E		0344	0706	1.9F
	1500	1825	2.4F		0959	1252	1.7E
	2144				1553	1924	2.1F
					2228		
7 Tu		0023	2.0E	22 W		0115	1.7E
	0330	0642	2.1F		0417	0742	1.9F
	0949	1236	2.2E		1037	1323	1.7E
	1545	1907	2.5F		1628	1957	2.1F
	2227				2303		
8 W		0106	2.1E	23 Th		0145	1.7E
	0414	0723	2.2F		0451	0811	1.9F
	1035	1322	2.2E		1115	1356	1.7E
	1631	1949	2.5F		1703	2026	2.0F
	2310				2338		
9 Th		0151	2.1E	24 F		0218	1.7E
	0458	0808	2.3F		0525	0843	1.9F
	1123	1409	2.2E		1154	1433	1.7E
	1718	2034	2.4F		1739	2058	1.9F
	2356						
10 F		0238	2.1E	25 Sa	0015	0253	1.7E
	0545	0857	2.3F		0601	0918	1.8F
	1215	1458	2.1E		1236	1512	1.6E
	1808	2123	2.3F		1819	2133	1.8F
11 Sa	0045	0326	2.0E	26 Su	0055	0332	1.6E
	0635	0948	2.2F		0641	0959	1.8F
	1310	1553	2.0E		1323	1557	1.5E
	1902	2218	2.1F		1902	2212	1.7F
12 Su	0138	0419	1.9E	27 M	0140	0419	1.6E
	0730	1048	2.0F		0726	1044	1.7F
	1411	1650	1.7E		1414	1645	1.4E
	2001	2320	1.9F		1952	2303	1.5F
13 M	0236	0518	1.7E	28 Tu	0230	0508	1.5E
	0831	1201	1.9F		0816	1139	1.6F
	1517	1756	1.5E		1511	1740	1.3E
	2107				2048		
14 Tu		0033	1.6F				
	0339	0624	1.5E				
	0937	1318	1.8F				
	1628	1912	1.3E				
	2219						
15 W		0153	1.5F				
	0446	0737	1.4E				
	1047	1433	1.8F				
	1739	2032	1.3E				
	2333						

Time meridian 75° W. 0000 is midnight. 1200 is noon.

At some locations on the west coast of the United States the pattern of floods, slacks, and ebbs is more complex. Slacks, for example, do not always follow a flood or ebb. These special current patterns are explained in the *Tidal Current Tables*.

The accuracy of these predictions is generally taken to be within one half hour, although deviations of as much as one hour or more can occur. Therefore, a prudent mariner plans to arrive at a particular entrance or strait at least one half hour before the time estimates given in the tables, to ensure passage at a slack or favorable current.

SUBORDINATE STATIONS

Table 2 of the *Tidal Current Tables* (excerpted in Table 8-10 of this text) provides the current differences and other constraints necessary for predictions at subordinate stations. The entries of this table include:

1. A station or substation identification number. For example, substation 2051 is assigned to the station located 0.8 miles northwest of Penikese Island. (There is no correspondence between the number assigned to a particular location in *Tide Tables* and that assigned in the *Tidal Current Tables*.)

2. A place name corresponding to each location for which predictions are available. As noted, the actual position should be plotted, rather than relying on the published place name.

3. The approximate position (latitude and longitude) of the station. As with the *Tide Tables*, these coordinates are approximate, and occasionally plot on dry land.

4. Time differences. Four time differences are given, that corresponding to minimum current (generally slack water) before flood, flood, minimum before ebb, and ebb. For Penikese Island, station 2051, these time differences are keyed to Pollack Rip Channel (look for this station in the Time Differences column) and are numerically equal to - 1 hour, 37 minutes, - 0 hours 25 minutes, - 0 hours 55 minutes, and -0 hours 57 minutes respectively. As with tidal predictions, it is convenient to use a structured worksheet (reproduced in Table 8-11) for tidal current computations. A worked out example is given in Table 8-12. In transcribing information from this table to the worksheet, pay particular attention to ensure that the correct numbers are entered. As with the tidal data, these time differences are to be added (algebraic sign important) to the corresponding times at the reference station. For example, the first current at Pollack Rip Channel on 27 February 1989 is a slack before ebb at 0140. The time difference corresponding to this current at Penikese Island is - 0 hours 55 minutes (55 minutes earlier). Therefore, the corresponding current occurs at (0140 - 0055) or 0045 at Penikese Island. The next current is an ebb current which occurs at Pollack Rip Channel at 0419 -- equivalent to 0322 at Penikese Island, from the - 57 minute time difference.

5. The next column entries are speed ratios for flood and ebb. These factors are to be multiplied by the drift of the corresponding current at the reference station. Numerically, the speed ratios are 0.6 for the flood and ebb current alike at station 2501, but they differ at many other locations. These are entered into the top data block of the worksheet in Table 8-12.

6. The next four columns in Table 2 of the *Tidal Current Tables* (Table 8-10 in this text) are the average speeds and directions of the various currents. Directions are given with respect to true north, and average speeds are given to the nearest 0.1 knot. These average speeds are of general interest, but are not used for individual predictions.

TABLE 8-10. EXCERPT FROM TABLE 2 OF THE *TIDAL CURRENT TABLES, 1989*

TABLE 2. – CURRENT DIFFERENCES AND OTHER CONSTANTS

NO.	PLACE	POSITION Lat. °' N	POSITION Long. °' W	METER DEPTH ft	TIME DIFFERENCES Min. before Flood h.m.	Flood h.m.	Min. before Ebb h.m.	Ebb h.m.	SPEED RATIOS Flood	Ebb	Minimum before Flood knots	deg.	Maximum Flood knots	deg.	Minimum before Ebb knots	deg.	Maximum Ebb knots	deg.
	VINEYARD SOUND Time meridian, 75°W				on POLLOCK RIP CHANNEL, p.28													
1931	West Chop, 0.2 mile west of..........	41 29.0	70 36.6		+1 19	+1 34	+1 50	+1 16	1.3	0.8	0.0	--	2.7	059	0.0	--	1.4	241
1936	Nobska Point, 1 mile southeast of..	41 30.1	70 38.6		+2 33	+2 15	+2 25	+2 19	1.3	1.4	0.0	--	2.6	071	0.0	--	2.4	259
1941	Norton Point, 0.5 mile north of.........	41 28.1	70 39.9		+1 55	+1 44	+2 01	+1 12	1.7	1.4	0.0	--	3.4	050	0.0	--	2.4	240
1946	Tarpaulin Cove, 1.5 miles east of......	41 28.3	70 43.5		+2 49	+2 07	+2 12	+2 33	1.0	1.4	0.0	--	1.9	055	0.0	--	2.3	232
1951	Robinsons Hole, 1.2 miles southeast of..	41 26.1	70 46.8		+2 30	+1 51	+2 11	+2 02	1.0	1.2	0.0	--	1.9	060	0.0	--	2.1	240
1956	Gay Head, 3 miles northeast of......	41 23.1	70 47.0		+2 25	+1 50	+1 42	+2 11	0.5	0.8	0.0	--	0.9	081	0.0	--	1.3	238
1961	Menemsha Bight <6>...........	41 21.3	70 46.3															
1966	Gay Head, 3 miles north of............	41 21.4	70 51.2		+2 13	+1 24	+1 55	+1 17	0.6	0.7	0.0	--	1.1	074	0.0	--	1.2	255
1971	Gay Head, 1.5 miles northwest of...	41 21.8	70 51.8		+1 30	+0 54	+1 42	+1 16	1.0	1.2	0.0	--	2.0	012	0.0	--	2.0	249
1976	Cuttyhunk Island, 3.2 miles southwest of	41 23	71 00		See table 5.													
1981	Browns Ledge............	41 19.8	71 05.9		See table 5.													
	VINEYARD SOUND-BUZZARDS BAY				on CAPE COD CANAL, p.22													
	Woods Hole																	
1986	South end............	41 30.8	70 40.2		+0 29	+1 40	+1 17	+0 08	0.4	0.2	0.0	--	1.5	135	0.0	--	1.1	318
1991	0.1 mile SW of Devils Foot Island...	41 31.2	70 41.1		+0 20	+1 41	+0 55	+0 31	0.9	0.8	0.0	--	3.5	094	0.0	--	3.6	276
1996	North end............	41 31.5	70 41.6		-0 29	+1 25	+1 09	-0 04	0.2	0.2	0.0	--	0.8	160	0.0	--	0.7	007
	Robinsons Hole																	
2001	South end............	41 26.7	70 48.2		+1 14	+1 42	+1 20	+1 01	0.2	0.2	0.0	--	0.8	162	0.0	--	1.0	339
2006	Middle............	41 27.0	70 48.4		+1 30	+2 00	+1 02	+0 47	0.7	0.6	0.0	--	2.8	146	0.0	--	2.9	316
2011	North end............	41 27.4	70 48.7		+1 54	+2 00	+0 52	+1 17	0.2	0.3	0.0	--	1.0	161	0.0	--	1.2	338
	Quicks Hole																	
2016	South end............	41 26.3	70 50.5		+2 18	+1 42	+1 17	+0 53	0.5	0.4	0.0	--	1.9	140	0.0	--	2.0	300
2021	Middle............	41 26.6	70 50.9		+2 21	+2 00	+1 26	+0 41	0.6	0.5	0.0	--	2.5	167	0.0	--	2.2	339
2026	North end............	41 27.1	70 51.0		+2 42	+2 06	+1 44	+0 23	0.5	0.6	0.0	--	2.0	165	0.0	--	2.6	002
2031	Canapitsit Channel............	41 25.4	70 54.5		+2 03	+2 27	+1 02	+0 26	0.6	0.4	0.0	--	2.6	156	0.0	--	1.7	312
					on POLLOCK RIP CHANNEL, p.28													
2036	Westport River entrance............	41 30.5	71 05.3		+0 09	-0 05	-0 26	-1 13	1.1	1.5	0.0	--	2.2	290	0.0	--	2.5	108
	BUZZARDS BAY <7>																	
2041	Gooseberry Neck, 2 miles SSE of.........	41 27	71 01		See table 5.													
2046	Ribbon Reef-Sow & Pigs Reef, between...	41 25.3	70 58.2		-0 19	-1 31	-2 44	-1 54	0.4	0.7	0.0	--	0.8	062	0.0	--	1.2	237
2051	Penikese Island, 0.8 mile northwest of...	41 27.9	70 56.2		-1 37	-0 25	-0 57	-0 57	0.6	0.6	0.0	--	1.2	050	0.0	--	1.1	254
2056	Penikese Island, 0.2 mile south of...	41 26.6	70 55.5		-1 43	-0 15	-1 30	-2 39	0.4	0.5	0.0	--	0.7	093	0.0	--	0.9	287
2061	Gull I. and Nashawena I., between...	41 26.2	70 54.2		-2 15	-0 57	-2 01	-2 41	0.5	0.6	0.0	--	0.9	091	0.0	--	1.1	247
2066	Weepecket Island, south of............	41 30.4	70 43.8		-3 16	-1 07	-1 28	-2 27	0.4	0.4	0.0	--	0.8	069	0.0	--	0.6	255
2071	Quamquisset Harbor entrance............	41 32.4	70 39.3		Current weak and variable												0.3	--
2076	West Falmouth Harbor entrance............	41 36.5	70 39.3		Current weak and variable													
2081	Megansett Harbor............	41 38.8	70 39.2		Current weak and variable													
2086	Abiels Ledge, 0.4 mile south of.........	41 41.1	70 40.4		+0 26	-0 36	-0 06	-0 23	0.4	0.6	0.0	--	0.8	035	0.0	--	1.0	216
2091	Dumpling Rocks, 0.2 mile southeast of...	41 32.0	70 55.1		-1 43	-1 03	-1 32	-2 09	0.4	0.6	0.0	--	0.8	066	0.0	--	1.1	190
2096	Apponagansett Bay............	41 35	70 57		Current weak and variable													
2101	Clarks Cove............	41 35	70 57		Current weak and variable													
2106	New Bedford Harbor and approaches......	41 36	70 55		Current weak and variable													

Endnotes can be found at the end of Table 2.

TABLE 8 - 11. COMPLETE CURRENT TABLE WORKSHEET

Substation: _____	Ref. Station: _____	Date: _____
Time Differences:	Speed Ratios:	Directions:
Min. Bef. Flood: _____	Flood: _____	Flood: _____
Flood: _____	Ebb: _____	Ebb: _____
Min. Bef. Ebb: _____		
Ebb: _____		

Look up these values from Table 2, "Current Differences and Other Constants." This section can be omitted if the desired location can be found in Table 1, "Daily Current Predictions." Pay careful attention to any footnotes applicable to the station.

CALCULATIONS:

Look up times and speeds for reference station in Table 1. Add or subtract time differences for substations to Table 1 times for reference station (pay attention to date). Estimate the drift at the substation by multiplying the appropriate speed ratio by the drift at the reference station. Remember, times given in these tables are standard time in the 24-hour system.

Ref. Station: _____

Condition	Time	Speed
Slack		
Ebb		
Slack		
Flood		
Slack		
Ebb		
Slack		
Flood		
Slack		
Ebb		

Substation: _____

Condition	Time	Speed
Slack		
Ebb		
Slack		
Flood		
Slack		
Ebb		
Slack		
Flood		
Slack		
Ebb		

VELOCITY OF CURRENT AT ANY TIME:

Location: _____ Time: _____ Date: _____

Interval Between Slack and Desired Time: _____

Time difference between desired time and nearest slack.

Interval Between Slack and Max Current: _____

Time difference between slack and maximum current that bracket desired time.

Max Current: _____

Drift of maximum current (ebb or flood) closest to desired time.

Tabled Correction: _____

From Table 3 -- be careful to use correct table if more than 1.

Calculated Velocity: _____

Multiply correction by max current.

Direction: _____

Take direction from top data block.

THE WORKSHEET

The top two blocks of the worksheet can be completed, and show the times of the slack and maximum currents at the subordinate station. To estimate the speed of the current at any time, it is necessary to use Table 3 from the *Tidal Current Tables,* reproduced here as Table 8-13. Note that two separate tables are given for this purpose, each referenced to different stations. (The same is true for the Pacific Coast stations.) Pay careful attention to ensure that the correct table is selected. The entries for this table are the factor to multiply the estimated maximum current at the substation to calculate the current at any time. Directions are given in the worksheet, and not repeated here.

DURATION OF SLACK

It is sometimes of interest to estimate the length of time at which a current will be slack, or nearly so. Divers, for example, are generally constrained to operate in circumstances where the current is nearly slack. As a second example, local knowledge may indicate that certain inlets or bridges are best transited during periods of near slack.

TABLE 8 - 12. COMPLETE CURRENT TABLE WORKSHEET

Substation: *Penikese*	Ref. Station: *Pollack*	Date: *27 February 1989*	Look up these values from Table 2, "Current Differences and Other Constants." This section can be omitted if the desired location can be found in Table 1, "Daily Current Predictions." Pay careful attention to any footnotes applicable to the station.
Time Differences:	Speed Ratios:	Directions:	
Min. Bef. Flood: *-1:37*	Flood: *0.6*	Flood: *050*	
Flood: *- :25*	Ebb: *0.6*	Ebb: *254*	
Min. Bef. Ebb: *- :55*			
Ebb: *- :57*			

CALCULATIONS :

Ref. Station: *Pollack Rip*			Substation: *Penikese*			Look up times and speeds for reference station in Table 1. Add or subtract time differences for substations to Table 1 times for reference station (pay attention to date). Estimate the drift at the substation by multiplying the appropriate speed ratio by the drift at the reference station. Remember, times given in these tables are standard time in the 24-hour system.
Condition	Time	Speed	Condition	Time	Speed	
Slack	*0140*	*0*	Slack	*0045*	*0*	
Ebb	*0419*	*1.6*	Ebb	*0322*	*1.0*	
Slack	*0726*	*0*	Slack	*0549*	*0*	
Flood	*1044*	*1.7*	Flood	*1019*	*1.0*	
Slack	*1414*	*0*	Slack	*1319*	*0*	
Ebb	*1645*	*1.4*	Ebb	*1548*	*0.8*	
Slack	*1952*	*0*	Slack	*1815*	*0*	
Flood	*2303*	*1.5*	Flood	*2238*	*0.9*	
Slack			Slack			
Ebb			Ebb			

VELOCITY OF CURRENT AT ANY TIME:

Location: *Penikese*   Time: *0900*   Date: *27 February 1989*

Interval Between Slack and Desired Time:	*0311*	Time difference between desired time and nearest slack.
Interval Between Slack and Max Current:	*0430*	Time difference between slack and maximum current that bracket desired time.
Max Current:	*1.0*	Drift of maximum current (ebb or flood) closest to desired time.
Tabled Correction:	*0.9*	From Table 3 -- be careful to use correct table if more than 1.
Calculated Velocity:	*0.9*	Multiply correction by max current.
Direction:	*050*	Take direction from top data block.

The time predictions for slack current, discussed above, attempt to give the *exact instant* of zero (or minimum) speed. However, there is a period on each side of slack water when the current is quite weak.

In principle, the estimated current at various times could be computed using the above procedure. A plot of the estimated current versus time could then be used to estimate the duration of interval within which the estimated current is arbitrarily small. But, such computations would be tedious, indeed, and subject to numerical error unless a computer were used.

Fortunately, a much simpler procedure has been devised by the architects of the *Tidal Current Tables*. This involves the use of Table 4 of these tables, termed the "Duration of Slack," which is reproduced as Table 8-14 of this text. Actually, two separate tables are used, as is the case for Table 3, each applicable to different stations.

TABLE 8-13. REPRODUCTION OF TABLE 3 FROM *TIDAL CURRENT TABLES*, 1989.

TABLE 3.—SPEED OF CURRENT AT ANY TIME

TABLE A

	Interval between slack and maximum current													
Interval between slack and desired time (h. m.)	h.m. 1 20	h.m. 1 40	h.m. 2 00	h.m. 2 20	h.m. 2 40	h.m. 3 00	h.m. 3 20	h.m. 3 40	h.m. 4 00	h.m. 4 20	h.m. 4 40	h.m. 5 00	h.m. 5 20	h.m. 5 40
0 20	0.4	0.3	0.3	0.2	0.2	0.2	0.2	0.1	0.1	0.1	0.1	0.1	0.1	0.1
0 40	0.7	0.6	0.5	0.4	0.4	0.3	0.3	0.3	0.3	0.2	0.2	0.2	0.2	0.2
1 00	0.9	0.8	0.7	0.6	0.6	0.5	0.5	0.4	0.4	0.4	0.3	0.3	0.3	0.3
1 20	1.0	1.0	0.9	0.8	0.7	0.6	0.6	0.5	0.5	0.5	0.4	0.4	0.4	0.4
1 40	------	1.0	1.0	0.9	0.8	0.8	0.7	0.7	0.6	0.6	0.5	0.5	0.5	0.4
2 00	------	------	1.0	1.0	0.9	0.9	0.8	0.8	0.7	0.7	0.6	0.6	0.6	0.5
2 20	------	------	------	1.0	1.0	0.9	0.9	0.8	0.8	0.7	0.7	0.6	0.6	0.6
2 40	------	------	------	------	1.0	1.0	1.0	0.9	0.9	0.8	0.8	0.7	0.7	0.7
3 00	------	------	------	------	------	1.0	1.0	1.0	0.9	0.9	0.8	0.8	0.8	0.7
3 20	------	------	------	------	------	------	1.0	1.0	1.0	0.9	0.9	0.9	0.8	0.8
3 40	------	------	------	------	------	------	------	1.0	1.0	1.0	0.9	0.9	0.9	0.9
4 00	------	------	------	------	------	------	------	------	1.0	1.0	1.0	1.0	0.9	0.9
4 20	------	------	------	------	------	------	------	------	------	1.0	1.0	1.0	1.0	0.9
4 40	------	------	------	------	------	------	------	------	------	------	1.0	1.0	1.0	1.0
5 00	------	------	------	------	------	------	------	------	------	------	------	1.0	1.0	1.0
5 20	------	------	------	------	------	------	------	------	------	------	------	------	1.0	1.0
5 40	------	------	------	------	------	------	------	------	------	------	------	------	------	1.0

TABLE B

	Interval between slack and maximum current													
Interval between slack and desired time (h. m.)	h.m. 1 20	h.m. 1 40	h.m. 2 00	h.m. 2 20	h.m. 2 40	h.m. 3 00	h.m. 3 20	h.m. 3 40	h.m. 4 00	h.m. 4 20	h.m. 4 40	h.m. 5 00	h.m. 5 20	h.m. 5 40
0 20	0.5	0.4	0.4	0.3	0.3	0.3	0.3	0.3	0.2	0.2	0.2	0.2	0.2	0.2
0 40	0.8	0.7	0.6	0.5	0.5	0.5	0.4	0.4	0.4	0.4	0.3	0.3	0.3	0.3
1 00	0.9	0.8	0.8	0.7	0.7	0.6	0.6	0.5	0.5	0.5	0.4	0.4	0.4	0.4
1 20	1.0	1.0	0.9	0.8	0.8	0.7	0.7	0.6	0.6	0.6	0.5	0.5	0.5	0.5
1 40	------	1.0	1.0	0.9	0.9	0.8	0.8	0.7	0.7	0.7	0.6	0.6	0.6	0.6
2 00	------	------	1.0	1.0	0.9	0.9	0.9	0.8	0.8	0.7	0.7	0.7	0.7	0.6
2 20	------	------	------	1.0	1.0	1.0	0.9	0.9	0.9	0.8	0.8	0.7	0.7	0.7
2 40	------	------	------	------	1.0	1.0	1.0	0.9	0.9	0.9	0.8	0.8	0.8	0.7
3 00	------	------	------	------	------	1.0	1.0	1.0	0.9	0.9	0.9	0.9	0.8	0.8
3 20	------	------	------	------	------	------	1.0	1.0	1.0	0.9	0.9	0.9	0.9	0.8
3 40	------	------	------	------	------	------	------	1.0	1.0	1.0	1.0	0.9	0.9	0.9
4 00	------	------	------	------	------	------	------	------	1.0	1.0	1.0	1.0	0.9	0.9
4 20	------	------	------	------	------	------	------	------	------	1.0	1.0	1.0	1.0	0.9
4 40	------	------	------	------	------	------	------	------	------	------	1.0	1.0	1.0	1.0
5 00	------	------	------	------	------	------	------	------	------	------	------	1.0	1.0	1.0
5 20	------	------	------	------	------	------	------	------	------	------	------	------	1.0	1.0
5 40	------	------	------	------	------	------	------	------	------	------	------	------	------	1.0

Use table A for all places except those listed below for table B.
Use table B for Cape Cod Canal, Hell Gate, Chesapeake and Delaware Canal and all stations in table 2 which are referred to them.

1. From predictions find the time of slack water and the time and velocity of maximum current (flood or ebb), one of which is immediately before and the other after the time for which the velocity is desired.
2. Find the interval of time between the above slack and maximum current, and enter the top of table A or B with the interval which most nearly agrees with this value.
3. Find the interval of time between the above slack and the time desired, and enter the side of table A or B with the interval which most nearly agrees with this value.
4. Find, in the table, the factor corresponding to the above two intervals, and multiply the maximum velocity by this factor. The result will be the approximate velocity at the time desired.

The duration of slack (in minutes) is found to be correlated with the strength of the maximum current. Thus, the tables provide the duration (in minutes) over which the estimated current will be less than a prespecified value of from 0.1 knots to 0.5 knots, in increments of 0.1 knots, for various values of the drift of the maximum current.

To illustrate, suppose that it is of interest to predict the approximate duration of the slack at 0549 at Penikese Island (substation #2051) on 27 February 1989 -- an example discussed above. Further, for purposes of this example, take "slack" to mean a current of less than 0.2 knots. Note that the estimated maximum ebb before this slack is 1.0 knot (see Table 8-12), as is the

TABLE 8 - 14. DURATION OF WEAK CURRENT NEAR TIME OF SLACK WATER

TABLE A

Maximum Current	Period with a speed not more than -				
	0.1 knot	0.2 knot	0.3 knot	0.4 knot	0.5 knot
KNOTS	MINUTES	MINUTES	MINUTES	MINUTES	MINUTES
1.0	23	46	70	94	120
1.5	15	31	46	62	78
2.0	11	23	35	46	58
3.0	8	15	23	31	38
4.0	6	11	17	23	29
5.0	5	9	14	18	23
6.0	4	8	11	15	19
7.0	3	7	10	13	16
8.0	3	6	9	11	14
9.0	3	5	8	10	13
10.0	2	5	7	9	11

TABLE B

Maximum Current	Period with a speed not more than -				
	0.1 knot	0.2 knot	0.3 knot	0.4 knot	0.5 knot
KNOTS	MINUTES	MINUTES	MINUTES	MINUTES	MINUTES
1.0	13	28	46	66	89
1.5	8	18	28	39	52
2.0	6	13	20	28	36
3.0	4	8	13	18	22
4.0	3	6	9	13	17
5.0	3	5	8	10	13

Table A should be used for all places except those listed below for Table B.

Table B should be used for Cape Cod Canal, Hell Gate, Chesapeake and Delaware Canal, and all stations in Table 2 which are referred to them.

estimated maximum flood at 1019. From Table 8-14 (top), the column headed (0.2 knots) is entered, as is the row (1.0 knot). The table entry, 46 minutes, is read. The estimated duration of slack is 46 minutes, or 23 minutes on either side of 0549. If slack were taken to mean a current of less than 0.5 knots, the estimated duration (from Table 8-14) would have been 120 minutes -60 minutes on either side of 0549.

In this example, the maximum current values on either side of the slack were identical, and equal to 1 knot. If this were not the case, Table 8-14 would be used twice to find a separate duration corresponding to each maximum speed, and the average of these two numbers used as the estimate.

ROTARY CURRENTS (ATLANTIC COAST ONLY)

The preceding discussion is applicable to what are termed *reversing currents* (termed *rectilinear* by the British). According to NOS, a *reversing current is defined as*, "A tidal current which flows alternately in approximately opposite directions with a slack water at each reversal of direction." However, experience shows that some currents are better described as *rotary*. A *rotary current is* "A tidal current that flows continually with the direction of flow changing through all points of the compass during the tidal period." Rotary tidal currents are generally found offshore where the direction of flow is not (or is less) restricted by shoreline or other barriers. The rotary currents tend to rotate clockwise in the northern hemisphere, and counter-clockwise in the southern hemisphere. The speed of a rotary current generally varies throughout the tidal current cycle.

Locations where rotary currents prevail are designated by the phrase "see Table 5" in the table of current differences and other constants. For example, look again at Table 8-10 (Table 2 of the *Tidal Current Tables*) for subordinate station #1976, "Cuttyhunk Island, 3.2 miles southwest of." The notation to see Table 5 is contained in the time differences columns.

Table 5 of the *Tidal Current Tables,* excerpted here in Table 8-15, contains information on the set (true) and drift of the rotary current, keyed to a defined reference station. For Cuttyhunk Island, the reference station is Pollack Rip Channel. Use of the table is virtually self-explanatory, so a brief example will suffice. Suppose that it is desired to estimate the set and drift of the current at this location at 1144 on 27 February 1989. Reference to the daily predictions for the reference station, Pollock Rip Channel, indicates that the maximum flood occurs at 1044, so the desired time is approximately 1 hour after the maximum flood. From Table 8-15 the set is 015 degrees (true), and the drift is 0.3 knots. The speeds shown in this table are *average* speeds. When the moon is full, new, or at perigee, the actual speeds will be 15 to 20 percent above the tabulated values. If syzygy and perigee are coincident, the actual current speeds will be 30 to 40 percent above the tabulated values. Quadrature or apogee lead to values 15 to 20 percent below the tabulated values. Finally, if quadrature and apogee are coincident, actual currents will be 30 to 40 percent less than predicted from these tables. Lunar or solar positions can be found in the inside back cover of the *Tidal Current Tables.*

TIDAL CURRENT DIAGRAMS

Tidal Current Diagrams are published for several well-traveled areas of the United States in the *Tidal Current Tables*. Figure 8-4 illustrates one such diagram for Vineyard and Nantucket sounds, covering a part of the area on the 1210-Tr chart. Other locations for which *Tidal Current Diagrams* are published include, the East River, New York, New York Harbor via Ambrose Channel, the Delaware Bay and River, and the Chesapeake Bay. These current diagrams represent *average* conditions of the surface currents in the middle of the channel.

For the illustration in Figure 8-4, easterly currents are designated "flood," and westerly currents "ebb." The small numbers in the diagram are the average speeds of the current in knots and tenths at various locations and times. All times, shown at the top and bottom axes of the diagram are keyed to slack waters at Pollock Rip Channel. These times can be estimated from the daily predictions given in the *Tidal Current Tables.*

Speed Lines are shown to the right of the diagram and are used directly with the diagram. By transferring to the diagram the direction of the speed line equal to the vessel's speed (with a paraline plotter or parallel rules), the diagram will show the general set and drift of the current

TABLE 8 - 15. EXCERPT TABLE 5 OF ROTARY TIDAL CURRENTS

Cuttyhunk I., 3 1/4 miles SW. of
L: 41°23' N., Lo: 71°00' W

Time	Direction (true)	Velocity
	Degrees	*Knots*
0	356	0.4
1	15	0.3
2	80	0.2
Hours after 3	123	0.3
maximum 4	146	0.5
flood at 5	158	0.5
Pollock Rip 6	173	0.4
Channel, see 7	208	0.3
page 28. 8	267	0.2
9	306	0.3
10	322	0.3
11	335	0.4

that would be encountered by any vessel passing through these waters, and the most favorable time for departing any place shown on the left margin. (Experience suggests that it is easier to use a parallel ruler or paraline plotter if this diagram is removed from the tables and placed on a flat surface.) To determine the set and drift of the current, use the parallel rulers to transfer from the speed lines to the diagram at the left, the direction of the speed line corresponding to the vessel's speed through the water (STW), moving the edge of the ruler to the point where the horizontal line representing the place of departure intersects the vertical line representing the time of day. If the ruler's edge lies within the shaded portion of the diagram, a flood current will be encountered, otherwise an ebb current will be encountered. If the ruler's edge lies along the boundary, slack water will be found.

To illustrate, suppose Coast Guard Auxiliary vessel 273007, capable of a STW of 12 knots, enters Pollock Rip Channel at 0340 on 27 February 1989 returning from a late night winter training and search and rescue (SAR) mission. Reference to the daily predictions (Table 8-9) indicates that the ebb begins at 0140 on this date and flood begins at 0726. The time, 0340, therefore, will be about 2 hours after ebb begins. With parallel rulers, transfer to the diagram the 12-knot speed line "westbound," placing the edge of the ruler on the point where the vertical line "2 hours after ebb begins at Pollack Rip Channel" intersects with the horizontal 47-mile line (the starting point). It will be found that the ruler passes through the unshaded (ebb current) portion of the diagram, the drift averaging approximately 1.4 knots. Vessel 273007 will, therefore, have a favorable ebb current averaging

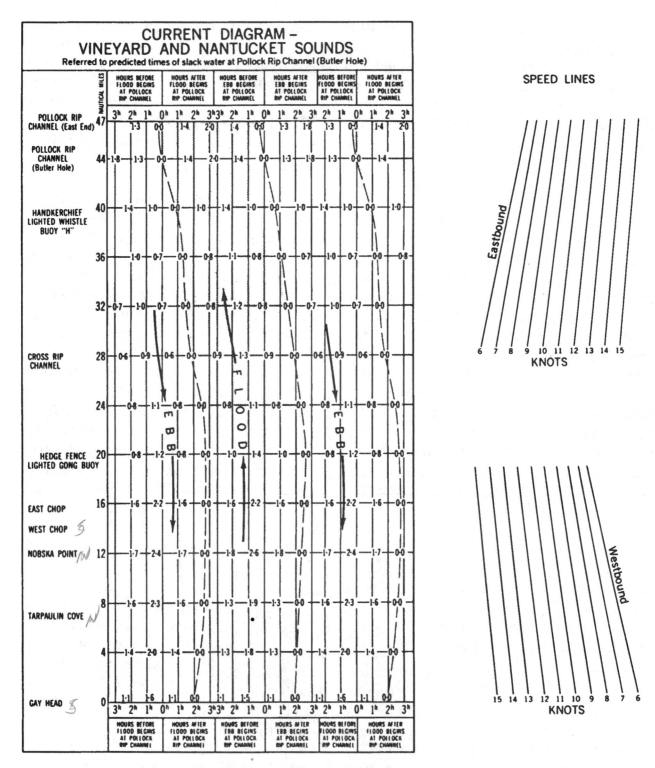

Fig. 8-4. Illustrative Tidal Current Diagram.

about 1.4 knots all the way to Gay Head, a welcome consolation after the night's activities. Note also that the edge of the ruler crosses the horizontal 16-mile line (at East Chop) about halfway between the figures 1.6 and 2.2 knots, indicating that the fair current will average nearly 2 knots at this point.

The most important use of these diagrams is to determine the most advantageous time of departure to maximize fair currents over the intended voyage route. Incidentally, it may not always be possible to ensure fair currents throughout the voyage, even if there is complete flexibility as to starting time. Whether or not a "free ride" is possible depends upon the speed of the vessel (too fast, and it may "outrun" the following current, too slow, and the current may reverse) and the tidal current patterns at the location in question. For example, it is not possible to ensure a fair current throughout an uninterrupted voyage for southbound vessels transiting the length of the Delaware River.

It is noted above that these diagrams represent average conditions. On any day, the currents calculated from the worksheet for Pollack Rip Channel may be larger or smaller than those given in the *Current Diagram*. The predicted current drift for the day in question can be used to determine approximate *correction factors* to adjust the averages in the *Tidal Current Diagrams* to the circumstances prevailing on the day when a prediction is required. For example, reference to the daily table for 27 February 1989 indicates that the maximum ebb on this tide is 1.6 knots, rather than the 1.8 knots shown on the *Tidal Current Diagram*. In this case, the drift determined from the *Tidal Current Diagram* could be corrected by the ratio 1.6/1.8, or approximately a factor of 0.89.

Differences in the vessel's estimated speed of advance (SOA) as a result of making appropriate use of these diagrams and selecting favorable times of departure can be substantial. In this case, ebb currents of as much as 2.4 knots can be encountered in the stretch from East chop to just west of Tarpaulin Cove. A 12-knot vessel, therefore, could make nearly 14.4 knots if the voyage were perfectly timed, versus only 9.6 knots if an inauspicious time were chosen, a difference of 50% in SOA (and fuel economy as well). These differences could be even more important in the case of slower sailing vessels. A 6-knot vessel could either average 8.4 knots or 4.6 knots, a difference of over 80%!

TIDAL CURRENT CHARTS

The last source of tidal current information discussed in this chapter are the *Tidal Current Charts*. These are published for locations in the United States by NOS for several areas including, Boston Harbor, Narragansett Bay, Narragansett Bay to Nantucket Sound, Block Island and East Long Island Sounds, New York Harbor, Delaware Bay and River, Upper Chesapeake Bay, Charleston Harbor, Tampa Bay, San Francisco Bay, Puget Sound (north), and Puget Sound (south).

Figure 8-5 provides an example, taken from the Narragansett Bay to Nantucket Sound charts. These charts (each a set of charts, really) include a series of 12 copies of a chart of the area covered, superimposed with arrows and numbers to indicate the typical set and drift of the current (at spring tides) for a specific hour in the tidal current cycle for a major reference station. In Figure 8-5, for example, the times are taken with respect to Pollock Rip Channel. Factors are also provided (in the text accompanying these charts) for adjusting the drift estimates from average spring tidal currents to those on the day in question. Therefore, for accurate results, it is necessary to use these charts in conjunction with the *Tidal Current Tables*. (The Narragansett Bay chart, keyed to Newport, RI, is unique in this series as it is based upon times of *tides,* rather than tidal currents, and is designed to be used with the *Tide Tables.*)

These charts are most useful for providing a synoptic view of the temporal and spatial distribution of currents--and eliminate an incredible amount of drudgery in making station-by-station computations of current set and drift. Many of the current patterns depicted on these charts are complex--at a given time currents may be going in one direction in one area, and another just a few miles away. Refer, for example, to the currents in Buzzards Bay and Vineyard South shown in Figure 8-5. As noted below, these diagrams can be used to advantage for determining the best overall routing to follow, the best timing of a voyage, or even if both the overall route and time are fixed, the specific route that is likely to maximize fair currents or minimize foul currents. Your only complaint after a care-

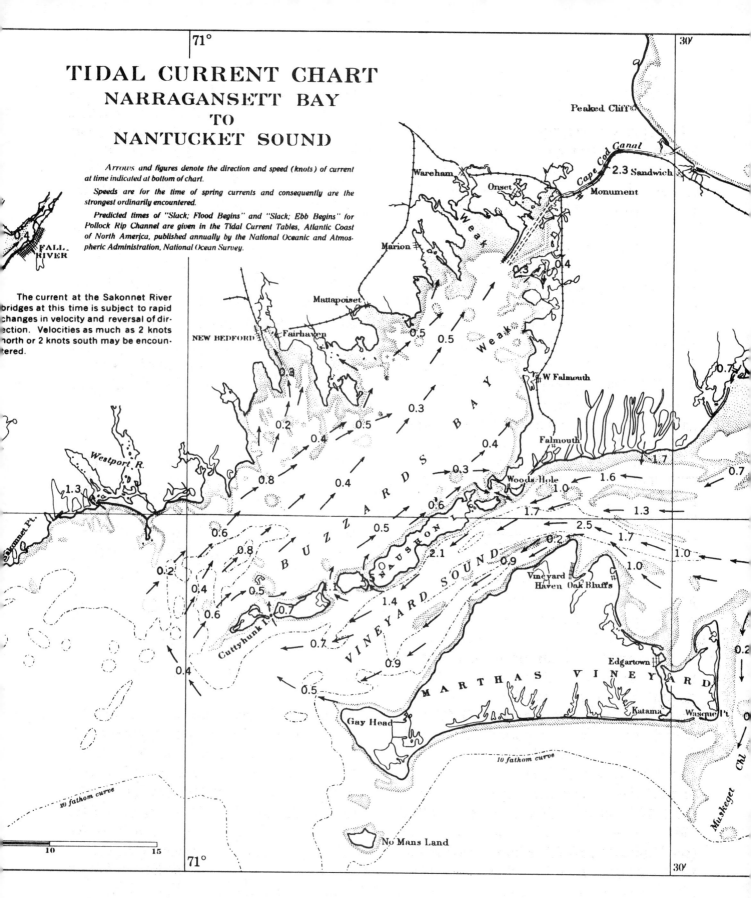

Fig. 8-5. Extract from *Tidal Current Chart.*

ful examination of these charts is that one may not be available for the waters where you cruise!

STRATEGIES FOR USING TIDAL CURRENT DATA

This section contains some brief concluding remarks about the use of tidal current information in voyage planning.

First, it is useful to annotate the voyage planning chart with the locations for which tidal current predictions are available. Browse through the index found at the back of the tables to identify the potentially relevant locations. In this way you can identify the available stations that can be used for planning each of the voyage legs. That is, for planning purposes, a different reference station or substation can be used as a surrogate for the current on each leg of the voyage.

Second, it is useful to make rough computations of the expected currents at various times of day. For this purpose, it is not necessary to make hourly computations, but rather to identify the times and strengths of slack water and maximum tidal current. These approximate calculations are sufficiently accurate for identifying the major timing options of the voyage. For example, it may be apparent that a delay of only a few hours in the start of a voyage offers the advantage of more favorable currents, or that one route option is superior to another in terms of the likely currents at voyage time. Remember, it is the speed with respect to the earth (SMG, SOA) over the course that is important, not the speed through the water (STW). A longer route (in distance) may actually be shorter (in time) than another if the currents are right. In the area of the 1210-Tr chart, a little time spent with the *Tidal Current Tables* or a *Tidal Current Chart* (see Figure 8-5) available for the area will convince you of the proposition that the currents are often flowing in opposite directions in Vineyard Sound and Buzzards Bay. That is, the currents are generally northeasterly in Buzzards Bay when they are southwesterly in Vineyard Sound and the converse. Starting from a point southwest of

Cuttyhunk Island on a voyage to Woods Hole, it might be much faster to go through Buzzards Bay and later south to Woods Hole, than to take the shorter route east through Vineyard Sound, depending, of course, on the voyage timing. Reference to the *Tidal Current Chart* also indicates that currents are generally stronger on the north side of Vineyard Sound when these currents are flowing to the southwest. So if Vineyard Sound is selected for the route at the time depicted in the chart, steering a course closer to Martha's Vineyard will result in reduced foul currents on average. Local knowledge, gained from experience, or a careful reading of such publications as the *Coast Pilot* (see Chapter 10), helps to establish the importance of currents at various locations and to identify potentially attractive voyage options.

The basis for making the determination that a longer distance route with fair currents will be a shorter time route when compared to a shorter distance route with foul currents can be made explicit. Let D_1 be the distance (M) on the longer route, X_1 the drift of the fair current along this route, D_2 the shorter distance, X_2 the drift of the foul current, and S the vessel's STW. Then, after a little algebra, it can be shown that the longer distance route will be the shorter time route provided that:

$$D_1/D_2 \leq (1 + X_1/S) / (1 - X_2/S).$$

Table 8-16 facilitates these computations. To illustrate the use of this formula, approximately one hour after flood begins at Pollock Rip Channel the currents are southwesterly in Vineyard Sound at approximately 1.5 knots and northeasterly in Buzzards Bay at between 0.5 and 0.6 knots. If sailing yacht *Despacio* can make 6.0 knots (STW), under what circumstances would a longer route through Buzzards Bay to Woods Hole require less time? Here, $X_1 = 0.5$, $X_2 = 1.5$, and $S = 6.0$, and, therefore, $X_1/S = 0.10$, $X_2/S = 0.25$. Substitution of these values into the above equation shows that the longer distance route is the shorter time route provided that $D_1 \leq 1.47$

Table 8-16. When to choose a longer route with fair currents compared to a shorter route with foul currents. Table entries are the ratio of the distances such that the voyage time is the same for both routes. If the actual ratio of distances is less than or equal to the tabulated value, the longer distance route is the shorter time route.

RATIO OF FOUL CURRENT TO VESSEL'S STW	RATIO OF FAIR CURRENT TO VESSEL'S SPEED THROUGH THE WATER																				
	0.00	0.02	0.04	0.06	0.08	0.10	0.12	0.14	0.16	0.18	0.20	0.22	0.24	0.26	0.28	0.30	0.32	0.34	0.36	0.38	0.40
0.00	1.00	1.02	1.04	1.06	1.08	1.10	1.12	1.14	1.16	1.18	1.20	1.22	1.24	1.26	1.28	1.30	1.32	1.34	1.36	1.38	1.40
0.02	1.02	1.04	1.06	1.08	1.10	1.12	1.14	1.16	1.18	1.20	1.22	1.24	1.27	1.29	1.31	1.33	1.35	1.37	1.39	1.41	1.43
0.04	1.04	1.06	1.08	1.10	1.13	1.15	1.17	1.19	1.21	1.23	1.25	1.27	1.29	1.31	1.33	1.35	1.38	1.40	1.42	1.44	1.46
0.06	1.06	1.09	1.11	1.13	1.15	1.17	1.19	1.21	1.23	1.26	1.28	1.30	1.32	1.34	1.36	1.38	1.40	1.43	1.45	1.47	1.49
0.08	1.09	1.11	1.13	1.15	1.17	1.20	1.22	1.24	1.26	1.28	1.30	1.33	1.35	1.37	1.39	1.41	1.43	1.46	1.48	1.50	1.52
0.10	1.11	1.13	1.16	1.18	1.20	1.22	1.24	1.27	1.29	1.31	1.33	1.36	1.38	1.40	1.42	1.44	1.47	1.49	1.51	1.53	1.56
0.12	1.14	1.16	1.18	1.20	1.23	1.25	1.27	1.30	1.32	1.34	1.36	1.39	1.41	1.43	1.45	1.48	1.50	1.52	1.55	1.57	1.59
0.14	1.16	1.19	1.21	1.23	1.26	1.28	1.30	1.33	1.35	1.37	1.40	1.42	1.44	1.47	1.49	1.51	1.53	1.56	1.58	1.60	1.63
0.16	1.19	1.21	1.24	1.26	1.29	1.31	1.33	1.36	1.38	1.40	1.43	1.45	1.48	1.50	1.52	1.55	1.57	1.60	1.62	1.64	1.67
0.18	1.22	1.24	1.27	1.29	1.32	1.34	1.37	1.39	1.41	1.44	1.46	1.49	1.51	1.54	1.56	1.59	1.61	1.63	1.66	1.68	1.71
0.20	1.25	1.28	1.30	1.33	1.35	1.38	1.40	1.43	1.45	1.48	1.50	1.53	1.55	1.58	1.60	1.62	1.65	1.68	1.70	1.73	1.75
0.22	1.28	1.31	1.33	1.36	1.38	1.41	1.44	1.46	1.49	1.51	1.54	1.56	1.59	1.62	1.64	1.67	1.69	1.72	1.74	1.77	1.79
0.24	1.32	1.34	1.37	1.39	1.42	1.45	1.47	1.50	1.53	1.55	1.58	1.61	1.63	1.66	1.68	1.71	1.74	1.76	1.79	1.82	1.84
0.26	1.35	1.38	1.41	1.43	1.46	1.49	1.51	1.54	1.57	1.59	1.62	1.65	1.68	1.70	1.73	1.76	1.78	1.81	1.84	1.86	1.89
0.28	1.39	1.42	1.44	1.47	1.50	1.53	1.56	1.58	1.61	1.64	1.67	1.69	1.72	1.75	1.78	1.81	1.83	1.86	1.89	1.92	1.94
0.30	1.43	1.46	1.49	1.51	1.54	1.57	1.60	1.63	1.66	1.69	1.71	1.74	1.77	1.80	1.83	1.86	1.89	1.91	1.94	1.97	2.00
0.32	1.47	1.50	1.53	1.56	1.59	1.62	1.65	1.68	1.71	1.74	1.76	1.79	1.82	1.85	1.88	1.91	1.94	1.97	2.00	2.03	2.06
0.34	1.52	1.55	1.58	1.61	1.64	1.67	1.70	1.73	1.76	1.79	1.82	1.85	1.88	1.91	1.94	1.97	2.00	2.03	2.06	2.09	2.12
0.36	1.56	1.59	1.63	1.66	1.69	1.72	1.75	1.78	1.81	1.84	1.88	1.91	1.94	1.97	2.00	2.03	2.06	2.09	2.13	2.16	2.19
0.38	1.61	1.65	1.68	1.71	1.74	1.77	1.81	1.84	1.87	1.90	1.94	1.97	2.00	2.03	2.06	2.10	2.13	2.16	2.19	2.23	2.26
0.40	1.67	1.70	1.73	1.77	1.80	1.83	1.87	1.90	1.93	1.97	2.00	2.03	2.07	2.10	2.13	2.17	2.20	2.23	2.27	2.30	2.33
0.42	1.72	1.76	1.79	1.83	1.86	1.90	1.93	1.97	2.00	2.03	2.07	2.10	2.14	2.17	2.21	2.24	2.28	2.31	2.34	2.38	2.41
0.44	1.79	1.82	1.86	1.89	1.93	1.96	2.00	2.04	2.07	2.11	2.14	2.18	2.21	2.25	2.29	2.32	2.36	2.39	2.43	2.46	2.50
0.46	1.85	1.89	1.93	1.96	2.00	2.04	2.07	2.11	2.15	2.19	2.22	2.26	2.30	2.33	2.37	2.41	2.44	2.48	2.52	2.56	2.59
0.48	1.92	1.96	2.00	2.04	2.08	2.12	2.15	2.19	2.23	2.27	2.31	2.35	2.38	2.42	2.46	2.50	2.54	2.58	2.62	2.65	2.69
0.50	2.00	2.04	2.08	2.12	2.16	2.20	2.24	2.28	2.32	2.36	2.40	2.44	2.48	2.52	2.56	2.60	2.64	2.68	2.72	2.76	2.80

D_2. That is, D_1 could be nearly 50% greater than D_2 and still be the shorter time route.

The phenomenon of currents going in opposite directions or at different speeds in contiguous waters is not unique to Buzzards Bay/Vineyard Sound. For example, the currents on opposite sides of Whidbey Island in Puget Sound (North) or Vashon Island in Puget Sound (South) exhibit the same patterns.

Third, the rough computations (referred to above) identify and narrow down the precise times (more accurately, time intervals or "windows") for which more exact current predictions are required or useful. In this more detailed planning phase, you may need or want to make hourly estimates of current. (As a practical matter, these detailed computations are tedious and always subject to numerical error. Just how many computations are made depend upon whether or not a computer is available to automate the computations. Use of the *Tidal Current Charts* or *Diagrams* reduces the computational drudgery if no computer is at hand.) In hazard-strewn waters and in conditions of poor visibility when fixes are not likely to be frequent, hourly computation of currents, estimated positions, and courses to steer (see Chapter 7) might be in order. Alternatively, in open water or if all-weather navigation aids, such as radar or loran are aboard, the use of average currents over a period of several hours might be appropriate.

Fourth, the navigator should consider the purchase of computer programs to automate the calculation of tide heights or tidal currents. Because the state-of-the-art of these programs is evolving rapidly, these are not discussed in this text. But software that is both powerful and easy to use is now on the market. Use of computer programs speeds up the planning process greatly, and means that many more voyage options can be considered and evaluated. Computers help ensure accuracy as well.

Finally, remember that tidal current predictions are not error free. These predictions should be checked frequently against the vessel's actual progress for voyage decision making.

REFERENCES

Bowditch, N. *American Practical Navigator, An Epitome of Navigation,* Vol. 1, Defense Mapping Agency, Washington, DC, 1984.

Defant, A. *Ebb and Flow, The Tides of Earth, Air, and Water,* University of Michigan Press, Ann Arbor, MI, 1958.

Hinz, E. *The Complete Book of Anchoring and Mooring,* Cornell Maritime Press, Centreville, MD, 1986.

Markell, J. *Coastal Navigation for the Small Boat Sailor,* TAB Books Inc., Blue Ridge Summit, PA, 1984.

Mays, J. "Thorough and Versatile Tide Prediction by Computer," *Sea Technology,* May 1987.

Graves, F. *Piloting,* International Marine Publishing Co., Camden, ME, 1981.

Maloney, E. S. *Chapman Piloting, Seamanship and Small Boat Handling,* Hearst Marine Books, New York, NY, 1985.

U.S. Department of Commerce, National Oceanic and Atmospheric Administration, National Ocean Service. *Tide Tables* also *Tidal Current Tables,* annual.

Chapter 9

Radionavigation

At several points in this text, "revolutionary developments" in marine navigation systems have been mentioned. Nowhere is evidence of this revolution more dramatic than in the area of radionavigation. In years past, small boat skippers were lucky to own a crystal-controlled marine radio, capable of transmitting on only four or five channels, and a radio direction finding (RDF) set. Dead reckoning positions were typically checked by piloting techniques for coastal mariners, and celestial fixes for bluewater sailors. Both radar and loran were bulky, expensive, and limited, for the most part, to merchant vessels and naval ships.

Now, advances in the state-of-the-art of electronics and computers have resulted in miniaturized and much less expensive components. Loran sets, for example, have decreased in price to levels well within reach of the average boater, and have become very much more sophisticated and "user friendly."

Additionally, advances in computers have resulted in navigation systems that do many of the tasks formerly done exclusively by the navigator. For example, a modern loran does much more than provide a continuous display of latitude and longitude. It can calculate speed and course made good (SMG, CMG), current set and drift, cross-track error, course to steer to reach an intended destination, time to go (TTG) to reach the destination, and sound an alarm to warn of arrival. Lorans can "talk" to radars, autopilots, and computer charting systems for a variety of purposes that would startle even a merchant marine skipper of 20 years ago.

It is virtually imperative that at least some of these new tools be covered in any modern course on coastal piloting. This chapter provides an *introduction* to these systems. Constraints on length and scope limit the discussion to only three of the most important systems, RDF, radar, and loran. Readers interested in more details about these systems and others not covered in this chapter are referred to the extensive bibliography.

RDF, radar, or loran sets from different manufacturers share many features, but also differ considerably in other features and details of operation. For this reason, it is impossible to write a single chapter that shows you how to use any specific model. Even if size constraints on this chapter did not prevent a model-by-model discussion, the rapid pace of innovation would quickly render any such discussion obsolete. Rather, this chapter describes the general principles of operation of the radionavigation system and common features of sets now in general use. In short, this chapter is not an owner's manual, but serves as a complement or introduction to that document.

Care has been taken in this chapter to avoid excessively technical descriptions. Most mariners, for example, are uninterested in the particular frequency of operation, pulse, length, beam width, etc., except insofar as this information is required to understand the use and limitations of the equipment. Again, look to the references in the bibliography for these details.

Finally, despite efforts at simplification, this is one of the longest and most technical chapters in the ACN course. It may require reading and rereading to ensure that the concepts are understood. Don't give up--this is important material, even if you don't own any of this equipment at present, you probably will in the near future.

RADIO DIRECTION FINDING (RDF)

RDF is the oldest (radiobeacons were placed in position on the Ambrose, Sea Girt, and Fire Island lightships on 1 May 1921, the first such stations in the world) of the three systems discussed in this chapter and was the first to provide a truly all-weather system of electronic navigation. RDF generally offers lower performance than loran in terms of accuracy and relative cost of equipment. The least expensive loran sets, for example, are now comparable in price to "inexpensive" RDFs and less expensive than the more elaborate automatic direction finders (ADF) being sold. Sales of loran sets have eclipsed those of RDF sets--a typical marine supply catalog will list one or two ADF units and perhaps 10 or 15 loran receivers.

None the less, the system of domestic RDF transmitter stations continues to be maintained by the Coast Guard (and will, until at least the year 2002). RDF offers coverage in many parts of the world not covered by other systems, such as loran. RDF is simple and reliable (transmitters routinely exceed the minimum 99% "on-air" specification), and many vessels are presently equipped with RDF sets. Used with skill and due regard to its limitations, RDF can provide fixes of "acceptable" (though by no means "state-of-the-art") accuracy. Some of the RDF sets can be powered by small dry cell batteries independent of the vessel's principal power source. Thus, in the event of an alternator or battery failure, the RDF set can still "get you home." This feature provides justification for purchase of an RDF as a "backup" navigation system.

However, there are also "portable" dry-cell powered lorans on the market that might be a better choice for this purpose.

RDF PRINCIPLE OF OPERATION

From the viewpoint of the mariner, the RDF system consists of a receiver with a *directional* antenna. The antenna can be rotated to produce either a minimum or maximum signal strength. Signal strength is greatest when the antenna is perpendicular to the transmitting station and least when the antenna is pointed directly at the transmitting station. (In principle, the antenna could be rotated so as to either minimize or maximize the signal strength and a bearing taken from either position. However, in practice the "null" or minimum is "sharper," hence more accurate.) The receiver is able to be tuned to stations in the low and medium frequency AM bands of approximately 200 to 400 kilohertz, just beneath the standard AM broadcast band. (Some receivers can also use the standard AM broadcast band for direction finding.) The significance of this technical detail is that transmission at these frequencies is not "line of sight," and reception at distances greater than the optical or radio horizon (see following sections) is possible. The directional antenna is used to determine the direction (usually relative direction) of the signal being emitted from a shore station. If the location of the transmitter is charted (as it is for marine radiobeacons) or otherwise known, the relative bearing can be converted to a line of position (LOP). Two or more crossed LOPs provide a fix, as discussed in Chapter 6.

MARINE RDF TRANSMITTERS

The Coast Guard operates approximately 200 transmitters, called *radiobeacons*, located in the Atlantic, Gulf, and Pacific coasts, and on the Great Lakes. These radiobeacons operate in the frequency range of 285 to 325 kilohertz and are often located on light structures or other ATONs. Additionally, there are similar radiobeacons located throughout the world and, if the receiver is properly equipped, standard AM stations can also be used (see below) for radio direction finding. Worldwide locations and frequencies can be found in DMA Publication 117, *Radio Navigational Aids*, published annually.

As noted, the operating frequency range of the RDF network is such that transmissions are not limited to "line of sight." But, because the number of discrete frequencies within the overall frequency band established for RDFs is limited, the power of each beacon must be reduced to avoid interference with other stations operating on the same (or nearly the same) frequency. Therefore, *radiobeacons are basically short-range navigational aids, limited in range from about 10 nautical miles to 175 nautical miles*. Radiobeacons are thus "final approach aids" to major harbors and generally located near major harbors for this reason. The location (latitude and longitude), frequency, morse code identifier, and range of these stations are given in the Light List (see Chapter 10), an excerpt of which is shown in Figure 9-1 from Volume II. Locations are also shown on nautical charts with a magenta circle, the symbol "R Bn," the frequency in kilohertz, and the Morse code identifier written nearby. A sample of RDF stations located on the 1210-Tr chart includes Point Judith, Brenton Reef, Buzzards, and Woods Hole.

As of this writing, U.S. marine radiobeacons are subdivided into two classes: **continuous** or **sequenced**. A **continuous** radiobeacon broadcasts without interruption on a discrete frequency. Referring to Figure 9-1, for example, the Brenton Reef beacon broadcasts its Morse code identifier (-... .-.) continuously on the frequency 295 kilohertz. More accurately, it transmits the Morse code identifier superimposed on a continuous carrier for 50 seconds, followed by a long tone for the remaining 10 seconds for maximum bearing accuracy during manual operation. The user merely tunes in this frequency (some receivers use "slide rule" tuning, and others digital), **verifies that this is the correct station** from the Morse code identifier (do not omit this step, otherwise you may tune in the wrong station!), and obtains a relative bearing from the set, as discussed below.

Operation with the **sequenced** stations, however, is slightly different. In order to permit more stations to operate on the same band, some stations are sequenced. That is, more than one station uses the same frequency--but not at the same time! Here's how this works. Typically, sequenced stations are organized into groups of six stations transmitting on the same frequency. One station in each group transmits for, say, one minute out of six, and is silent for the remaining five minutes. Referring to Figure 9-2, for example, which shows characteristics of sequenced radiobeacons, Highland, Nantucket LNB, Montauk Point, Ambrose, Great Duck Island, and Manana Island stations all share the same frequency. Highland transmits first in sequence, identifier (.... ..), etc. The user tunes in the station (286 kilohertz) and listen for the appropriate code, and takes a bearing during the long tone after this code is broadcast. In some cases, fewer than six stations are included in the group, and stations may transmit more than one minute in six. Referring to Figure 9-2, for example, the stations using a frequency of 316 kilohertz have this characteristic. Execution Rocks will transmit during the first and fourth minute of the six-minute cycle.

Obviously, sequenced radiobeacons are less convenient to use and this system is now being phased out in favor of continuous stations. Hopefully, this description will only be of historical interest by the time you read this. Check the Light List for the most authoritative and up-to-date information.

OTHER BEACONS

Aeronautical beacons (sometimes shown on marine charts) and standard AM broadcast stations can also be used with an RDF. Some aeronautical beacons may also transmit weather information at 15 and 45 minutes past the hour. The weather information is of particular interest to aircraft pilots (e.g., surface winds, ceiling and visibility, etc.) but is also of interest to mariners. The location of aeronautical beacons or standard AM stations are determined by factors

RADIOBEACON SYSTEM - ATLANTIC AND GULF COASTS

CONTINUOUS – By Frequency

Freq kHz	Station	Characteristic	Range (n.m.)	Lat. (N)	Long. (W)
286	DRY TORTUGAS	OE (——— .)	110	24 37 54	82 55 16
288	PUNTA TUNA	X (—..—)	150	17 59 25	65 53 08
290	CHESAPEAKE LIGHT	CO (—.—. ———)	50	36 54 15	75 42 47
290	FRYING PAN SHOALS	FP (..—. .——.)	50	33 29 07	77 35 24
290	FREEPORT	R (.—.)	20	28 56 27	95 18 04
290	YANKEETOWN	Y (—.——)	65	28 57 35	82 41 49
291	HALFWAY ROCK	HR (.... .—.)	10	43 39 21	70 02 15
291	NOBSKA POINT	NP (—. .——.)	20	41 30 58	70 39 20
291	FIRE ISLAND	RT (.—. —)	15	40 38 18	73 18 53
293	OCEAN CITY INLET	OC (——— —.—.)	10	38 19 30	75 05 18
294	JUPITER INLET	J (.———)	110	26 56 54	80 04 54
295	SCITUATE HARBOR	SH (... ....)	10	42 11 56	70 43 12
295	BRENTON REEF	BR (—... .—.)	10	41 25 35	71 23 22
296	GALVESTON	G (——.)	150	29 19 44	94 44 10
299	HILLSBORO INLET	Q (——.—)	125	26 15 33	80 04 52
300	MOBILE POINT	C (—.—.)	150	30 13 38	88 01 24
301	PORTLAND LIGHTED HORN BUOY P (LNB)	PH (.——. ....)	30	43 31 37	70 05 31
301	BLOCK ISLAND	BI (—... ..)	20	41 09 09	71 33 07
302	EAST ROCKAWAY INLET	ER (. .—.)	10	40 35 11	73 45 11
304	BOSTON LIGHTED HORN BUOY B (LNB)	BH (—... ....)	30	42 22 42	70 47 00
304	ARANSAS PASS	Z (——..)	125	27 50 18	97 03 32
306	ST. JOHNS	R (.—.)	125	30 23 09	81 23 51
307	SOUTHWEST PASS ENT.	OT (——— —)	50	28 54 19	89 25 43
308	CLEVELAND LEDGE	CL (—.—. .—..)	10	41 37 51	70 41 42
308	MANASQUAN INLET	MI (—— ..)	20	40 06 03	74 02 03
308	INDIAN RIVER INLET	IR (.. .—.)	10	38 36 35	75 04 06
309	HATTERAS INLET STATION	HI (.... ..)	30	35 12 27	75 42 21
310	SMITH POINT	SP (... .——.)	20	37 52 47	76 11 03
310	GEORGETOWN	F (..—.)	30	33 13 21	79 11 06
310	EGMONT KEY	H (....)	170	27 36 02	82 45 39

Fig. 9-1. Excerpt From the Light List Describing Continuous RDF Stations

other than utility to the mariner, however. In particular, use of inland stations entails reduced accuracy. Moreover, for obvious reasons, it is necessary to know the location of the broadcast antenna which may require access to aeronautical charts or other maps that are unlikely to be on board. Be careful in using commercial AM stations; although the station may identify its location as part of the legally required identification, what is relevant is the location of the **transmitting antenna,** not the "downtown" location where the studio is located.

RADIOBEACON SYSTEM - ATLANTIC AND GULF COASTS

SEQUENCED – By Frequency

Freq kHz	Sequence	Station	Characteristic	Range (n.m.)	Lat. (N)	Long. (W)
286	I	HIGHLAND	HI (.... ..)	100	42 02 24	70 03 40
	II	NANTUCKET LNB	NS (-. ...)	50	40 30 00	69 28 00
	III	MONTAUK POINT	MP (-- .--.)	125	41 04 02	71 51 47
	IV	AMBROSE	T (-)	125	40 27 32	73 49 52
	V	GREAT DUCK ISLAND	GD (--. -..)	50	44 08 32	68 14 47
	VI	MANANA ISLAND	MI (-- ..)	100	43 45 48	69 19 38
298	I	OAK ISLAND	OA (--- .-)	70	33 53 33	78 02 06
	II	CAPE HENLOPEN	HL (.... .-..)	125	38 47 39	75 05 26
	III	CHARLESTON	S (...)	125	32 45 28	79 50 36
	IV	CAPE HENRY	CB (-.-. -...)	150	36 55 35	76 00 27
	V	OREGON INLET	PI (.--. ..)	125	35 46 06	75 31 24
	VI	FORT MACON	CL (-.-. .-..)	150	34 41 53	76 41 00
306	I, IV	CLINTON HARBOR	CL (-.-. .-..)	20	41 16 00	72 31 10
	II	LITTLE GULL	J (.---)	20	41 12 22	72 06 29
	III, VI	HORTON POINT	HP (.... .--.)	20	41 05 06	72 26 48
	V	WATCH HILL	WH (.-- ....)	10	41 18 36	71 55 30
308	II	PARTRIDGE ISLAND (C)	U (..-)	50	45 14 13	66 03 17
	III	SOUTHWEST HEAD (C)	N (-.)	50	44 36 03	66 54 20
	IV	WEST QUODDY	WQ (.-- --.-)	20	44 48 54	66 57 04
	VI	SEAL ISLAND (C)	H (....)	40	43 23 28	66 00 53
316	I, IV	EXECUTION ROCKS	XR (-..- .-.)	20	40 52 41	73 44 18
	II, V	OLD FIELD POINT	OP (--- .--.)	20	40 58 36	73 07 08
	III, VI	STRATFORD POINT	SP (... .--.)	20	41 09 06	73 06 13

Fig. 9-2. Excerpt From the Light List for Sequenced RDF Stations

HOW TO USE AN RDF

Directions for use of an RDF differ slightly depending upon the features of the RDF, but generally follow the steps below.

First, the RDF should be positioned in a fixed and precalibrated (see below) location with the base of the antenna located so that the bearing 000 on the azimuth dial is parallel to the fore-an-aft- axis of the vessel.

Second, tune in the radiobeacon and verify its identification with the Morse code identifier. *This step should be followed even in sets with digital tuning to ensure positive station identification.*

Third, rotate the antenna to obtain a good "null," or position of minimum signal strength. If the RDF is equipped with a null meter, the antenna is turned until the minimum signal strength is observed on the meter. If the RDF is equipped with earphones, rather than a null meter, the antenna is rotated until the minimum volume is heard. The bearing of the antenna is read on an attached bearing scale, and recorded for later plotting. Some of the more expensive RDFs, called automatic direction finders (ADFs), automate this process and a relative bearing is read directly on a dial or digital readout.

Fourth, correct the relative bearing just determined by a precalculated *deviation* (see below) which depends on the *observed relative bearing*, not the ship's heading. For example, if the observed relative bearing were 270 degrees, and the deviation on this bearing were 5 degrees east, the corrected relative bearing would be 270 + 005 or 275 degrees relative (correcting add east).

Fifth, determine the vessel's true heading using the compass heading corrected for deviation and variation. For example, if the vessel's compass heading were 050 degrees, deviation on this heading were 5 degrees east and variation in the area were 15 degrees west, the vessel's true heading would 050 + 005 - 015 = 040 degrees.

Finally, add the *corrected* relative bearing, 275 degrees in this example, to the vessel's true heading, 040 degrees, to calculate the bearing to the beacon, 315 degrees true. A worksheet to simplify these calculations is given in Table 9-1.

LIMITATIONS AND BEARING ERROR

RDF is subject to a number of limitations and sources of error, such as night effect, land effect, and deviation, as shown in Figure 9-3.

Perhaps chief among these is that, similar to a compass, the RDF has *deviation*, which must be taken into account to calculate a correct relative bearing. Unlike the compass, where deviation is a function of the ship's *heading*, RDF deviation

depends upon the *relative bearing* to the station. This said, it is generally a simple matter to prepare a deviation curve for the RDF. If a pelorus is available, visually determined relative bearings are compared to the observed RDF bearing and the deviation calculated. Otherwise, a hand-held compass is used and relative bearings computed for comparison with the RDF bearing. The deviation curve will change with the location of the RDF set on the vessel; so it is convenient to establish one location for the RDF.

USE AND ACCURACY OF RDF

The above discussion shows how an RDF can be used to determine a single LOP. This single LOP can be used to determine an estimated position (EP) as discussed in Chapter 6, or combined with a subsequent LOP to establish a running fix. Alternatively, if two or more radiobeacons can be received, a conventional fix can be determined. *(Fixes determined by one or more RDF bearings are denoted with a triangle on the plot and, optionally, the letters RDF.)* The accuracy of an LOP determined by RDF depends upon many factors but is often taken to be within plus or minus 2 or 3 degrees. RDF installations on small vessels may actually have a greater bearing uncertainty--perhaps as much as 5 or even 10 degrees. It is sometimes recommended that these error bounds (e.g., plus or minus 3 degrees) be plotted on the chart to get some idea of the possible uncertainty of the fix so determined.

RDF bearings can also be used for *tracking* or *homing* purposes. It is possible to *"home in"* on a radiobeacon (located, for example at the mouth of a harbor) by adjusting the vessel's heading so that the bow continually points to the station. The resultant ground track may be a straight line in the absence of wind or current but more typically is "bent" or "bowed" in the direction of the prevailing current. *Tracking* differs from homing in that the vessel's bow is not necessarily pointed at the station, but rather a few degrees to one side or another to compensate for the wind or current. The objective of

TABLE 9-1. WORKSHEET FOR RDF BEARINGS

ITEM	REMARKS
1. Relative bearing of RDF _____ degrees.	From measurement of null or ADF readout
2. Deviation on this bearing _____ degrees.	From RDF deviation curve
3. Corrected relative bearing _____ degrees.	Line 1 plus or minus line 2, add easterly subtract westerly deviations.
4. Vessel's compass heading _____ degrees.	Taken when RDF bearing read
5. Deviation on this heading _____ degrees.	From compass deviation curve
6. Vessel's magnetic heading _____ degrees.	Line 4 plus deviation east or minus deviation west
7. Variation _____ degrees.	From chart of area and DR position
8. Vessel's true heading _____ degrees.	From line 6 plus variation east or minus west
9. True bearing to station _____ degrees.	Line 3 plus line 8 (360 may have to be subtracted.)

tracking is to travel to the radiobeacon in a straight line with respect to the bottom. In practice, the vessel's bow is first pointed directly toward the station (relative bearing 000 degrees) and this compass heading maintained for a few minutes. If the relative bearing to the station remains constant, no subsequent course adjustments are necessary. However, if the RDF/ADF needle drifts to the right (left), the compass heading should be adjusted to the right (left) to compensate for the current setting the vessel to the left (right). By trial-and-error a compass heading can be established such that the relative bearing to the radiobeacon remains constant--not necessarily equal to zero--differing from the vessel's course by an amount equal to the current correction angle. Tracking is much more convenient if an ADF, rather than an RDF, is used.

Care must be taken when either tracking or homing to stay out of dangerous waters. *Remember that the mere determination of a bearing to a station does not guarantee that there is safe water between the vessel and the beacon.* Additionally, it is necessary to establish some means to know when to stop homing and alter course, otherwise you could track right into the radiobeacon or land! (For example, homing could be interrupted periodically to determine RDF position fixes, water depth could be monitored, DR information could be used or, if visibility permits, piloting could be used.) This may seem an obvious comment, but there are several recorded instances where homing or tracking vessels have neglected this precaution and run into danger. Some years ago, for example, the *S.S. Olympic* ran into the Nantucket lightship (which was equipped with a radiobeacon) for just this reason!

Fig. 9-3. A Brief Summary of RDF/ADF Limitations and Error Sources

Factor	Description
Track of Radio Waves	Radio waves travel along great circle, rather than rhumb line, paths. At distances of more than approximately 50 miles, this difference should be corrected for, using a procedure described in the U. S. Coast Pilot.
Using Station Out of Range	The range at which a particular marine radiobeacon will be heard depends upon receiver/antenna characteristics and atmospheric conditions. Although bearings can be obtained at ranges greater than those given in the Light List, these bearings will be of doubtful accuracy and should be used with caution.
Coastal Refraction (Land Effect)	Bearings that cut an intervening coastline at an oblique angle or cross higher elevations of intervening land may be in error of 4 degrees or 5 degrees. Where possible, use stations located on the water or on the coast to minimize or eliminate land effect.
Night Effect	Bearings obtained from about half an hour before sunset until half an hour after sunrise (and particularly during twilight) may be subject to an additional error termed night effect.
Electrical Disturbances	Lightning and precipitation static can cause bearing errors, particularly with ADF sets, where the needle may briefly "point" to an electrical discharge rather than the station.
Calibration Necessary	Radio waves include weak electromagnetic fields in the vessel and its equipment that can cause deviation in RDF bearings, much like compass deviation. Therefore, it is necessary to develop a deviation curve for the RDF. The deviation is a function of the relative bearing to station, the position of the RDF, and the presence and operation of other electronic gear.
Ambiguity Error	A null is produced when the directional antenna points either directly towards or away from the radiobeacons. This ambiguity error can usually be resolved from the vessel's DR position. Some RDF/ADF sets have internal circuitry to resolve this error directly, and others have an additional "sense antenna" for ambiguity resolution.
Operator Error	It requires some practice before consistently very accurate bearings can be taken using an RDF. (ADF operation is very much simpler.)

LORAN

Loran is a highly reliable (stations typically have greater than 99.9% availability) and accurate long-range navigation system now in use. It was an outgrowth of research during the 1930s in England and later in the United States. The first practical system for civilian maritime navigation (later termed loran-A) was replaced by loran-C during the 1970s. The loran-C system will be maintained until at least the year 2002, according to announced plans, but most observers believe that loran-C will remain in place well beyond this date.

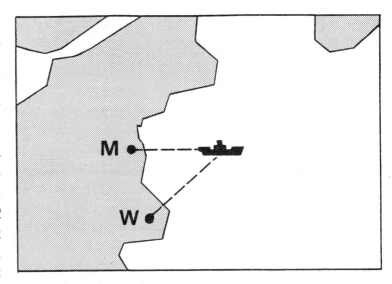

Fig. 9-4. Master and Secondary

PRINCIPLE OF OPERATION I

In highly simplified form, loran operates as follows. It consists of two components, an on-board receiver, and a *chain* of three to five land-based *transmitting stations* (maintained in the United States by the Coast Guard), generally separated by several hundred miles. The on-board receiver can be "tuned" (placed in quotation marks because the tuning principle differs from selection of a frequency) to receive the transmissions from all stations in the chain. One station in the chain is designated the *master* (denoted by the symbol M), and the remaining two to four stations are designated *secondaries* (denoted by the letters W, X, Y, and Z). The master transmits a signal (actually a complex pulse), followed at predetermined intervals by a transmission from each of the secondaries. The on-board receiver measures the slight time difference (TD) required for these separate signals to reach the vessel. Figure 9-4 (taken from the *Loran-C User Handbook*, published by the Coast Guard) illustrates two stations from a hypothetical chain, the master (M) and the whiskey (W), secondary. The time difference (TD) between arrival of the signals from the master and any of the secondaries is typically very small, and measured in

millionths of a second, designated microseconds, and abbreviated usec. (Radio waves propagate at essentially the speed of light, 161,829 nautical miles per second--at this speed it requires approximately 6.179 usec for the signal to travel one nautical mile.) Modern loran receivers can measure TDs to within 0.1 usec. In the illustration in Figure 9-5 the measured TD is 13,370 usec (shown in the upper right-hand corner) and, therefore, the vessel lies somewhere along the 13,370 LOP. This LOP is curved rather than a straight line, because the locus of points located a constant difference in distance between two points is mathematically a hyper-

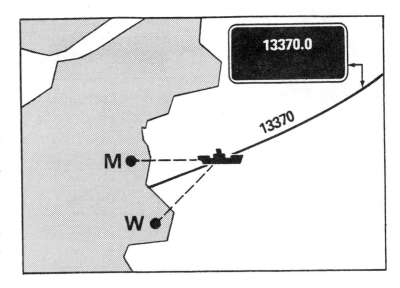

Fig. 9-5 LORAN LOP

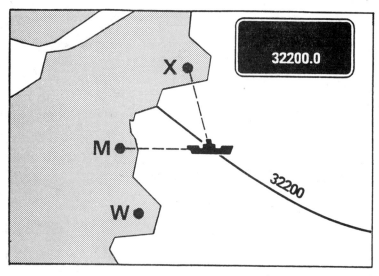

Fig. 9-6. Another LORAN LOP

bola. (Because of this, loran is sometimes called a *hyperbolic system.*) However, on larger scale charts the apparent curvature is very slight.

Now, suppose another similar TD measurement is taken between the arrival times for the signals from the master and the X ray secondary as illustrated in Figure 9-6. The measured TD, 32,200 usec, is displayed in the receiver, indicating that the vessel lies somewhere along the 32,200 LOP. The intersection of these two LOPs fixes the vessel's position as shown in Figure 9-7. Of course, the TDs for other station pairs also determine LOPs, and could be used to determine a fix as well. (Signal strength, crossing

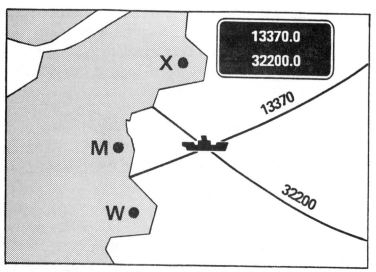

Fig. 9-7. LORAN Fix Determined By TDs

angles, and other factors determine the "best" station pair for position determination.) *Loran fixes are denoted with a triangle (as are other electronic fixes) and, optionally, the word "loran" written next to the fix symbol.*

PRINCIPLE OF OPERATION II

(This section is more technical and can be skipped without loss of continuity.) Unlike other navigation systems that use discrete frequencies for different stations, all loran chains transmit on the same frequency in the low frequency band, 100 kilohertz. At this frequency, radio is not limited to line-of-sight, and reception ranges of hundreds of miles are possible. To prevent interference between stations, each chain employs a different time sequence of transmissions, termed the Group Repetition Interval (GRI). In the loran-C chains, these intervals are between 40,000 and 99,990 usec. The chain designations are four digit numbers derived from the repetition interval by dividing by ten, e.g., the group repetition interval of the Northeast Chain is 99,600 usec, and so this chain is designated GRI 9960.

The chains, their designations, and coverage data can be found in the *Loran-C User Handbook,* published by the US Coast Guard, Publication 117, of DMA, and other sources. For example, Figure 9-8 shows the location and coverage of the Northeast US chain. For this chain the master is located in Seneca, NY, and the secondaries are located in Caribou, ME (Whiskey), Nantucket, MA (X ray), and Carolina Beach, NC (oddly enough, Yankee). The coverage area, enclosed by the dotted lines in Figure 9-8, is defined by two criteria, a minimum signal-to-noise (S/N) ratio, and an accuracy specification. The accuracy criterion used for this coverage diagram is that 95% of the fixes determined should be within 0.25 nautical mile.

The transmission sequence operates as follows. First, the master station transmits a signal (actually a series of pulses). Next, after receiving the master signal, one of the secondary stations transmits. But, to allow time for the signal from the master to propagate through the coverage area, the secondary station delays its transmission by a prespecified length of time, termed the *secondary coding delay*. The secondary coding delay for each station in each chain can be read from a loran coverage diagram, published in the *Loran-C User Handbook*. For the Northeast US chain, the secondary coding delay is 11,000 usec, for example. In turn, after another coding delay, the third station in sequence transmits, etc., until the transmission cycle is completed. The process is initialized again with the transmission of the master. The GRIs are selected so as to avoid overlap with other chains using the same frequency.

The computation of the expected time difference between the arrival of the signal from the master and that from one of the secondaries is illustrated as follows. Suppose that the vessel is located at latitude 41° 20'N and longitude 71° 20'W, approximately seven miles south of Newport Neck on the 1210-Tr chart, and that the receiver is set to receive the 9960 chain. The master station at Seneca, NY, is located approximately 258 miles from this assumed position (great circle computation), so the signal from the master will require approximately 6.18 (258) or 1,594 usec to reach the on-board receiver. (Strictly speaking, radio waves propagation differences over land and sea water should be included, but these can be neglected for this illustration.)

The distance between the master and Whiskey station in Caribou, ME, is approximately 451 miles, equivalent to a time delay of 2,787 usec (i.e., 6.18(451) = 2,787). The secondary station transmits after an 11,000 usec secondary coding delay (given in the *Loran-C User Handbook*). The secondary station in Caribou, ME, is approximately 360 nautical miles from the as-

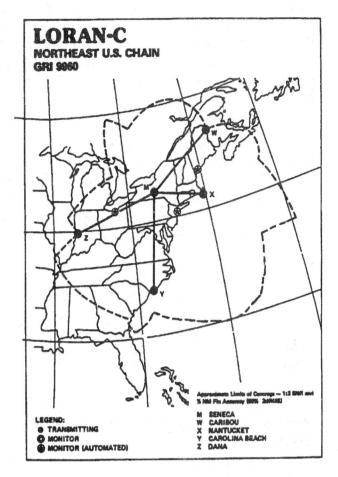

Fig. 9-8. GRI 9960, The Northeast U. S. LORAN Chain

sumed position, and therefore it will take an additional 6.18 (360) or 2,225 usec for the secondary signal to reach the assumed position.

The loran receiver measures the *time difference* (TD) between the arrival of the master signal and the secondary signal, or 2,225 + 11,000 + 2,787 -1,594 = 14,418 usec in this example. Aside from rounding errors and slight corrections to allow for variations in signal propagation speed as a result of terrain and other factors, the on-board loran should record this TD for the Whiskey secondary if located at the assumed position.

Examination of the 1210-Tr chart shows that the assumed position is located almost exactly on the 14,420 TD contour, shown in light blue, so this approximate calculation is remarkably accurate.

LORAN CHARTS

Most nautical charts (e.g, the 1210-Tr) of coastal scale or smaller are "overprinted" with the loran TD contours shown as faint grey, light blue, or magenta line with the GRI, station, and usec printed somewhere along the contour. (Harbor charts typically do not come with loran overprinting.) The TD contours are typically printed at convenient intervals. On the 1210-Tr, for example, these are printed at 5 or 10 usec intervals. Obtaining a position from the loran receiver amounts to nothing more than reading the TD display, noting the TDs, and locating their position on the chart. Options differ, but most loran sets automatically select the best GRI, and the best two TDs for use. Users wishing to select a different GRI or master-secondary pair can override the automatic feature and select these manually. The specific TDs being displayed by the loran are generally obvious from inspection of the magnitude of the TDs. However, most sets have the capability of displaying these directly, possibly on a different "page" of the electronic display. Interpolation of TDs (i.e., position location for TDs between those printed on the contour lines) can be done by eye or, for more precision, by using the interpolator printed on the chart or available as a separate plastic or cardboard overlay.

As noted above, loran TD contours are printed on many nautical charts. The accuracy of location of these contours is generally quite high, but not all nautical charts are of equivalent accuracy. With older charts, the location of the TD contours is determined by a slight variation of the simple calculation illustrated above to account for differences in the speed of the propagated signal over land versus water. In such cases, a disclaimer is written on the chart to the effect that "the lines of position shown have been adjusted based on theoretically determined overland signal propagation delays...They have not been verified by comparison with survey data." This is exactly the wording on the 1210-Tr chart, for example. However, in some cases survey data are available, and more sophisticated adjustments are possible. For charts that have these additional adjustments included the disclaimer is reworded to the effect that "the lines of position shown here have been adjusted based on survey data." TD contours are located with more accuracy if adjusted based upon survey data, and so, generally speaking, these charts are more accurate.

It was noted above that Harbor charts are not overprinted with TD contours at present. One important reason why this is so is that the corrections for signal propagation are more complex and variable for near shore areas than for outlying areas. Additionally, the requirements for navigational accuracy when operating in restricted waterways are often greater than the 0.1 to 0.25 nautical mile accuracy advertised for loran.

Unless the user has a loran with the capability to automatically convert from TDs to latitude and longitude (see below) or has visited the harbor before and noted the TDs corresponding to key features of navigational interest (e.g., buoys, channels, anchorages, etc.) the lack of loran TD overprinting amounts to an insuperable obstacle to the use of loran for navigation within harbors. Even if the on-board receiver has the capability of direct lat/lon readout, there are many experienced navigators who would argue that this feature should not be used, because of the possible inaccuracy in the TD to lat/lon conversion in harbor areas. Although this cautious advice is certainly "conservative," it overlooks the possible benefits of loran use in harbors. The advice offered here is to use loran (if possible), but as a secondary or supplemental navigation tool. That is, navigate using the tradiional methods (e.g., DR plots, visual fixes if visibility permits, RDF bearings, soundings, etc.), and supplement the available information with loran readings. Particularly if the navigator has local knowledge and has "calibrated" the loran by comparison of loran positions with "ground truth" (knowledge of the actual positions), loran can be a valuable aid for harbor navigation.

Inspection of the loran TD lines as printed on the nautical chart provides two additional important pieces of information to the navigator. First, the navigator can see the *crossing angles* of the various loran TD lines. Recall from the discussion on the accuracy of fixes in Chapter 6 that crossing angles of 90 degrees are optimal. The loran receiver generally selects the TDs automatically--criteria used by the various manufacturers vary, but may or may not include crossing angles. The alert navigator can determine the loran LOPs in use and alter these if necessary to ensure that good crossing angles result. Referring to the 1210-Tr chart, for example, it can be seen that in this area the crossing angles for the magenta (X ray) and blue (Whiskey) LOPs are generally much less than 90 degrees. Were these selected by the receiver, a manual override to select another TD pair would be in order.

Second, it is useful to introduce the concept of *gradient.* The gradient as used in this discussion is the ratio of the spacing between adjacent loran TDs, as measured in nautical miles, and the number of microseconds difference between these lines. For example, in the general area of Brenton Light on the 1210-Tr chart, the X ray TD gradient is approximately 0.82 M per 10 usec interval, or 0.082 M/usec. Generally speaking, the smaller the gradient, the better in terms of fix accuracy. Suppose, for example, that the onboard receiver could resolve TDs to 0.1 usec. With a gradient of 0.082 M/usec, a 0.1 usec resolution would translate into a possible position error of 0.1 (0.082) = 0.0082 nautical miles, or approximately 50 ft. In this same area the gradients for the Yankee and Whiskey secondaries are 0.138 and 0.118 nautical miles per microsecond, respectively. Considering both gradient and crossing angle, the "best" TDs in this small area would be X-ray and Yankee. (Gradient alone would suggest X ray and Whiskey, but, as noted, these TDs have a poor crossing angle.)

The above calculations are simple, but tedious if a large number of computations is re-quired. The Coast Guard publishes a useful document, *Specifications of the Transmitted loran-C Signal* that contains charts depicting the possible error of position estimates arising from the "geometric component" of signals from loran-C chains (actually, in terms of "triads" of master-secondary pairs). Inspection of these diagrams (together with the range limits of loran coverage can enable the user to find the "best" station pairs for use.

AUTOMATIC COORDINATE CONVERSION

With earlier loran sets, TD information was all that was available, which required the user to make the conversions manually from TDs to latitude and longitude using the published loran chart. This procedure is not difficult, but time-consuming none the less, and decidedly inconvenient if "single-handling." Indeed, a long section of the earlier edition of this text was devoted to a detailed exposition of the tricks of TD interpolation. Now, however, all loran sets being manufactured have automatic coordinate conversion routines built in, so all that is necessary is to enable this function and read out latitude and longitude directly. (Some of the earliest sets had crude conversion routines that did not take into account certain propagation corrections, termed additional secondary phase factors (ASF). With these earlier sets, use of TDs was clearly preferable for maximum accuracy. However, nearly all the new sets now have highly accurate conversion routines programmed in, so there are now only small differences in accuracy obtainable by using TDs in place of latitude and longitude readouts. Even so, as of this writing, there is no industry standard for lat/lon conversion routines and, for the most demanding applications, TDs are to be preferred over lat/long readouts.) Figure 9-9, for example, shows a modern loran receiver with latitude and longitude displayed.

LORAN ACCURACY

Loran-C is a highly accurate navigational system. Its *absolute accuracy* is of the order of 0.1 nautical mile to 0.25 nautical mile. Absolute accuracy is calculated by comparing the loran's estimate of the vessel's position with a known position (ground truth). Thus, for example, if you were to go to the Buzzards Light on the 1210-Tr chart and read the loran display, the latitude and longitude displayed on the receiver would be within less than 0.1 to 0.25 nautical miles of the charted position. Accuracy is a function of gradient, crossing angle, and other factors.

However, another accuracy concept is also relevant here, *repeatable accuracy*. To return to the example, if you were to note the *apparent* TDs or latitude and longitude of the Buzzards Light on the loran and either write these down or save them in the loran's memory and later return to the same indicated position, the accuracy of the system would be much higher--perhaps of the order of 75 ft. or even less. Indeed, some mariners claim to have nearly collided with buoys and fixed aids to navigation once the apparent coordinates were entered into the memory!

LORAN ERRORS AND LIMITATIONS

The various loran chains in the system has a very high availability--i.e., the fraction of the time on the air with signals within tolerance. As noted above, the required availability of the system is 99.9%, a number routinely exceeded in practice. None the less, the system is subject to some errors and limitations. These are summarized in Figure 9-10 and should be noted by the reader.

The availability of the loran system from the point of view of the mariner will be lower than the 99.9% figure noted above, because this estimate measures only the transmitting stations

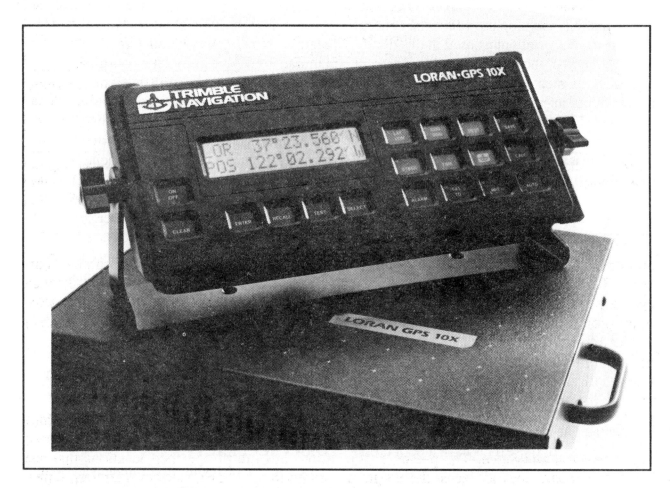

Fig. 9-9. Modern LORAN Receiver Displaying Latitude and Longitude Readouts.
This Model Integrates LORAN and GPS, Another Radionavigation System.
(Photograph Courtesy of Trimble Navigation)

9-14

Fig. 9-10. A Brief Summary of LORAN Limitations and Error Sources

FACTOR	DESCRIPTION
Coverage Limitations	Loran is not yet a worldwide system. Although certain areas (e.g., the coastal United States and Canada) have excellent coverage, there are some large gaps (e.g., the South Pacific and Atlantic) in coverage.
Operation in Areas of Baseline Extension	The baseline extension is the extension of a line connecting a master-secondary pair. Operation in this area may lead to ambiguous position information. This situation may or may not be detected by the loran receiver, depending upon the model. However, it can be detected and corrected by the alert navigator. Coverage diagrams show the locations of the transmitting stations and, therefore, the baseline extension areas. All that is generally necessary to "cure" this problem is to select a different master-secondary pair using the manual override feature of the loran.
External Interference	Some broadcast stations (particularly certain military transmitters) will interfere with loran reception. Most receivers contain adjustable "notch" filters to remove this interference.
Master or Secondary Off Air	If the master station is off the air no navigation using the entire chain will be possible. In these rare instances it may be possible to switch to another chain. Alternatively, if a secondary is off the air, a special "blink" chain is transmitted. The solution here is to switch to another TD.
Others	A variety of special problems may result including low signal-to-noise ratios (SNR), cycle slippage, and other problems. Consult the owner's manual to determine how these errors are detected, displayed, and corrected in the particular make and model loran being used.
Internal Radio Frequency Interference (RFI)	Many shipboard items, e.g., bilge pumps, an ignition system, windshield wipers, fluorescent lights, tachometers, etc., can cause RFI and lower the SNR of the received signals. This can often be cured by installation of filters on the offending equipment or noise source.

and does not consider the loran on-board receiver. Receivers are susceptible to water damage, power systems or antennas may fail, and other problems may limit the reliability of the on-board receiver. Even a cursory examination of the literature on bluewater sailing indicates that failure of all types of on-board electronic systems, including loran, is not all that rare. This fact has two implications. *First, it underscores the need for the mariner to avoid over-reliance on any single system of navigation.* The presence of a loran set on-board does not excuse the navigator from parallel navigation by more traditional means. *Second, it suggests that the mariner consider carrying a second "portable" loran receiver.*

Portables are made that use self-contained batteries and a separate portable antenna. Although the performance and features of these portables may not be the equal of the vessel's principal loran, these are very useful backup systems.

WAYPOINT NAVIGATION WITH LORAN AND OTHER FEATURES

One of the very useful features of all modern lorans is the ability to define *waypoints*. These waypoints are prespecified locations that are stored in the loran's memory. (Options differ, but many lorans enable the user to enter latitude/longitude, TDs, or even range and bearing from the present position or another waypoint.)

Most lorans can accommodate 99 or more such waypoints. These waypoints could correspond to the mariner's dock, ATONs such as lights or buoys, wrecks, areas of productive fishing, or simply imaginary reference points that would be used as turn points or leg markers for an intended voyage.

Waypoints can be entered in advance of a voyage, using the latitude and longitude or TDs of the position identified on the chart. Alternatively, waypoints can be entered by actually voyaging to the waypoint and entering the coordinates automatically in the loran's memory. The advantage of this latter method is that, because repeatable accuracy rather than absolute accuracy is involved, the waypoints are more accurate. The trick is to enter these waypoints on a day with excellent visibility when these can be readily identified. For example, the entrance buoys to an inlet or harbor can be "memorized" by the loran while on a leisurely cruise. Then, on a later day when the ceiling and visibility are "zero/zero," these loran waypoints prove their worth. Incidentally, most lorans have built in batteries that are used to power the memory, so waypoints are not "lost" whenever the external power is cut or the unit is switched off. Still, it is a good idea to write down the coordinates in a "waypoint log" for future reference.

Many lorans have some "route" capability, enabling the user to input a set of waypoints to describe the intended track of the vessel. Lorans with this feature automatically display not only the vessel's current position, but also the course (either true or magnetic) and distance to the next waypoint in sequence, ground speed towards the waypoint, TTG to reach the waypoint, and the vessel's *cross track error* (distance away from a straight line between the waypoints) and other useful navigational information. Figure 9-11 shows a loran receiver displaying waypoint information. This particular model (as do others) also provides an electronic "arrow" or *course deviation indicator* (CDI) which indicates to the helmsman what course correction to make to return to the direct track between waypoints. In this example, the CDI located on the top line of the display in Figure 9-11, is pointing to the left, indicating the vessel should be steered left to rejoin the course to the waypoint.

Waypoints, routes, and CDIs are so convenient to use that the navigator may become "sloppy." As with RDF, it is possible to make unrecognized and catastrophic blunders using loran. For example, the loran will not "complain" if adjacent waypoints in a route are located on opposite sides of an island! Unless you are operating a dredge this will have unpleasant consequences.

Still on the subject of a need for care in using electronics, it is important to check loran fixes by as many additional means as possible, proximity to DR position, visual fixes, water depth, etc.

OTHER FEATURES

Loran sets have a variety of other features that facilitate navigation. For example, the loran can be coupled to an autopilot. With this setup, the autopilot will steer towards the waypoints in the route, obtaining course corrections automatically from CDI in the loran.

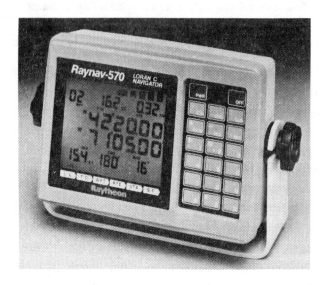

Fig. 9-11. Waypoint Navigation With LORAN (Photograph Courtesy of Raytheon Marine Company)

Some lorans have the ability to be connected to instruments that measure the vessel's speed through the water (STW) and heading (e.g., a fluxgate compass). By comparing the vessel's ground track with this information, the loran can automatically calculate current set and drift using mathematical routines similar to those discussed in Chapter 7.

Most lorans have some sort of *arrival alarm*, and will sound an audible tone when the vessel is within a predefined and adjustable distance from a waypoint. Some lorans also have a *cross track error alarm* that will warn the mariner when the distance off course to a particular waypoint exceeds an adjustable threshold. Additionally, some lorans are equipped with an *anchor watch*, which sounds an alarm whenever the vessel moves more than a defined amount from a fixed location. The location where the anchor is dropped is used to define a waypoint, and the alarm can be set to ring whenever the vessel moves a distance greater than the amount of anchor line deployed.

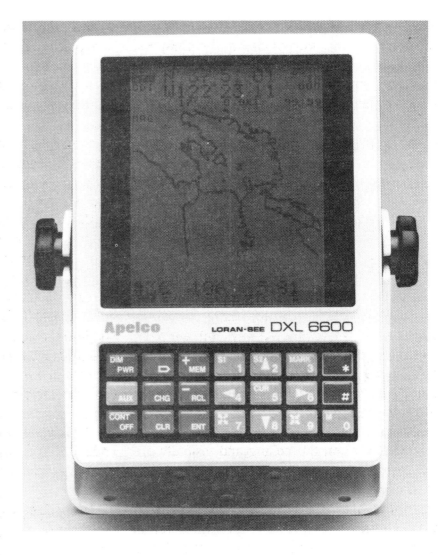

**Fig. 9-12. Some Lorans Can Display
Chart Information As Well
(Photograph Courtesy of Apelco Electronics)**

Other features of loran sets now sold include the ability to interface with *electronic charts*, or even to display this information on the loran screen itself, as shown in Figure 9-12. The navigator can enter waypoints from the small electronic chartlet, measure their course and distance from the vessel's present position, integrate these points into routes, etc. Loran sets can "talk" to radars, and display loran coordinates (and even waypoints) on the radar display. Display technology is rapidly evolving, and should be followed with interest by the mariner.

This completes the discussion of loran. The reader interested in additional detail is referred to the references given in the bibliography.

RADAR: GENERAL

Radar is the last of the electronic systems to be described in this text. Introduced in Chapter 4, it is described in detail here. Unlike RDF or loran, which require ground-based transmitters for operation, radar is completely self-contained. A radar set consists of a transmitter, receiver, antenna (either *open array* or *radome*), and display unit, as illustrated in Figure 9-13.

The radar set alternately transmits, then "listens" for the reflected signal and measures the time for the reflected signal to return. This time is translated into a distance (radar waves travel at the speed of light) and the reflected signal or *radar echo* is displayed on a circular screen termed a *plan position indicator* (PPI), that shows the azimuth (bearing) and range of the *target* or *pip*.

The maximum range of the radar is determined by several factors, including the radar's *power* and the *antenna height*. Radar signals are broadcast on frequencies that are essentially line-of-sight, so antenna height is often critical to range. (The actual equations for distance in nautical miles to the visible and radar horizons are $1.17\sqrt{H}$ and $1.22\sqrt{H}$ respectively, where H is the antenna height in feet and apply to the *standard* atmosphere. Under certain circumstances, the distance could be substantially greater or lesser than given by these formulas.) Table 9-2 shows the distance to the radar horizon in nautical miles as a function of the height of the antenna in feet and the height of the target in feet. Compare this with Table 6-2.) Table 9-2 shows only the distance at which *it is normally possible* that a target can be "seen" by the radar. As discussed below, *detection* and *identification* are complex phenomena and detection ranges may be appreciably shorter than given in Table 9-2.

Fig. 9-13. Marine Radar Set and Antenna
(Photograph Courtesy of Raytheon Marine Electronics)

TABLE 9-2:

THE DISTANCE TO THE RADAR HORIZON IN NAUTICAL MILES AS A FUNCTION OF THE ANTENNA HEIGHT IN FEET AND THE TARGET HEIGHT SHOWS WHY HIGH ANTENNAS ARE DESIRABLE. NOTE THAT THESE RANGES ARE TYPICALLY LESS THAN THE "ADVERTISED" RANGE OF THE RADAR.

HEIGHT OF TARGET (FT.)	HEIGHT OF ANTENNA IN FEET							
	0.0	2.5	5.0	7.5	10.0	15.0	20.0	30.0
0.0	0.0	1.9	2.7	3.3	3.9	4.7	5.5	6.7
2.5	1.9	3.9	4.7	5.3	5.8	6.7	7.4	8.6
5.0	2.7	4.7	5.5	6.1	6.6	7.5	8.2	9.4
7.5	3.3	5.3	6.1	6.7	7.2	8.1	8.8	10.0
10.0	3.9	5.8	6.6	7.2	7.7	8.6	9.3	10.5
12.5	4.3	6.2	7.0	7.7	8.2	9.0	9.8	11.0
15.0	4.7	6.7	7.5	8.1	8.6	9.5	10.2	11.4
17.5	5.1	7.0	7.8	8.4	9.0	9.8	10.6	11.8
20.0	5.5	7.4	8.2	8.8	9.3	10.2	10.9	12.1
22.5	5.8	7.7	8.5	9.1	9.6	10.5	11.2	12.5
25.0	6.1	8.0	8.8	9.4	10.0	10.8	11.6	12.8
27.5	6.4	8.3	9.1	9.7	10.3	11.1	11.9	13.1
30.0	6.7	8.6	9.4	10.0	10.5	11.4	12.1	13.4
35.0	7.2	9.1	9.9	10.6	11.1	11.9	12.7	13.9
40.0	7.7	9.6	10.4	11.1	11.6	12.4	13.2	14.4
45.0	8.2	10.1	10.9	11.5	12.0	12.9	13.6	14.9
50.0	8.6	10.6	11.4	12.0	12.5	13.4	14.1	15.3
55.0	9.0	11.0	11.8	12.4	12.9	13.8	14.5	15.7
60.0	9.5	11.4	12.2	12.8	13.3	14.2	14.9	16.1
65.0	9.8	11.8	12.6	13.2	13.7	14.6	15.3	16.5
70.0	10.2	12.1	12.9	13.5	14.1	14.9	15.7	16.9
75.0	10.6	12.5	13.3	13.9	14.4	15.3	16.0	17.2
80.0	10.9	12.8	13.6	14.3	14.8	15.6	16.4	17.6
85.0	11.2	13.2	14.0	14.6	15.1	16.0	16.7	17.9
90.0	11.6	13.5	14.3	14.9	15.4	16.3	17.0	18.3
95.0	11.9	13.8	14.6	15.2	15.7	16.6	17.3	18.6
100.0	12.2	14.1	14.9	15.5	16.1	16.9	17.7	18.9
110.0	12.8	14.7	15.5	16.1	16.7	17.5	18.3	19.5
120.0	13.4	15.3	16.1	16.7	17.2	18.1	18.8	20.0
130.0	13.9	15.8	16.6	17.3	17.8	18.6	19.4	20.6
140.0	14.4	16.4	17.2	17.8	18.3	19.2	19.9	21.1
150.0	14.9	16.9	17.7	18.3	18.8	19.7	20.4	21.6
175.0	16.1	18.1	18.9	19.5	20.0	20.9	21.6	22.8
200.0	17.3	19.2	20.0	20.6	21.1	22.0	22.7	23.9

Radar also has a *minimum* range at which targets may be detected. This minimum range is related to the radar's *pulse length*. Radar waves travel at the speed of light so if, for example, the pulse length were 1 usec, the wave could travel approximately 984 feet, or 492 feet "out and back." With this pulse length, any target closer than 492 feet cannot be detected, because the radar will still be emitting a signal when the return wave "bounces back" and the receiver will still be off. If p is the pulse length in microseconds, then the minimum radar range is at least 492 p (in feet). (Some radars have a variable pulse length.) The minimum range for most small boat radars is about 30 yards or so, and is usually given in the manufacturer's specifications.

RADARSCOPE INTERPRETATION.
GENERAL

For navigational applications--determination of position from *range* and *bearing* of known objects as discussed in Chapter 6--radar can be very useful if its characteristics and limitations are understood. Determining a radar fix from observation of the range and bearing of a charted, isolated, and well-defined radar-reflective object is relatively simple. It becomes much more complex, however, if the shoreline is not well defined and/or prominent, radar-reflective targets are few and far between. The reaction of many first-time radar users to the image on the radar screen is often one of disappointment. Novices are often preconditioned to expect a literal image (e.g., as seen by eye or as in a photograph) rather than the initially confusing mass of electronic "blobs" on the screen. A prominent inlet (see below) may be virtually "invisible" to the radar (at a given range), as may fiberglass or wooden vessels, while a small radar reflector held aloft from a rowboat may "bloom." Hilly ground surrounded by low-lying areas may appear as a series of "islands." A visually prominent tower on land may present only a small echo because its rounded shape scatters the return signal, whereas a much smaller structure of different shape and materials of construction may present a larger target. With time, patience, and a clear understanding of the characteristics and limitations of radar, navigators can learn to interpret radar imagery with almost the same ease as photo interpretation. Textbook discussions are valuable, but no substitute for on-the-water experience with radar.

The PPI provides a "chartlike" presentation (plan view). But, the image "painted" by the sweep of the antenna is not a literal representation of the shore. The width of the radar beam and the length of the transmitted pulse are two factors which distort the image as it appears on the scope. More specifically, the width of the radar beam acts to distort the shoreline features in bearing and the pulse length may cause offshore features to appear as part of the landmass. Inlets, for example, cannot generally be seen on radar until the vessel is sufficiently close that the size of the inlet is wider than the antenna's beam width. Knowledge of the beam width, from the manufacturer's specifications, enables an approximate computation of the maximum distance at which an inlet will be able to be identified. For this and other reasons, the actual radar image of a scene depends upon the range at which it is observed.

It is not easy to determine which features in the vicinity of the shoreline are actually reflecting the echoes painted on the scope. Any uncertainty or ambiguity, of course, undermines the accuracy of the resulting fix.

Additionally, certain features on the shore will not be visible on the scope, even if they have good reflecting properties, if they are hidden from the radar beam by other physical features or obstructions. This phenomenon is called *masking* or *radar shadow*.

LAND TARGETS

Landmasses are readily recognizable because of the generally steady brilliance of the relatively large areas painted on the PPI. Knowledge of the vessel's position relative to nearby land is an important clue to interpretation. (This is one of the reasons why it is desirable to integrate navigation information, for example, from a loran, on the radar screen.) On relative motion displays (discussed below), landmasses apparently move in directions and at rates opposite and equal to the actual motion of the observer's ship. Actually, landmasses are readily recognizable-the real problem is to identify *specific features* so that these features can be used for determining a fix. Identification of specific features can be quite difficult because of various factors, including distortion resulting from beam width and pulse length and uncertainty as to just which charted features are reflecting the echoes. Often the identification of a specific feature (e.g., a tower or light) is based on a contextual association. For example, a light on the end of a recognizable landmass may be identified based upon the fact that the landmass has a characteristic shape and the light is the only radar prominent object on the tip of the landmass. The following clues or "keys" are suggested in DMA Publication 1310:

■ Sandpits and smooth, clear beaches normally do not appear on the PPI at ranges beyond one or two miles because these targets have almost no area that can reflect energy back to the radar antenna. Ranges determined from these targets are not reliable. If waves are breaking over a sandbar, echoes may be returned from the surf. Waves may, however, break well out from the actual shoreline, so that ranging on the surf may be misleading when a radar position is being determined relative to the shoreline.

- Mud flats and marshes normally reflect radar pulses only a little better than a sandpit. The weak echoes received at low tide disappear at high tide. Mangroves and other thick growth may produce a strong echo. Areas that are indicated as swamps on a chart, therefore, may return either strong or weak echoes, depending on the density and size of the vegetation growing in the area.

- When sand dunes are covered with vegetation and are well back from a low, smooth beach, the apparent shoreline determined by radar appears as the line of the dunes rather than the true shoreline. Under some conditions, sand dunes may return strong echo signals because the combination of the vertical surface of the vegetation and the horizontal beach may form a sort of corner reflector.

- Lagoons and inland lakes usually appear as blank areas on a PPI because the smooth water surface returns no energy to the radar antenna. In some instances, the sandbar or reef surrounding the lagoon may not appear on the PPI because it lies too low in the water.

- Coral atolls and long chains of islands may produce long lines of echoes when the radar beam is directed perpendicular to the line of the islands. This indication is especially true when the islands are closely spaced. The reason is that the spreading resulting from the width of the radar beam causes the echoes to blend into continuous lines. When the chain of islands is viewed lengthwise, or obliquely, however, each island may produce a separate pip. Surf breaking on a reef around an atoll produces a ragged, variable line of echoes.

- Submerged objects do not produce radar echoes. One or two rocks projecting above the surface of the water, or waves breaking over a reef, may appear on the PPI. Obviously, when an object is submerged entirely and the sea is smooth over it, no indication is seen on the PPI.

- If the land rises in a gradual, regular manner from the shoreline, no part of the terrain produces an echo that is stronger than the echo from any other part. As a result, a general "haze" of echoes appears on the PPI, and it is difficult to ascertain the range to any particular part of the land. Land can be recognized by plotting the contact. Care must be exercised when plotting because, as a vessel approaches or retreats from a shore behind which the land rises gradually, a plot of the ranges and bearings to the land may show an "apparent" course and speed.

- "Blotchy" signals are returned from hilly ground because the crest of each hill returns a good echo although the valley beyond is in a shadow. If high receiver gain (one of the adjustable controls on some radars) is used, the pattern may become solid except for the very deep shadows.

- Low islands ordinarily produce small echoes. When thick palm trees or other foliage grow on the island, strong echoes often are produced because the horizontal surface of the water around the island forms a sort of corner reflector with the vertical surfaces of the trees. As a result, wooded islands given good echoes and can be detected at a much greater range than barren islands.

VESSELS AS TARGETS

Vessels, unlike landmasses present only a small pip on the PPI. But other objects, such as small islands, rocks, and ATONs also present small targets. Other clues, in addition to target size, are required to classify the target as a vessel. For example, a check of the vessel's position can indicate that no land is within radar range. The size of the pip can also be used to exclude the possibility of land or precipitation, both usually having a massive appearance on the PPI. The rate of movement of the pip on the PPI can eliminate the possibility of aircraft.

Having eliminated the foregoing possibilities, the appearance of the pip at a medium range as a bright, steady, and clearly defined image on the PPI indicates a high probability that the target is a steel ship. Unless equipped with special "radar reflectors," detection of wooden or fiberglass vessels is more problematic.

The pip of a ship target may brighten at times and then slowly decrease in brightness. Normally, the pip of a ship target fades from the PPI only when the range becomes too great. In heavy seas, however, small vessels can be lost in radar shadow and appear only as an intermittent target.

RADAR SHADOW

While PPI displays are approximately chart-like when landmasses are being scanned by the radar beam, there may be sizable areas missing from the display because of certain features being blocked from the radar beam by other features. A shoreline which is continuous when the ship is at one position may not be continuous when the ship is at another position and scanning the same shoreline.

The radar beam may be blocked from a segment of this shoreline by an obstruction such as a promontory. An indentation in the shoreline, such as a cove or bay, appearing on the PPI when the ship is at one position may not appear when the ship is at another position nearby. Thus, radar shadow alone can cause considerable differences between the PPI display and the literal chart presentation. This effect in conjunc-

tion with beam width and pulse length distortion of the PPI display can cause even greater differences.

RADAR USES

From the above it should be clear that marine radar is useful for two broad applications, *navigation* and *collision avoidance*.

With respect to *navigation*, radar can be used to "see" land objects and ATONs under conditions of darkness or otherwise restricted visibility. In this sense, radar navigation might be thought analogous to "electronic piloting." That is, the techniques of navigation with radar are nearly identical to those used for visual piloting (e.g., determination of range or bearing to identified objects, determination of LOPs, fixes, etc.) except that the objects are detected and identified with the radar rather than the eye. The "trick" in using radar for this purpose involves nothing more than learning the appearance of targets on a radar screen, rather than as seen by eye. As noted above, this is not a simple process and facility comes only with experience.

The second major application of radar is for *collision avoidance*. That is, radar is used to detect and identify other vessels and the radar data are used to assess the likelihood of collision. This generally, but not always, requires familiarity with radar plotting as discussed below.

RADAR PLOTTING:
REGULATORY IMPLICATIONS

The following sections have been written to simplify radar plotting as much as possible. But, it may be necessary to study this material carefully before mastering the topic. None the less, it is important that the operator of any radar-equipped vessel *fully* understand radar interpretation and plotting.

Mastery of any on-board navigational tool is arguably important--why, after all, own something you can't use? But, knowledge of the use of

TYPE OF MOTION	TYPE OF DISPLAY	KEY CHARACTERISTICS	ADVANTAGES	DISADVANTAGES
RELATIVE MOTION	UNSTABILIZED (SHIP'S HEAD UP SHU)	Relative motion display with own ship at center and instantaneous relative bearing of targets displayed. Plan view rotates in direction opposite to turn.	Relatively low cost (no gyrocompass input required). Relative bearings of targets may be easier to see than with stabilized (NU) displays.	Off-screen plotting on maneuvering board required to determine target speed and direction. Bearing accuracy adversely affected by yaw.
	STABILIZED (NORTH UP NU)	Relative motion display with own ship at center. Linked to gyrocompass to display continuous north-up picture on PPI. Absolute bearing of targets displayed. Own ship's heading displayed by heading flash.	Direct readout of actual target bearing and on screen plotting is possible. Target smearing due to ship's yaw is reduced. Targets retain same position on-screen when own ship turns, lowering the likelihood that targets will be lost.	Unless "base course up" mode available, can cause interpretation difficulties when ship's course is far from north. Units are more expensive than SHU radar.
TRUE MOTION	North up or ship's head up alternatives exist, but North up more common.	Own ship and other moving objects displayed in true motion. Stationary objects such as land, buoys, etc., remain stationary. Display most resembles "chart view" on PPI.	Simplest to understand and visualize. True motion radars can generally be operated as relative motion radars so has all advantages of relative motion display if necessary.	Cost, complexity of operating controls, need to reset display as own ship moves to edge of display.

ALL → RELATIVE MOTION, TRUE MOTION

TABLE 9-3. TYPES OF RADAR DISPLAY

radar is important for an additional reason. The NAVRULES (explicitly or implicitly) mention radar in several sections and specifically state (in Rule 7, "Risk of Collision") that, "*proper use* shall be made of radar equipment if fitted and operational, *including long-range scanning to obtain early warning of risk of collision and radar plotting or equivalent systematic observation of detected objects.*" [Emphasis added.] In other words, if you have working radar aboard, it must be used and used properly. Because this common sense dictum is made so explicit, the mariner may risk a legal liability in the event of a collision for any failure to use the radar *properly.*

Radar ownership thus involves certain responsibilities. A complete discussion of this topic is beyond the scope of this section and this brief mention does not purport to give legal advice. Navigators interested in following up on this should contact an appropriate professional.

OUTLINE OF DISCUSSION

The remainder of this chapter is structured as follows. First, a brief discussion on the types of radar displayed is presented. Next, radar plotting techniques are given in the context of several examples. Finally, other relevant details and situations of interest are covered.

RADAR DISPLAYS

Teaching experience with the ACN course has indicated that students are frequently confused by the different types of radar display now in use--particularly as many of the texts on this subject assume (without explicit mention) that a so-called stabilized north-up display is used, whereas most displays on small boats are unstabilized with ship's head up. This section has been added for clarification.

Three principal types of display are used on marine radar--a relative motion display (ship's head up), a relative motion display (north up), and a true motion display (which can be either ship's head up or north up). Key characteristics, advantages, and disadvantages of each of these displays are summarized in Table 9-3. Although some radars can be switched from one display mode to another, many radars have only one fixed type of display. These three principal types are discussed below.

UNSTABILIZED SHIP'S HEAD UP (SHU) DISPLAY

Figure 9-14 shows a stylized replica of a radar display or PPI, so named because it presents a plan view (top view) of the scene to the observer. Although this display is particularly convenient, it is important to remember that it was not created by observation from above. Rather, it is "painted" from a point near the ground. "Radar shadow" (discussed earlier), though not necessarily obvious from the display, is none the less an important phenomenon. Smaller vessels, for example, can be masked or hidden from view behind larger ships even though the perspective of the PPI would encourage the naive observer to believe that he/she can "see" what's on the other side of a target. Radar observers should be particularly alert to the possibility that previously unseen targets can emerge suddenly from behind larger targets in congested waterways.

To simplify interpretation of Figure 9-14, extraneous features, such as land echoes, side lobe echoes, sea or rain clutter, etc., are suppressed in this view of the PPI. On the outer edge of this PPI is a ring displaying bearing information. A series of concentric rings (six in this figure) sometimes called *Fixed Range Markers* (FRM) is also shown. The scale of these FRMs is generally adjustable from a switch on the console. (The number and spacing of the FRMs vary among sets of different manufacture.) Additionally, some radars have an adjustable *intrusion alarm* which alerts the navigator if any target penetrates an adjustable range ring. In this example (see top of diagram), the scale is set so that a *target* or *pip* located at the outermost ring is 6 M distant and, therefore, each of the concentric rings is 1 M apart. The range of the target can be estimated from its position relative to the FRMs. But, to increase the accuracy of range estimates, most radars are also equipped with one or more *Variable Range Markers* (VRM) (not shown in Figure 9-14), which insert additional ring(s) in the display at an adjustable distance from the center. The range of the VRM is generally shown on a separate digital readout located on the screen.

It is recommended that the VRM (if available) be used rather than the FRMs to estimate the target range. This recommendation is offered for two reasons. First, the VRM generally enables a more precise estimate of range to be made. Second, it occasionally happens that the operator inadvertently switches the range setting on the radar. In this event, the distance corresponding to each range ring is altered. (Chapter 12 provides an example where a vessel grounded because the range corresponding to each of the FRMs was misinterpreted.) The VRM display prevents this error from being made.

It is important to note that, in general, it is not possible to tell the orientation or even the size of the target from the size or the intensity of the radar image alone. As noted above, target detection is a function of many variables including the target's height, size, shape, aspect, texture, composition, and range. Local knowledge, contextual clues, and radar plotting can often be

RANGE SET AT = ___6 M___

RANGE MARKERS = ___1 M___

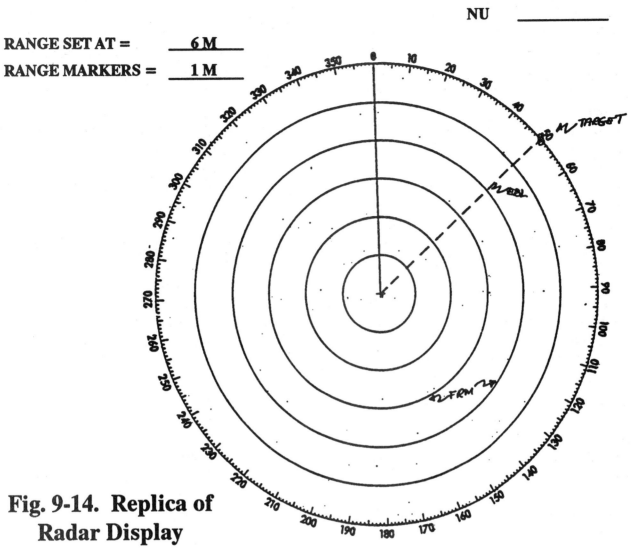

Fig. 9-14. Replica of Radar Display

used to classify the target (e.g., land targets versus targets at sea, vessel versus ATON, fishing vessel versus merchant ship, etc.), as discussed later in this chapter. But, until this classification process is complete all detected objects are referred to as simply targets or pips.

In the display shown in Figure 9-14, the observer's vessel (termed *own*, or *reference ship*, or *vessel*) is located at the center, and the target's location is, therefore, a relative position.

The radar display type shown in Figure 9-14 is termed *unstabilized with ship's head up* (SHU). (The notation SHU is checked in the top right

corner of Figure 9-14.) This is the most common display on small boat radars. The word "unstabilized" is used because the image in the PPI will change with the reference vessel's heading. A turn to starboard, for example, will cause the target(s) in the image to appear to rotate in a counter-clockwise direction. Only relative bearings (to the ship's head) of targets can be read from this display. The target shown in Figure 9-14 has a relative bearing of 050 degrees. To calculate a true bearing from this relative information it is appropriate to note the reference ship's compass heading at the time of observation, convert this heading to true heading from the CDMVT sequence, and finally, to add the target's relative bearing to the reference ship's heading. Thus, for example, if the reference vessel were heading 030 compass, the deviation on the heading were 2 degrees east, and the variation were 10 degrees west, the true bearing of the target would be 030+002-010+050, or 072 degrees. With the unstabilized SHU display, true (or magnetic) bearings must be calculated, rather than simply read off the screen. Moreover, it is necessary to note the reference vessel's heading at the instant the relative bearing is measured, otherwise yaw errors are introduced.

Some unstabilized SHU displays are capable of displaying the vessel's heading (e.g., from a fluxgate compass) or CMG (e.g., from a loran input). These are often termed *north referenced unstabilized displays*. Care must be used, however, because the CMG may be very different from the vessel's heading. Heading, not CMG is required for bearing calculations.

To increase the accuracy with which relative bearings can be read (particularly for targets that are not located near the edge of the screen), most modern radars have one or more *electronic bearing markers* (EBM) or *electronic bearing lines* (EBL). These appear as an adjustable "spoke" on the screen with an off-screen (or on-screen) digital bearing readout. The EBL can be rotated until it is aligned with a target, and the relative bearing read directly. In Figure 9-14, a dotted EBL is shown (actual lines may be solid on the screen but are shown as dotted in this illustration to avoid confusion with other markers).

STABILIZED NORTH UP (NU) DISPLAY
In contrast to the unstabilized display, some radars (typically more expensive models that would be found on larger vessels) feature a *stabilized display with north up* (NU) *presentation*. The stabilized display accepts heading information from the ship's gyrocompass or, alternatively, from a fluxgate or electronic compass. This information is shown in Figure 9-15, which presents a NU display for the same case as shown in Figure 9-14. In this display, a *heading*

flash (shown by the dashed line) notes own ship's instantaneous heading. (The heading flash shows the vessel's true or magnetic heading, depending on whether a gyrocompass or fluxgate compass is used. In the example above, the true heading would be 030+002-010, or 022 degrees, as shown in Figure 9-15.) If the reference vessel were to change course, the radar image would not change (as it would with an unstabilized display)--only the heading flash would change position--hence the name "stabilized display." As most vessels yaw somewhat, even if the helmsman attempts to maintain a steady course, "target smear" is sometimes a problem with unstabilized displays. Bearing accuracies, in consequence, are generally higher with a stabilized display. Additionally, true (or magnetic) target bearings can simply be read directly from the NU display, without any calculation.

Finally, because the target location does not change when the reference ship changes course, targets are less likely to be the "lost" (e.g., confused with other targets in the display) by the observer in the event that the reference ship maneuvers. In the example shown in Figure 9-14, there is only one target in view, so the target is unlikely to be lost. However, in a "target-rich environment" (i.e., if many targets are present) it can be difficult to keep track of the individual targets on the SHU display.

TRUE MOTION DISPLAY
Both the stabilized and unstabilized displays discussed above present a picture of relative, rather than true motion. Rates of movement of the target, for example, are relative to the reference vessel and not to the ocean or the bottom. For example, if one vessel were steaming north at 10 knots and meeting another vessel on a southbound course moving at the same speed, the relative closure rate is 20 knots--this would be the apparent speed of the target as calculated from successive observations of the target on a relative motion radar. Similarly, land and other fixed features will have an apparent velocity when observed from a relative motion radar.

(As noted above, these objects will have apparent motion opposite, but at a speed equal to that of the reference vessel.)

Some radars are so-called *true motion radars*, in that they are able to display the actual movements of the reference vessel as well as that of the other targets. (This requires additional computers and some means of determining the ship's true course and speed.) Land and other fixed targets remain fixed on the display and the vessels move about in very much the same fashion as would be seen by an overhead observer. But this advantage comes about at the expense of complexity in operation and cost. Because

true motion radars are (at present) priced out of the reach of all but a small proportion of recreational boaters, these are not discussed further in this chapter.

DISPLAY SCREENS

The display *types* discussed above should not be confused with the display *screen*. Conventional screens, also called analog displays, were standard at one time. The image displayed on a conventional screen *decays* (becomes less bright) over time until it is *refreshed* with the next revolution of the antenna. Conventional displays require the use of a viewing hood during daytime hours.

EXAMPLE _____

RANGE SET AT = ___6 M___
RANGE MARKERS = ___1 M___

DISPLAY MODE: SHU   _____

                NU   ___✓___

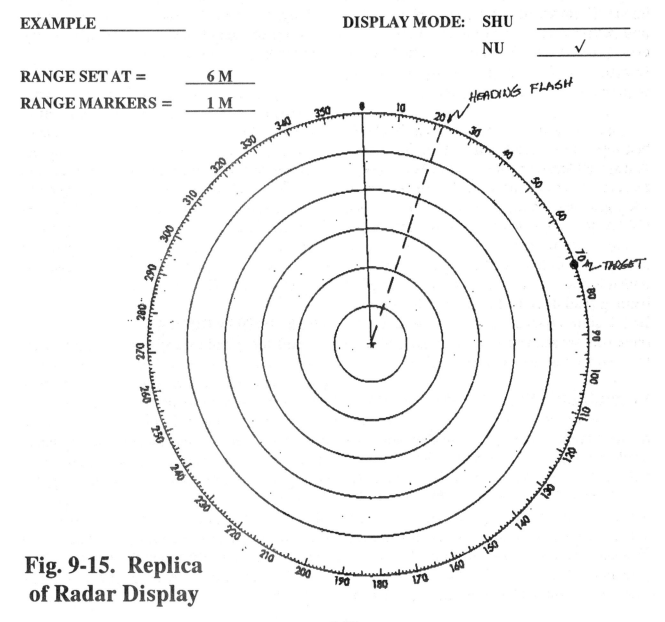

Fig. 9-15. Replica of Radar Display

Within the past few years, digital or digitized displays, also called *raster scan displays* have become available. Raster scan displays are an outgrowth of modern television technology. The principal advantage of these new displays is that the image does not decay, but rather remains bright as the antenna revolves. Viewing hoods are not generally required with this display.

Some radars are equipped with *color*, rather than *monochrome* displays. On some models, different colors are used only to differentiate fixed or variable range markers (see below), but on others, different hues are used to denote the intensity of the echo.

RADAR PLOTTING--A FIRST EXAMPLE

Radar observations of targets are generally *plotted* to determine the answers to key questions regarding the likelihood of collision, speed, and course of the target, etc. Plotting may be done manually, as discussed here, or automatically if the radar has this feature.

Radar plotting is better described by example than abstract discussion of theory. So, let's suppose that you are the navigator aboard the yacht, *Altair*, maintaining a course of 112 degrees at 5 knots, outbound for Bermuda just south of the shipping channel off the mouth of the Delaware Bay. *Altair* is equipped with a

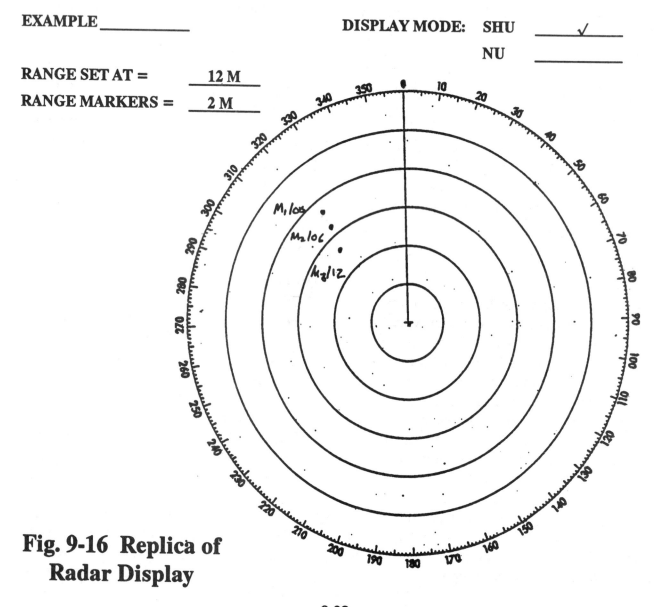

EXAMPLE _____

DISPLAY MODE: SHU ____ ✓ ____

NU _____

RANGE SET AT = _____ 12 M _____
RANGE MARKERS = _____ 2 M _____

Fig. 9-16 Replica of Radar Display

radar with unstabilized SHU display. At 1000, a radar target can be identified bearing 322 degrees relative (using the EBL) at a range of 7.3 M (using the VRM). Means for identification of targets are discussed later in this chapter. Factors considered in target identification include the vessel's location relative to charted ATONs, known fishing areas, the water depth at the target's location, the range at which the target is detected, and the apparent course and speed of the target. In this example, suppose that there are no ATONs or fixed obstructions at the target's location. *Altair's* navigator tentatively identifies that target as another vessel and decides to monitor the target's progress.

Because *Altair* has an unstabilized display, the navigator calls "mark" when using the EBL to determine the relative bearing, and records the helmsman's response. At 1000, *Altair's* heading is 112 degrees. The navigator records the observation (target bearing, *Altair's* heading, time, and target range) and attends to other duties. *Altair* maintains course and speed. At 1006, the process is repeated and a second observation recorded. The target vessel bears 321 degrees relative at range 6.3 M while *Altair* is on a heading of 110 degrees. (Although range and bearing information can be taken at any interval of time, it is customary to take observations at equally spaced instants in time. Moreover, to simplify later calculations, observations are often taken at intervals of 3, 6, or 12 minutes. For example, if observations are taken every 6 minutes (0.1 hour), the speed of the relative motion is simply 10 times the distance traveled during the interval.) Because the target's relative bearing appears nearly constant and the target's range is decreasing a so-called *constant bearing decreasing range* (CBDR) situation, the navigator decides to monitor the target more closely and to prepare a radar plot on a *maneuvering board* (M board). Interpretation of radar plot is considerably simplified if the reference ship maintains course and speed, so the navigator ensures that *Altair* keeps on course and speed until all observations are completed.

Whether or not to initiate a radar plot requires some judgment--it is generally impractical and unnecessary to plot all targets that appear on the screen. (This is particularly true in congested areas, such as harbor entrances, fishing grounds, etc., where the sheer number of targets would preclude plotting of all targets.) However, if a collision results, the failure to maintain a plot may have legal implications. At a minimum, all CBDR targets should be plotted or systematically observed, particularly where visibility is reduced.

At 1012, when *Altair's* heading is 111 degrees, the target bears 316 degrees, at range 5.3 M. Figure 9-16 shows the position of the target as it would be seen at successive times of observation--noted /XX, where XX refers to the number of minutes past the hour when the observation was taken. As can be seen from the successive PPI images in Figure 9-16, the *relative* motion (SHU) of the target is generally "southeastward" (moving "downscope" and closing from left to right) on the SHU display, and some danger of collision may exist, so an M board plot is judged to be appropriate. To facilitate the preparation of the M board plot, the worksheet shown in Table 9-4 has been developed, directions for filling in the worksheet and the preparation of the plot are given below.

WORKSHEET PREPARATION AND PLOTTING

The worksheet shown in Table 9-4 has three sections, a data section, a space for remarks on the plot, and finally a guide to the computations. Experience has shown that the use of the worksheet simplifies plotting and interpretation of the results. The first section of the worksheet to be filled in is the data section. Accordingly, the data on the time of observation, target range, own ship's heading, and target relative bearing are entered along with own ship's course and speed. To simplify the calculations for the first example, assume that the ship's compass has no deviation. Additionally, this problem is solved in magnetic, rather than true directions to elimi-

TABLE 9-4. BASIC WORKSHEET FOR SOLVING RADAR PROBLEMS ON MANEUVERING BOARD

BASIC WORKSHEET FOR SOLVING RADAR PROBLEMS ON MANEUVERING BOARD

DATA FOR PLOTTING: EXAMPLE/CASE:_____   OWN SHIP'S COURSE AND SPEED:_____

TIME	DISTANCE IN MILES OR YARD NOTE UNITS	OWN SHIP'S HEADING (TRUE OR MAG)	TARGET RELATIVE BEARING	TARGET TRUE/MAG BEARING	REMARKS
0130	9.0	295	310	245	DISTANCE AND TARGET TRUE OR MAGNETIC BEARING ARE TO BE PLOTTED ON MANEUVERING
0136	7.5	295	311	246	BOARD. IF TRUE BEARINGS ARE DESIRED ITS NECESSARY TO CONVERT FROM COMPASS
0142	6.0	295	313	248	HEADING TO TRUE HEADING USING CDMVT ADD
					EAST LOGIC. CHOOSE AND LABEL BOTH SPEED
					AND DISTANCE SCALES ON THE BOARD. ENSURE
					POINTS ARE PLOTTED CAREFULLY USING THE
					CORRECT SCALE!

HOW ENTRIES ARE OBTAINED	RECORDED AT TIME OF OBS.	READ FROM RANGE RING OR VRM	READ FROM COMPASS OR GYRO	READ FROM EBL ON RADAR SCOPE	CALCULATED FROM SH + RB (360 MAY HAVE TO BE SUBTRACTED)

SCALE DISTANCE _____ SD VALUE
SPEED _____

INSERT REMARKS HERE ON MANEUVERING BOARD PLOTS:

COMPUTATIONS:

TOPIC	QUANTITY	VALUE	REMARKS ON CALCULATION
RELATIVE MOTION	DIRECTION OF RELATIVE MOTION:	060	MEASURED FROM RELATIVE MOTION PLOT-DO NOT ERR BY 180 DEG!
	DIST BETWEEN OBSERVATIONS:	3 mi	TAKEN FROM LINEAR PORTION OF RELATIVE MOTION PLOT (RMP)
	TIME BETWEEN OBSERVATIONS:	12 min	TAKEN FROM INPUTS ON LINEAR PORTION OF RMP
	SPEED OF RELATIVE MOTION:	15 kt	CALCULATED FROM ABOVE TWO ENTRIES S = 60D/T
CPA	DISTANCE TO CPA:	6.0	EXTRAPOLATED OR INTERPOLATED FROM RELATIVE MOTION PLOT
	TRUE OR MAGNETIC BEARING OF CPA:	150	FROM DRM PLUS OR MINUS 90 DEGREES
	RELATIVE BEARING OF CPA:		FROM TRUE OR MAGNETIC BEARING MINUS OWN SHIP'S HEAD
	DIST FROM LAST OBS TO CPA:	6.0	MEASURED FROM RELATIVE MOTION PLOT
	TIME TO TRAVERSE THIS DIST:	24	FROM T = 60D/S $\frac{60 \times 6.0}{15}$
	TIME OF CPA:	0142+24 = 0206	FROM ABOVE PLUS TIME OF LAST OBSERVATION
TARGET MOVEMENT	TARGET COURSE:		FROM COMPANION VECTOR PLOT ON MANEUVERING BOARD
	TARGET SPEED:		FROM COMPANION VECTOR PLOT ON MANEUVERING BOARD

nate the need to consider variation. With these conventions, the target's magnetic bearing can be calculated from the equation, reference ship's head + relative bearing equals bearing to target. For example, in the first observation at /00, the target's magnetic bearing is 112 + 322 or 434 degrees. Since this exceeds 360, 360 is subtracted and the calculated magnetic bearing is 074 degrees. The other times, distances, relative bearings, and calculated magnetic bearings are similarly recorded and entered into the worksheet, as shown in Table 9-5.

TABLE 9--5.   COMPLETED WORKSHEET FOR FIRST EXAMPLE

BASIC WORKSHEET FOR SOLVING RADAR PROBLEMS ON MANEUVERING BOARD

DATA FOR PLOTTING: EXAMPLE/CASE: __Altair__   OWN SHIP'S COURSE AND SPEED: __112° 5 KTS__

TIME	DISTANCE IN (MILES) OR YARD NOTE UNITS	OWN SHIP'S HEADING (TRUE OR (MAG)	TARGET RELATIVE BEARING	TARGET TRUE (MAG) BEARING	REMARKS
1000	7.3	112	322	074	DISTANCE AND TARGET TRUE OR MAGNETIC BEARING ARE TO BE PLOTTED ON MANEUVERING BOARD. IF TRUE BEARINGS ARE DESIRED ITS NECESSARY TO CONVERT FROM COMPASS HEADING TO TRUE HEADING USING CDMVT ADD EAST LOGIC. CHOOSE AND LABEL BOTH SPEED AND DISTANCE SCALES ON THE BOARD. ENSURE POINTS ARE PLOTTED CAREFULLY USING THE CORRECT SCALE!
1006	6.3	110	321	071	
1012	5.3	111	316	067	

					SCALE	SD	VALUE
					DISTANCE	1	1M
					SPEED	1	1KT

HOW ENTRIES ARE OBTAINED	RECORDED AT TIME OF OBS.	READ FROM RANGE RING OR VRM	READ FROM COMPASS OR GYRO	READ FROM EBL ON RADAR SCOPE	CALCULATED FROM SH + RB (360 MAY HAVE TO BE SUBTRACTED)

INSERT REMARKS HERE ON MANEUVERING BOARD PLOTS:

Straight Line & Constant Interval Between
Points on RMP indicate Both Vessels
Maintaining Course & Speed

COMPUTATIONS:

TOPIC	QUANTITY	VALUE	REMARKS ON CALCULATION
RELATIVE MOTION	DIRECTION OF RELATIVE MOTION:	271	MEASURED FROM RELATIVE MOTION PLOT-DO NOT ERR BY 180 DEG!
	DIST BETWEEN OBSERVATIONS:	2.1	TAKEN FROM LINEAR PORTION OF RELATIVE MOTION PLOT (RMP)
	TIME BETWEEN OBSERVATIONS:	12 Min.	TAKEN FROM INPUTS ON LINEAR PORTION OF RMP
	SPEED OF RELATIVE MOTION:	10.5	CALCULATED FROM ABOVE TWO ENTRIES S = 60D/T
CPA	DISTANCE TO CPA:	2.2	EXTRAPOLATED OR INTERPOLATED FROM RELATIVE MOTION PLOT
	TRUE OR MAGNETIC BEARING OF CPA:	001	FROM DRM PLUS OR MINUS 90 DEGREES
	RELATIVE BEARING OF CPA:	249	FROM TRUE OR MAGNETIC BEARING MINUS OWN SHIP'S HEAD
	DIST FROM LAST OBS TO CPA:	4.9	MEASURED FROM RELATIVE MOTION PLOT
	TIME TO TRAVERSE THIS DIST:	28 Min.	FROM T = 60D/S
	TIME OF CPA:	1040	FROM ABOVE PLUS TIME OF LAST OBSERVATION
TARGET MOVEMENT	TARGET COURSE:	254	FROM COMPANION VECTOR PLOT ON MANEUVERING BOARD
	TARGET SPEED:	6.1	FROM COMPANION VECTOR PLOT ON MANEUVERING BOARD

Next, it is necessary to plot these data. In principle, the *relative motion plot* (RMP) could be prepared either with grease pencil on a transparent plastic overlay on the radar screen itself, on an M board, or on another special purpose chart such as a *radar transfer plotting sheet* (RTPS).

But because an unstabilized display is being used, the radar screen is small, and the navigator may wish to change range scales as the target vessel draws closer, a M board is used for plotting rather than plotting on the radar screen. Two separate plots are prepared--a *relative mo-*

tion plot and a *speed* or *vector diagram*. It is essential that these plots are not confused. For convenience, these two separate graphs are generally plotted on the same M board, but the plots are logically distinct. The first plot required is the RMP. The RMP is used to determine whether or not a danger of collision exists, the *closest point of approach* (CPA), the *direction of relative motion* (DRM), the *time to closest point of approach* (TCPA), and other quantities if required. The second of these plots, the *vector diagram* (VD), is used to determine the target's course and speed.

RELATIVE MOTION PLOT (RMP)

To prepare the RMP it is necessary to plot successive observations of the target's distance and either true or magnetic bearing. Although a useful plot can be made from as few as two observations, generally three or more are plotted if time and circumstances permit. Our vessel *(Altair)* is termed the *reference ship* or vessel and is labeled "R" if required. (Symbols for the RMP are, by convention, all uppercase.) In a RMP, own ship is located at the origin (center of the plot) at all times.

The target is termed the *maneuvering ship,* and is labeled "M." Successive data points for the maneuvering ship are denoted with the symbol M_i/XX to denote the ith observation and the time when it was made. In this example, the first observation would be denoted $M_1/00$, the second observation $M_2/06$, and the third observation $M_3/12$. The target range and true or magnetic (magnetic in this example) bearings are plotted on the *polar diagram* (M board). M boards are discussed in Chapter 7. For ease in plotting, it is sometimes appropriate to plot the target at a different scale than 1 scale division (SD) equals 1 nautical mile (M). However, a scale of 1 SD equals 1 M is convenient in this example. There is provision on the worksheet to note the scale, but additionally, it is useful to write the scale on the M board. If scales other than 1:1 are used, it is necessary to factor the scale into the calculations.

Care should be taken in preparing the plot. Small plotting errors are carried through the calculations and can influence the final results substantially. Common errors include failing to use the scale factors (if other than 1:1) and misreading the bearing scale (e.g., plotting 074 degrees as 066 degrees, etc.).

Figure 9-17 shows the M board RMP. The three observations are plotted--the coordinates are range, (M), and magnetic bearing. Passing a straight edge or paraline plotter through these points indicates that all lie approximately on the same straight line and are equally spaced. This situation will occur whenever the reference ship and the maneuvering ship both maintain course and speed. *Altair* has maintained speed and course (by design), so this plot enables the conclusion to be drawn that the target vessel has also maintained course and speed. This conclusion is noted in the worksheet in Table 9-5.

From the RMP it is possible to calculate several useful quantities. First, the *direction of relative motion* (DRM) can be estimated. This is done by connecting the points on the line and sliding the paraline plotter to a line parallel to the DRM but through the origin. The DRM (271 degrees in this example) can be read on the outer (bearing) scale of the M board. The DRM is noted on the M board and the worksheet. It is important to avoid reading the reciprocal direction on the M board. In this instance, successive points lie generally to the left of each other, and this determines the direction. (Note that the DRM, nearly westward in this case, differs from the apparent "southeastward" motion of the target on the SHU display. These two directions will only be the same when the reference ship is heading north.) The DRM is the first entry on the third (bottom) section of the worksheet.

Next, it is useful to calculate the *speed of relative motion* (SRM) from the RMP. If the points are equally spaced and lie in a straight line, the speed is constant. The SRM can be calculated by measuring the distance between

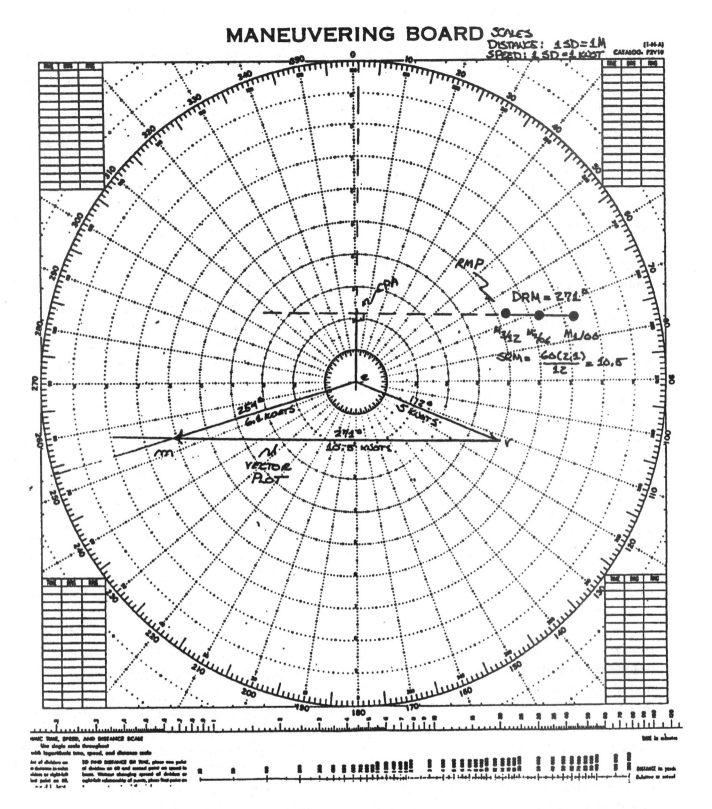

Fig. 9-17. Radar Plot For *"Altair"* Example

the first and last observations on the RMP with a pair of dividers, and calculating the speed using the formula $S = 60D/T$. In this example, the SRM works out to approximately 10.5 knots. Alternatively, the nomogram on the bottom of the M board (not shown in this illustration) can be used to estimate the SRM. These entries are also given on the completed worksheet in Table 9-5. This completes the relative motion calculations.

CLOSEST POINT OF APPROACH (CPA)

As the name implies, the CPA is the smallest distance that the maneuvering ship (the target) will approach the reference ship, to use the common terminology. It is determined by either extrapolating or interpolating the RMP. The CPA is found by drawing a line from the origin perpendicular to the RML. The point where the perpendicular and the RML intersect is the CPA. Although this can be done graphically, it is easier to calculate the bearing from the DRM plus or minus 90 degrees. The distance, approximately 2.2 nautical miles in this example, can be transferred to one of the distance scales with a pair of dividers. By extending the line from the origin through the CPA to the bearing scale, a true (magnetic) bearing of the CPA can be obtained. In this example the magnetic bearing of the target at the CPA is approximately 001 degrees. These entries are also shown on the worksheet in Table 9-5. The relative bearing of the CPA can be calculated from the true (magnetic) bearing minus the ship's head. In this example, the relative bearing is 001 degrees magnetic minus 112 degrees (360 must, therefore, be added) or 249 degrees. In other words, at the point of closest approach the target vessel will be approximately 21 degrees abaft *Altair's* port beam.

Finally, the TCPA can be determined, by measuring the distance between the last observation, M_3, and the CPA, approximately 4.9 M, and calculating how long it would take to traverse this direction at the SRM. In this example, the TCPA is estimated to be 1040.

To summarize the results for this example, the RMP has enabled the following estimates to be made. The target vessel will pass as close as 2.2 M to *Altair* at 1040 with relative bearing of closest approach 249 degrees. Actions to be taken by *Altair's* crew in this case depend upon additional factors, such as *Altair's* ability to maneuver, visibility, etc. In good weather, *Altair's* skipper would probably elect to maintain course and speed, alert the lookout(s) to the

target's position, and continue to monitor the situation until the target vessel was well clear. Other options include attempting to contact the target vessel on VHF/FM (Channel 13) to arrange details of passage, or altering course or speed to increase the separation at CPA. The effect of course or speed adjustments can be evaluated on an M board, but this is beyond the scope of this chapter.

THE VECTOR DIAGRAM

The second plot generally required for complete solution of the radar problem is the *speed triangle* or *vector diagram*. It is used to estimate the target's course and speed. There are two principal methods for plotting the vector diagram. The method discussed here can be found in the *Maneuvering Board Manual* or the *Radar Navigation Manual* published by the Defense Mapping Agency, and cited in the attached references. Another method, called the *Real Time Method* (RTM), is gaining favor among radar users. This is also described in some of the references, but is not discussed here.

Unlike the RMP which shows *distances and bearings*, the vector diagram shows *speeds and courses* of the maneuvering and reference ships. Therefore, it is possible that a different scale would be appropriate for plotting the vector diagram. In this example, however, a scale of 1 knot equals 1 SD is appropriate, and is so noted on the M board and worksheet alike.

The vector diagram is a graphical method for vector addition, and is used to obtain the course and speed of the maneuvering ship. It is simple to use and interpret, and described in the three steps shown below.

First, the reference vessel's course and speed vector is plotted. This vector, labeled er (lowercase letters are used on the vector plot to avoid confusion with the uppercase symbols on the RMP), is plotted on the M board. The vector is drawn outward from the origin in the direction of the course of the reference vessel. The length of vector er is proportional to the speed of the reference vessel. In this example, *Altair's* speed vector has a length of 5 SDs (5 SDs correspond to 5 knots at a 1:1 scale) and is drawn outward on a heading of 112 degrees.

Next, the relative motion vector is laid out on the M board. The "tail" of the relative motion vector is the DRM (271 degrees in this example), and is conveniently laid out by moving the paraline plotter parallel to the DRM on the RMP. The length of the relative motion vector is the SRM (10.5 knots, or 10.5 SDs at the 1:1 scale used in this example), determined from the RMP.

Finally, the maneuvering vessel's vector, denoted em, is drawn from the origin to the head of the relative motion vector. The orientation of this vector (254 degrees in this example) is the course (magnetic in this example) of the maneuvering or target vessel. The length of this vector (measured as 6.1 SDs or 6.1 knots at a 1:1 scale) is equal to the speed of the target. The fact that the target's estimated speed is positive confirms the navigator's initial classification of the target as another vessel. If the target were stationary, or nearly so, it could have been a vessel at anchor (the plausibility of this hypothesis could be checked from the depth of water), dead in the water, or possibly a fixed ATON.

This completes the radar plot for the first example. Inspection of both plots shows that *Altair* and the target vessel are almost on opposite courses, and should pass port-to-port at a distance of approximately 2.2 M if both vessels maintain course and speed. In practice, the RMP would probably be continued or otherwise systematically observed to monitor the progress of the maneuvering vessel and ensure that no subsequent course or speed adjustments were required to avoid collision.

RADAR PLOTTING
--A SECOND EXAMPLE

As a second example, range and bearing data are presented from one reconstruction of a collision that occurred in clear weather between the Polish M/V *Nowy Sacz* and the Cypriot ship, *Olympian,* under conditions of darkness early one morning on 14 February 1972 approximately 20 M south of Cape St. Vincent, off the Iberian Peninsula, along the coast of Portugal. Although both ships were using radar for navigation, radar observations were not taken nor were M board plots actually made in this case. None the less, sufficient information exists to reconstruct the sequence of radar observations that would have resulted had these actually been taken. To make the problem concrete, suppose that you are the master of the *Nowy Sacz,* enroute from Casablanca in North Africa to Gdynia, Poland. At 0245, *Nowy Sacz* is making 12.5 knots on a true course of 341 degrees. A radar target is identified with a relative bearing of 124 degrees, approximately 3.7 miles distant. (For purposes of this example, assume that *Nowy Sacz* has an unstabilized SHU display.) By 0300 the target has closed to approximately 2.9 M while still bearing 124 relative. A third observation is taken at 0315, when the target bears 124 degrees relative at a range of approximately 2.2 M. Assume that, because an autopilot was in use, *Nowy Sacz's* heading and speed remained constant at 341 degrees and 12.5 knots, respectively, while the bearings were taken. Prepare an M board plot for these observations, estimate the CPA, course and speed of the target. What actions, if any, should you take as the master of the *Nowy Sacz* on the basis of these data?

SOLUTION TO SECOND EXAMPLE

Table 9-6 and Figure 9-18 shows the completed worksheet and M board plot, respectively, for this example. From the RMP, it is determined that the DRM is 285 degrees and the SRM is 3 knots. From the M board plot it is clear that the CPA is 0 M, i.e., a collision situation exists. The TCPA--time of estimated collision in this case--is 0359, and the target's course

TABLE 9--6.   *NOWY SACZ/OLYMPIAN* COLLISION

BASIC WORKSHEET FOR SOLVING RADAR PROBLEMS ON MANEUVERING BOARD

DATA FOR PLOTTING: EXAMPLE/CASE: *NOWY SACZ*   OWN SHIP'S COURSE AND SPEED: *341° 12.5KTS*

TIME	DISTANCE IN MILES OR YARD NOTE UNITS	OWN SHIP'S HEADING (TRUE OR MAG)	TARGET RELATIVE BEARING	TARGET TRUE/MAG BEARING	REMARKS
0245	*3.7*	*341*	*124*	*105*	DISTANCE AND TARGET TRUE OR MAGNETIC BEARING ARE TO BE PLOTTED ON MANEUVERING
0300	*2.9*	*341*	*124*	*105*	BOARD. IF TRUE BEARINGS ARE DESIRED ITS NECESSARY TO CONVERT FROM COMPASS
0315	*2.2*	*341*	*124*	*105*	HEADING TO TRUE HEADING USING CDMVT ADD EAST LOGIC. CHOOSE AND LABEL BOTH SPEED AND DISTANCE SCALES ON THE BOARD. ENSURE POINTS ARE PLOTTED CAREFULLY USING THE CORRECT SCALE!

					SCALE	SD	VALUE
					DISTANCE	*2*	*1M*
HOW ENTRIES ARE OBTAINED	RECORDED AT TIME OF OBS.	READ FROM RANGE RING OR VRM	READ FROM COMPASS OR GYRO	READ FROM EBL ON RADAR SCOPE	CALCULATED FROM SH + RB (360 MAY HAVE TO BE SUBTRACTED)	SPEED *1*	*2KTS*

INSERT REMARKS HERE ON MANEUVERING BOARD PLOTS:

CBDR Situation--Straight Line Plot

COMPUTATIONS:

TOPIC	QUANTITY	VALUE	REMARKS ON CALCULATION
RELATIVE MOTION	DIRECTION OF RELATIVE MOTION:	*285°*	MEASURED FROM RELATIVE MOTION PLOT-DO NOT ERR BY 180 DEG!
	DIST BETWEEN OBSERVATIONS:	*1.5M*	TAKEN FROM LINEAR PORTION OF RELATIVE MOTION PLOT (RMP)
	TIME BETWEEN OBSERVATIONS:	*30 Min.*	TAKEN FROM INPUTS ON LINEAR PORTION OF RMP
	SPEED OF RELATIVE MOTION:	*3*	CALCULATED FROM ABOVE TWO ENTRIES S = 60D/T
CPA	DISTANCE TO CPA:	*0!*	EXTRAPOLATED OR INTERPOLATED FROM RELATIVE MOTION PLOT
	TRUE OR MAGNETIC BEARING OF CPA:	*NA*	FROM DRM PLUS OR MINUS 90 DEGREES
	RELATIVE BEARING OF CPA:	*NA*	FROM TRUE OR MAGNETIC BEARING MINUS OWN SHIP'S HEAD
	DIST FROM LAST OBS TO CPA:	*2.2*	MEASURED FROM RELATIVE MOTION PLOT
	TIME TO TRAVERSE THIS DIST:	*44 Min.*	FROM T = 60D/S
	TIME OF CPA:	*0359*	FROM ABOVE PLUS TIME OF LAST OBSERVATION
TARGET MOVEMENT	TARGET COURSE:	*331°*	FROM COMPANION VECTOR PLOT ON MANEUVERING BOARD
	TARGET SPEED:	*14.6*	FROM COMPANION VECTOR PLOT ON MANEUVERING BOARD

and speed are estimated to be 331 degrees and 14.6 knots respectively. (Incidentally, the Cypriot vessel claimed to be on a course of 290 degrees making only 13 knots, a claim that was rejected by the court on the basis of the evidence presented.) From the M board plot it is clear that the *Olympian* is overtaking the *Nowy Sacz*, so under the NAVRULES (assuming that the vessels were in sight of one another) the *Nowy Sacz* was the stand-on vessel and the *Olympian* should have altered course/speed to avoid collision. (The actual situation was somewhat more com-

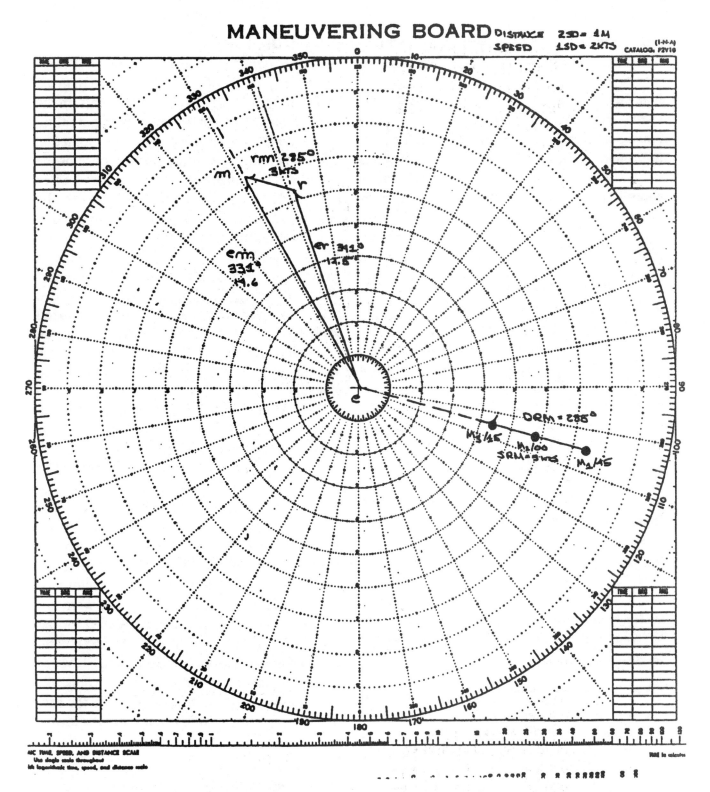

Fig. 9-18. *NOWY SACZ/OLYMPIAN*

plex and the *Nowy Sacz* was initially held responsible for the collision that resulted. However, on appeal, this verdict was reversed and the *Olympian* was held to be partially at fault. The actual collision occurred at 0358 in agreement with the predicted TCPA.)

This example is instructive in that it shows the value of an M board plot, rather than simple examination of the radar scope images alone. (However, even the radar observations alone should have alerted both vessels that a collision was likely.) Note that, the same succession of radar images could have resulted from many combinations of reference and target ship movements. For example, if the *Nowy Sacz* were dead in the water rather than on the course and at the speed indicated, the identical series of radar images could have resulted if the *Olympian* were approaching on a course of 285 degrees at 3 knots. In fact, there are an infinite number of combinations of speed and course for the reference and maneuvering ships that could have produced the same RMP. It is only the vector plot that enables the actual course and speed of the maneuvering ship to be determined.

A THIRD EXAMPLE

The third example presented here is taken with minor modification from a problem given in the Student Study Guide (SSG). It is of interest because the plot is somewhat complex and presents more of a challenge to interpretation. In all the problems given above, the M board plot was linear and the distances were constant between evenly spaced observations. As noted, this situation results only when both the reference and maneuvering vessels maintain course and speed. Indeed, it is important to note that the reference vessel should maintain course and speed throughout the plotting interval if valid data are to be obtained. However, even if the reference vessel maintains course and speed, the maneuvering vessel(s) may not do so. Thus, it is important to consider some cases involving a maneuvering target.

In this example, the M/V *Pollux* is proceeding due north at a speed of 9 knots inbound to Valdez, Alaska. At XX29 a target is identified bearing 111 degrees at a range of 2.3 M. To avoid tedious computations, it is assumed that a NU display is available and true bearing information is given directly as shown below.

TIME	RANGE (M)	BEARING (DEGREES)
xx29	2.30	111
xx35	1.20	111
xx38	0.60	111
xx41	0.35	140
xx47	0.60	225
xx53	1.20	243

SOLUTION

The M board plot shown in Figure 9-19 presents a somewhat more complex picture than the earlier examples. In this case, the points on the RMP do not plot as one straight line, but rather appear to fall along two straight lines joined at xx38, indicating that either the reference or the target vessels changed course and/or speed. Since *Pollux* did not change either course or speed, the target vessel must have--possibly to avoid collision. Note that the first three points at 29, 35, and 38 past the hour indicate the classic CBDR pattern. The object of this exercise is to determine what happened. It is solved by making two RMPs and two vector diagrams--note the speed scale of 2 SD = 1 knot is used. After plotting the RMP and *Pollux's* speed vector, the relative motion vector should be inserted in the speed diagram. But, in this example there are two relative motion vectors--one valid for the first period, denoted rm_1, and another valid after xx38, denoted by rm_2. From the plot of the first three points it is determined that the DRM is 291 degrees, and the SRM is approximately 11.6 knots. Connecting rm_1 to er enables determination of the target vessel's initial course and speed to be 321 degrees and 17 knots, respectively. To determine the target's course and speed after xx38, it is necessary to plot another vector diagram. But, *Pollux's* course and speed were unchanged, so the same vector, er, is used for the second vector diagram. The RML for the second time period shows that the DRM and SRM are approximately 259 degrees and 6.6 knots, respectively. These computations define the second rm vector, rm_2, which is plotted as shown.

Examination of the second vector diagram indicates that the target's speed was reduced to approximately 10 knots, but that the course was unchanged, because rm_2 lies along the same radial (approximately) as rm_1. This example is particularly interesting because it clearly illustrates the value of plotting. It would be clear from inspection of the radar screen alone that "something" has happened, but only the M board

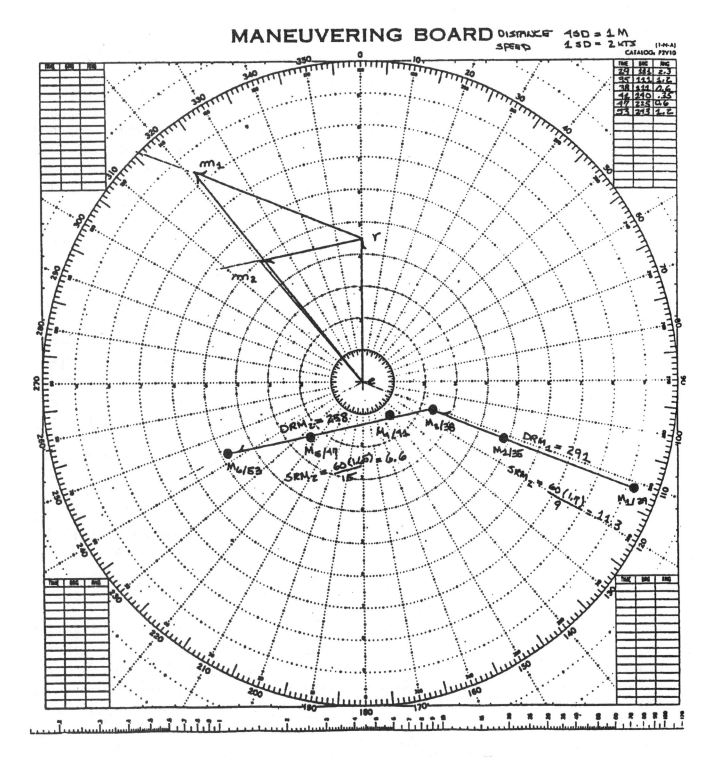

Fig. 9-19. Radar Plots For *M/V Pollux*

plot enables the navigator to determine exactly what action was taken by the target vessel.

It is useful to consider this example from another perspective, that of the NAVRULES. In this connection, it is instructive to consider the circumstances of visibility. Suppose first that the prevailing visibility is such that *Pollux* and the target vessel are in sight of one another throughout the encounter. In this case, *Pollux* is the "give way" vessel, because the target is in *Pollux's* "danger zone," that is between 0 degrees and 112.5 degrees relative bearing. The target, therefore, is a "crossing vessel" within the meaning of

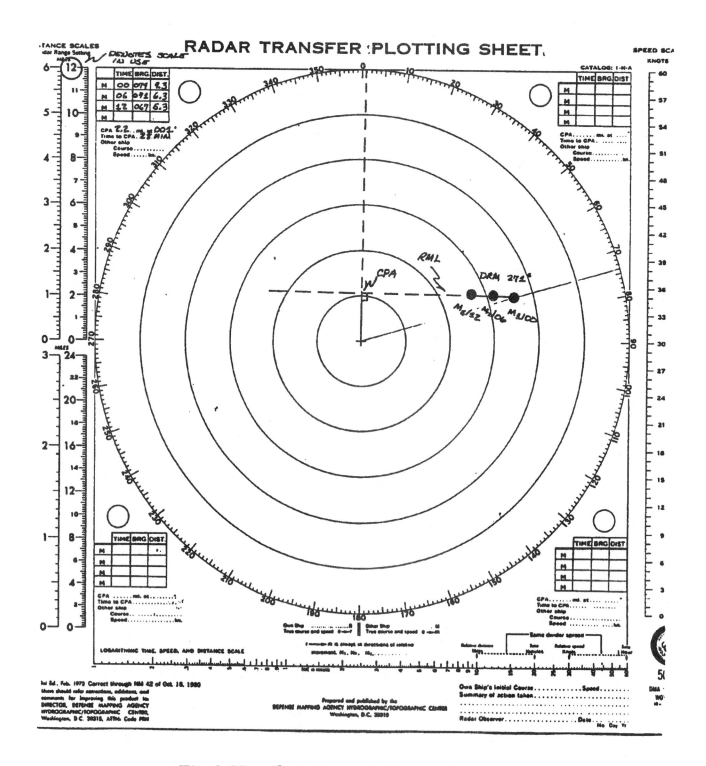

Fig. 9-20. *Altair* **Example Plotted On RTPS**

the NAVRULES. (Although the situation is close, and the target is within 2 degrees of being an "overtaking," and thus the "give way" vessel.) Close or not, *Pollux* should have given way, by either alteration of course or speed to ensure that the vessels passed at a safe distance (see Rule 15).

Now suppose that this encounter took place in restricted visibility. In this situation, unlike that of vessels in sight of one another, there are no "stand on" or "give way" vessels. However (Rule 19), "a vessel which detects by radar alone the presence of another vessel shall determine if a close-quarters situation is developing or risk of collision exists." The rule continues, "If so, she shall take avoiding action in ample time..." Because *Pollux* was equipped with operating radar and able to determine that a risk of collision existed, *Pollux* should have taken appropriate action to minimize the risk of collision.

Therefore, regardless of the prevailing visibility, *Pollux* should have initiated action to avert collision, albeit for different reasons.

A complete discussion of the NAVRULES, radar, and collision-avoidance is beyond the scope of this text. However, the reader is advised to review the references given in the bibliography for more details.

USE OF THE RTPS

As noted above a *radar transfer plotting sheet* (RTPS) can be used as an alternative to an M board for radar plotting. The RTPS is also available from the Defense Mapping Agency (No. 5089, DMA Stock No. WOXZP 5089), but is produced in only one size (10-inch).

Figure 9-20 shows the RML for the first example as plotted on the RTPS. Before discussing the plot in detail, a brief review of the RTPS is in order. Basically, it offers a similar presentation to the M board, except that 6 FRMs are given, and scales are adjusted to be multiples of 6 (i.e., 3 miles, 6 miles, 12 miles, and 24 miles). Suppression of a radiating distance (or speed) scale found on the M board presents a less "cluttered" plot, but auxiliary scales, given on the right- or left-hand side, need to be used and distances (or speed) transferred with a pair of dividers from the auxiliary scales to the plot. Thus, for example, observation $M_1/00$ is located 7.3 miles at a bearing 074 magnetic. If a 12-mile scale is assumed (i.e., FRMs located 2 miles apart) as denoted by placing a circle around the 12 in the auxiliary scale on the right-hand side, the distance (7.3M) is first measured with a set of dividers on this scale and then transferred to the radar scope facsimile in the center.

Use of an RTPS is particularly convenient if the range scales on your radar set match those on the RTPS. The auxiliary scales eliminate the need to convert from SDs to either distance or speed. However, as most small boat radars have range scales that differ from the choices presented on the RTPS, use of an M board is recommended.

RADAR PLOTTING: THE STEPS SUMMARIZED

As illustrated in the above examples, the overall steps in radar plotting are as follows:

1. *Observation and Detection*--a continuous radar watch is maintained and the appearance of targets noted. On the basis of early observation of the range and bearing of the target(s) and other factors, a decision is made whether or not to plot or otherwise monitor the target(s). If practical, the reference ship should maintain course and speed.

2. *Plotting and Analysis*--if the target(s) is plotted, the plot is used to determine the risk of collision (CPA, TCPA), and nature of the encounter (true and relative bearings). Alternatively, this can be done automatically if the radar has this feature.

3. *Selection of Evasive Action*--although not discussed in this chapter, M boards can be used to evaluate the effects of course and speed changes to ensure that the vessels pass at a safe distance.

4. *Monitoring Results*--radar plots are maintained to monitor the results of any collision avoidance maneuvers to verify their success, and/or to select alternative maneuvers.

OTHER SITUATIONS OF INTEREST

There are several other salient points that should be made with respect to the interpretation of radar for collision avoidance.

First, it is important to note that if the reference ship is *dead in the water* (DIW), aside from whatever drift and/or yaw may be present, the relative motion display behaves almost as though it were a true motion display. Thus, if presented with an ambiguous situation and conditions otherwise permit, you can simply halt the vessel to enable the course and speed of other targets to be observed directly.

Second, it should be evident that a target which is apparently stationary when viewed from the radar screen of a moving vessel is *not* DIW, but rather maintaining the same course and speed as the reference ship. Such targets are often observed by vessels transiting inlets or enroute to popular destinations as they "keep station" relative to other vessels.

Third, it is often of interest to identify stationary targets such as buoys, or other ATONs. There are several ways to do this. Often the location of the target and absence of other targets will render identification of buoys self-evident. (This also highlights the importance of knowing the reference vessel's position accurately and is one of the many reasons why it is convenient to have a loran that "talks" to the radar and displays the vessel's latitude and longitude on the radar screen.) In some cases, for example, with a transponder equipped buoy, the identification is likewise self-evident. Buoys can frequently be identified from the range at which detection first occurs. Detection ranges for buoys range from perhaps 1/4 M for a conical buoy to 6 M or more for a buoy with a radar reflector. (This also shows the value of a continuous radar watch. Sporadic observation will not enable the target's detection range to be estimated with any accuracy.) A target detected at 10 or more miles distance, for example, is unlikely to be a buoy. If two targets are present, reducing the gain may enable differentiation to be made--the buoy will disappear first, while the echo of a nearby ship may remain visible. As well, M board plots can be used to differentiate between DIW targets, such as, buoys and moving vessels. A target that is DIW will have a DRM opposite that of the reference vessel and a speed the same as the reference vessel. This can be determined solely from a RMP, although a vector diagram will, of course, confirm the stationary position of the target. In practice, a vector diagram for a DIW target will result in a small apparent speed due to observation errors, but values close to zero are sufficient confirmation of the target's status.

From the above, it should be clear that targets on identical (or nearly) courses from the reference ship that have the same speed as the reference vessel appear stationary. Targets moving "downscope" on the SHU display at *greater* speed (SRM) than the reference vessel are other vessels on (nearly) reciprocal courses. And "upscope" targets apparently moving downscope at *slower* speeds (SRM) than the reference ship are vessels being overtaken by the reference ship. These simple rules of thumb can easily be verified with the use of an M board.

Fourth, it is important to emphasize that the material presented in this chapter gives only a sampling of the possible uses of M boards. Examination of one of the many texts given in the list of references will show additional applications.

CONCLUDING COMMENTS

Finally, proficiency in radar interpretation and plotting comes only with practice. Although plotting can (and should) be practiced in the living room or study, there are important differences from the shipboard environment (e.g., the time available for plotting, the size of the plotting table, the need to divide your attention between plotting and other duties), and on-the-water practice is essential. The problems in the SSG serve as a useful opportunity to test your mastery of the subject. But nothing short of extensive on-the-water practice (in good visibility) will enable the mariner to become fully familiar with radar.

REFERENCES

Anderson, J.*Exercises in Pilotage*, David and Charles, London, England, 1987.

Block, R. A., editor. *Radar Observer Manual (Fifth Revision)*, Marine Navigation Textbooks, Houma, LA, 1983.

Bole, A. G. and K. D. Jones. *Automatic Radar Plotting Aids Manual*, Cornell Maritime Press, Centreville, MD, 1981.

Brooke, G. A. G. and S. Dobell *Radar Mate*, Adlard Coles Ltd., London, England, 1986.

Burger, W. *Radar Observer's Handbook for Merchant Navy Officers*, 6th edition, Brown, Son & Ferguson, Glasgow, Scotland, 1978.

Cahill, R. A.*Collisions and Their Causes*, Fairplay Publications, London, England, 1983.

Carpenter, M. and W. Waldo. *Real Time Method of Radar Plotting*, Cornell Maritime Press, Centreville, MD, 1975.

Clissold, P. *Radar in Small Craft*, Thomas Reed Publications Limited, London, England, 1970.

Coolen, E. *Nicholls's Concise Guide to Navigation*, Vol. 1, Brown, Son & Ferguson, Ltd., Glasgow, Scotland, 1987.

Coolen, E. *Nicholls's Concise Guide to Navigation Examinations*, Vol. 2, Brown, Son & Ferguson, Ltd., Glasgow, Scotland, 1984.

Dahl, B. *The Loran-C Users Guide*, Richardsons' Marine Publishing Inc., Streamwood, IL, 1986.

Defense Mapping Agency, Hydrographic/Topographic Center. *American Practical Navigator,* Pub. No. 9, Vols. I and II, 1984, 1981 respectively.

Defense Mapping Agency, Hydrographic/Topographic Center. *Loran-C Correction Table, Northeast, USA, 9960,* DMA Stock No. LCPUB 2211 200"C, Washington, DC, 1983.

Defense Mapping Agency, Hydrographic/Topographic Center. *Maneuvering Board Manual,* Pub. No. 217, 4th edition, 1984.

Defense Mapping Agency, Hydrographic/Topographic Center. *Radar Navigation Manual*, Pub. No. 1310, 4th edition, 1985.

Defense Mapping Agency, Hydrographic/Topographic Center. *Radar Navigational Aids,* Pub. No. 117, DMA Stock No. RAPUB 117, 1988.

Departments of Transportation and Defense. *Federal Radionavigation Plan 1988*, NTIS, Springfield, VA, 1988.

French, J. *Small Craft Radar,* Van Nostrand Reinhold Company, New York, NY 1977.

Hoffer, W. *Saved! The Story of the Andrea Doria-- The Greatest Sea Rescue in History*, Summit Books, New York, NY, 1979.

Holdert, H. M. C. and F. J. Bozek. *Collision Cases--Judgements and Diagrams,* Lloyd's of London Press Ltd., Legal Publishing and Conferences Divisions, London, UK, 1984.

Maloney, E. S. *Chapman Piloting Seamanship and Small Boat Handling,* Hearst Marine Books, NY, 1983.

Maloney, E. S. *Dutton's Navigation & Piloting,* 14th edition, Naval Institute Press, Annapolis, MD, 1985.

McClench, D., Ed. *Primer of Navigation by George W. Mixter,* 5th edition, Van Nostrand Reinhold Co., New York, NY, 1967.

Melton, L. *The Complete Loran-C Handbook,* International Marine Publishing Co., Camden, ME, 1986.

Melton, L. *Piloting with Electronics*, International Marine Publishing Co., Camden, ME, 1987.

Ministry of Defense (Navy) BR 45(1). *Admiralty Manual of Navigation,* Volume 1, Her Majesty's Stationary Office (HMSO), London, UK, 1987.

Moss, W. D. *Radar Watchkeeping*, The Maritime Press Ltd., London, England, 1965.

Motte, G. A. and T. M. Stout, *Chartwork and Marine Navigation for Fishermen and Boat Operators,* Second Edition, Cornell Maritime Press, Centerville, MD, 1984.

Oudet, L. *Radar and Collision*, D. Van Nostrand Company, Princeton, NJ, 1960.

Pierce, J. A. "Memoirs of John Alvin Pierce: Development of Loran," *Journal of the Institute of Navigation,* Vol. 36, No. 1, Spring 1989, pp. 1-8.

Pike, D., *Electronic Navigation For Small Craft,,* Granada Publishing, London, England, 1977.

Safford, E. L. *Modern Radar: Theory, Operation and Maintenance,* Tab Books, Blue Ridge Summit, PA, 1971.

Sonnenberg, G. J. *Radar and Electronic Navigation*, 6th edition, Butterworths, London, England, 1988.

United States Coast Guard Academy, New London, Conn, *Loran-C Engineering Course,* 1990.

United States Department of Transportation, U. S. Coast Guard. *Loran-C User Handbook,* COMDTINST M16562.3, Washington, DC, 1980.

United States Department of Transportation, U. S. Coast Guard, *Radionavigation Systems,* G-NRN, 1984.

United States Department of Transportation, U. S. Coast Guard. *Specifications of the Transmitted Signal*, COMDINST 16562.4, Washington, DC.

Van Wyck, S. M. and M. H. Carpenter. *The Radar Book,* Cornell Maritime Press, Centreville, MD, 1984.

Walsh, G. "Coastal Navigation, the Basics: Radar Tactics and the Rules of the Road," *Ocean Navigator*, September/October 1988, pp. 55, et seq.

West, J. *Boatowner's Guide to Radar*, International Marine Publishing Company, Camden, ME, 1988.

West, J. *Radar for Marine Navigation and Safety*, Van Nostrand Reinhold Company, New York, NY, 1978.

Wylie, F. J., ed. *The Use of Radar at Sea*, Royal Institute of Navigation, Naval Institute Press, Annapolis, MD, 1982.

Chapter 10

Navigation Reference Publications

By this point in the course/text you should be quite familiar with the 1210-Tr chart and, more generally, the tremendous amount, variety, and utility of material that can be found on the modern nautical chart. None the less, space and format constraints limit the amount of information that can be placed on the nautical chart. Therefore, the mariner also has need for additional material to help provide for the safe and efficient navigation of the vessel. A variety of additional publications are available, some published by commercial enterprises, and others of government origin. This chapter provides a brief overview of relevant *government publications,* including the *Coast Pilot, Light List,* and *Notices to Mariners.* These three publications supplement the nautical chart. Additionally, commercially produced "Cruising Guides" and/or "Boating Almanacs" often contain valuable information and are worthwhile additions to the "ship's library."

COAST PILOT

The *United States Coast Pilot,* to use its formal title, is published annually by the National Ocean Service (NOS), Charting and Geodetic Services (C&GS), National Oceanic and Atmospheric Administration (NOAA). It is published in nine volumes covering the Atlantic and Pacific coasts (including Alaska and Hawaii), and the Great Lakes and their connecting waterways. (The area covered by the 1210-Tr chart, for example, is contained in the *Coast Pilot,* Vol. 2, Atlantic Coast: Cape Cod to Sandy Hook.)

The *Coast Pilot* supplements the navigational information given in the nautical chart. This information is developed in several ways, including field inspections conducted by NOAA, excerpts from Notices to Mariners (discussed following), and information furnished by other federal agencies and state and local governments, maritime and pilotage associations. Mariners are also encouraged to recommend changes to the *Coast Pilot,* which can be sent to NOAA on Form 77-6, copies of which are found at the back of each *Coast Pilot.* Topics covered in the *Coast Pilot* include coast and channel descriptions, anchorages, communication frequencies, drawbridge schedules and signals (both differ from bridge to bridge), bridge and cable clearances, currents, tide and water levels, prominent features, pilotage, towage, weather, ice conditions, wharf descriptions, dangers, routes, traffic separation schemes, small craft facilities, and federal regulations applicable to navigation. In short, the *Coast Pilot* serves as an encyclopedia of local knowledge. Corrections to the *Coast Pilot* since the date of publication are published in the Notices to Mariners.

USE OF THE *COAST PILOT*: AN EXAMPLE

The value of the *Coast Pilot* is best indicated by example, rather than lengthy discourse. Suppose, therefore, that you are in a 32 ft. sailboat with a 3.5 ft. draft located in the basin at Menemsha, on Martha's Vineyard, and wish to voyage to Fairhaven, on the east side of New Bedford Harbor. The auxiliary engine has been acting up, but you have replaced the plugs and feel that the problem is solved. Winds are out of the south at 10 to 15 knots. The current is setting eastward through Vineyard Sound.

As can be seen by referring to the 1210-Tr chart, there are two broad options for this voyage; try to make passage through one of three channels (termed *Holes* in that part of the country) between the Elizabeth Islands (Canapitsit Channel, Quicks Hole, or Robinsons Hole), or detour west and pass clear to the west of Cuttyhunk Island. The distance "the long way around" is at least 28 miles (equivalent to 5.6 hours at 5 knots, but it could be longer considering the eastward set of the current in Vineyard South), whereas if you go through Quicks Hole (which appears fairly broad and deep on the chart) the distance is only about 19 miles (3.8 hours at 5 knots). What should you do?

A glance at the *1988 Coast Pilot* descriptions for either Canapitsit Channel or Robinsons Hole (refer to Figure 10-1) suggests that either of these options would be a "white knuckle special," best left either to experts or the foolhardy. Quicks Hole (see Figure 10-2 for the *Coast Pilot* excerpt) looks to be a better option--in particular, the remark about avoiding possibly heavy seas in the entrance to Vineyard Sound is tantalizing. However, the advice that sailing vessels should not attempt to pass through Quicks Hole unless with favorable winds *and* a favorable current is more than a little unsettling because, with an eastward current in Vineyard Sound, foul currents in Quicks Hole are to be expected. (Perhaps the engine cannot be relied upon.)

Hmmm, looks like the long way around is not such a bad idea after all. If the seas are ugly at the entrance to Vineyard Sound, you can turn around and try to use the engine, or run east to some location like Tarpaulin Cove. The *Coast Pilot* would be a good place to look to identify possible alternatives. Of course, you could always remain where you are and await more favorable conditions.

The point of this example is not to recommend a particular course of action or to offer a discourse on voyage decision making, but rather to illustrate the value of the *Coast Pilot*. It puts a wealth of information and local knowledge in your hands that cannot be provided by the chart alone. Coast Guard and Coast Guard Auxiliary vessels (in some Districts) are required to have the latest editions of these aboard, and this simple example shows you why.

LIGHT LIST

First published in 1838, the *Light List* is now published annually by the Coast Guard. Seven volumes cover the United States. (The area covered by the 1210-Tr chart, for example, is contained in Volume 1, Atlantic Coast, St. Crois River, Maine to Toms River, New Jersey.) Briefly stated, the purpose of the *Light List* is to provide more complete information concerning aids to navigation than can be shown on nautical charts.

Charts 13233, 13230, 13229.-Robinsons Hole is a narrow buoyed passage from Vineyard Sound to Buzzards Bay between the western end of Naushon Island and the eastern end of Pasque Island. *It has numerous rocks and ledges, and strong tidal currents. The buoys often tow under, and the passage should never be attempted by strangers; it is used occasionally by local fishermen. It has been reported that currents sometimes reach a velocity of 5 knots in the passage.* The velocity in the narrow part is about 3 knots. The flood sets southeastward and the ebb northwestward into Buzzards Bay. (See the Tidal Current Tables for predictions, and the Tidal Current Charts, Narragansett Bay to Nantucket Island, for the hourly velocities and directions of the current.)

Canapitsit Channel, between the east end of Cuttyhunk Island and Nashawena Island, is used by small boats and is partially marked by buoys. In November 1980, the channel had a controlling depth of 5 1/2 feet. *The buoys at this entrance are often dragged off station by strong currents and heavy seas. The channel should never be used during a heavy ground swell. With southerly winds, heavy seas will break across the entrance.*

Fig. 10-1. Excerpt from the 1988 U. S. Coast Pilot.
[Emphasis added.]

The *Light Lists* contain useful general information on such topics as buoyage, bridge markings, and electronic aids to navigation (including radar, loran, and RDF).

The "heart" of the *Light List* is a massive series of tables that describe nearly every aid to navigation in the area covered by the specific volume of the *Light List*. Entries in the table include the name and location of the ATON, position (latitude and longitude), light color and characteristic, height and nominal range (see discussion below), nature of structure, and a catchall category titled "remarks." Figure 10-3, for example, provides an excerpt from the *1988 Light List* relevant to the 1210-Tr chart. The first entry shown in this figure (No. 650) provides information on the Buzzards Bay entrance light. Although some of this information can be read from the nautical chart, the *Light List* provides additional details, for example, on the location, description of the structure, existence of an emergency light, and the pattern of sound signals. Other useful information could include, for example, the note that the **ATON** is seasonal, or that it might be removed if threatened by ice, the *true* bearings of range lights, limits to visibility, etc.

The *Light List* employs a number of abbreviations that may be unfamiliar to the mariner. These abbreviations are:

Quicks Hole, between Pasque Island and **Nashawena Island** is the only passage between Vineyard Sound and Buzzards Bay eastward of Cuttyhunk available for vessels of over 10-foot draft. The clearly defined entrance from Vineyard Sound, about 0.6 mile wide, is about 4 miles southwestward of Tarpaulin Cove and about 5 miles north of Gay Head. *The passage is used considerably by tows, especially during westerly or southerly winds, to avoid the very heavy sea in the entrance to Vineyard Sound,* and also because a secure anchorage from these winds can be had, if necessary, on the north side of Nashawena Island. The passage is considered unsafe for a long tow at night, but otherwise it may be used by steamers either night or day.

Vessels should follow a midchannel course through the passage. The channel is nearly straight with a width of about 0.2 mile. General depths are 30 feet or more, but there are several spots of 16 to 18 feet and others of 21 to 27 feet. Because of the broken nature of the bottom, the passage is not recommended for a stranger drawing more than 21 feet. Buoys marks the channel.

The aids in Quicks Hole are colored and numbered for passage from Vineyard Sound to Buzzards Bay.

The eastern side of Quicks Hole is foul, and no attempt should be made to pass eastward of the lighted buoy. **Felix Ledge,** 0.2 mile off the eastern shore of Nashawena Island, is covered 16 feet and marked by a buoy.

In November 1985, a sunken wreck was reported on the west side of the passage in about 41° 26.5' N., 70° 51.0' W.

Lone Rock, covered 4 feet and marked by a lighted buoy, is off the northern entrance, about 0.7 mile northward of **North Point,** the northeastern extremity of Nashawena Island.

Tides and currents.—The mean range of tide is 2.5 feet at the south end and 3.5 feet at the north end of Quicks Hole. *The tidal currents have considerable velocity in Quicks Hole, about 2 to 2.5 knots, and a sailing vessel should not attempt to pass through unless with a strong favorable wind on a favorable current.* Deep-draft vessels should be careful not to be set off their courses. With a strong westward current through Vineyard South, there is a northward current through Quicks Hole; *with a strong eastward current in Vineyard Sound, the current sets southward through Quicks Hole.* Strong winds affect the regularity of the currents. (See the Tidal Current, Tables for predictions, and the Tidal Current Charts, Narragansett Bay to Nantucket Sound, for the hourly velocities and directions of the current.)

Fig. 10-2. Excerpt from the *1988 U. S. Coast Pilot*
[Emphasis added.]

Al	-	Alternating
bl	-	blast
C	-	Canadian
ec	-	Eclipse
ev	-	Every
F	-	Fixed
fl	-	flash
Fl	-	Flashing
FS	-	Fog Signal
Fl(2)	-	Group flashing
F	-	Green
I	-	Interrupted
Iso	-	Isophase (Equal interval)
kHz	-	Kilohertz
LFl	-	Long Flash
lt	-	Light
LNB	-	Large Navigational Buoy
MHz	-	Megahertz
Mo	-	Morse Code
Oc	-	Occulting
ODAS	-	Anchored Oceangraphic Data Buoy
Q	-	Quick (Flashing)
Ra ref	-	Radar reflector
R	-	Red
RBN	-	Radiobeacon
s	-	seconds
si	-	Silent
SPM	-	Single Point Mooring Buoy
W	-	White
Y	-	Yellow

VISIBILITY OF LIGHTS

The *Light List* also contains a useful graph for estimating the distance of visibility of lights at night. This is reproduced in the logarithmic chart of Figure 10-4. The abscissa, or x axis, shows the *nominal range* of the light in nautical miles. *The nominal range of the light is the maximum distance a light can be seen in clear weather (meteorological visibility of 10 nautical miles).* This value is listed for all lighted aids to navigation except range lights, directional lights, and private aids to navigation. Referring to Figure 10-3, the nominal range of the Buzzards Bay entrance light is 22 nautical miles.

The ordinate, or y axis of Figure 10-4, shows the *luminous range* of the light in nautical miles. *The luminous range of the light is the greatest distance a light can be expected to be seen given its nominal range and the prevailing meteorological visibility.* Figure 10-4 shows the relationship between the nominal and luminous range of the light. To convert from the nominal range, enter the figure with the nominal range and read upwards to the line that best describes the prevailing visibility. For example, in looking for the Buzzards Bay entrance light (nominal range 22 nautical miles read from the *Light List*) when the prevailing visibility could be classified as "haze" (category 5 on the chart, visibility 1.1 to 2.2 miles), the luminous range would be between 3.3 and 7 nautical miles (the smaller figure corresponding to a visibility of 1.1 nautical miles, and the larger to a visibility of 2.2 nautical miles). To be more accurate, if the visibility were 2.2 miles, the luminous range would be 7 miles.

Neither the nominal range nor the luminous range makes any allowance for the curvature of the earth, distance to the horizon, or geographic range. *The geographic range is the greatest distance the curvature of the earth permits an object of a given height to be seen from a particular height of eye without regard to luminous intensity or visibility conditions (synonym: distance to the optical horizon).* This concept was discussed in Chapters 6 and 9. In particular, Table 6-2 provides a convenient basis for estimating geographic ranges. For example, if the height of eye were 10 ft. on a vessel, and the height of the object were 100 ft. (note from Figure 10-3 that the height of the Buzzards Bay entrance light is 101 ft.), then the geographic range would be approximately 15.4 nautical miles.

The procedure for estimation of the actual distance a light might be expected to be seen is as follows. *First,* read the nominal range from the *Light List. Second,* use Figure 10-4 to convert the nominal range to a luminous range, lr, considering the prevailing visibility. *Third,* using esti-

(1) No.	(2) Name and location	(3) Position	(4) Characteristic	(5) Height	(6) Range	(7) Structure	(8) Remarks

SEACOAST (Massachusetts) – First District

(1) No.	(2) Name and location	(3) Position	(4) Characteristic	(5) Height	(6) Range	(7) Structure	(8) Remarks
	N/W **APPROACHES TO NEW YORK - NANTUCKET SHOALS TO FIVE FATHOM BANK (Chart 12300)**						
	Thorofare Channel						
600	– Buoy 5	38 21.3 75 05.9				Green can.	Private aid.
605	– Buoy 6	38 21.4 75 06.1				Red nun.	Private aid.
610	Old Man Ledge Buoy 3 On north end of Rocky Shoal.					Green can.	
615	Lone Rock Buoy 5					Green can.	
620	*Nomans Land Lighted Whistle Buoy 2*	41 12.2 70 50.0	Fl R 4s		4	Red.	
625	Nomans Land Gong Buoy 4					Red.	
630 14230	**Gay Head Light**	41 20.9 70 50.1	Al (3) W R 40s 2s Wfl 8s ec. 2s Wfl 8s ec. 2s Wfl 8s ec. 2s Rfl 8s ec.	170	W 21 R 17	Red brick tower. 51	Obscured from 342° to 359° by Nomans Land; light occasionally visible through notches in hilltop. Emergency light of reduced intensity when main light is extinguished. Al (3) WR 30s .09s Wfl 4.91s ec .09s Wfl 4.91s ec .09s Wfl 9.91s ec .09s Rfl 9.91s ec Nominal range 13W, 11R.
640 14245	Vineyard Sound Whistle Buoy VS	41 17.6 71 00.1				Red and white stripes; red spherical topmark.	

SEACOAST (Rhode Island) – First District

(1) No.	(2) Name and location	(3) Position	(4) Characteristic	(5) Height	(6) Range	(7) Structure	(8) Remarks
	APPROACHES TO NEW YORK - NANTUCKET SHOALS TO FIVE FATHOM BANK (CHART 12300)						
645 14630	*Narragansett-Buzzards Bay Approach Lighted Horn Buoy A*	41 06.0 71 23.4	Mo (A) W		6	Red and white stripes with red spherical topmark.	HORN: 1 bl ev 10s (1s bl). RACON: N (—•).

SEACOAST (Massachusetts) – First District

(1) No.	(2) Name and location	(3) Position	(4) Characteristic	(5) Height	(6) Range	(7) Structure	(8) Remarks
	APPROACHES TO NEW YORK - NANTUCKET SHOALS TO FIVE FATHOM BANK (Chart 12300)						
650 14635	**Buzzards Bay Entrance Light**	41 23.8 71 02.0	Fl W 2.5s	101	22	Tower on red square superstructure, on four black piles. Worded BUZZARDS on sides.	Emergency light of reduced intensity when main light is extinguished. RBN: 314 kHz BB (—••• —•••). Antenna on top of light tower. HORN: 2 blasts ev 30s (2s bl-2s si-2s bl-24s si).

Fig. 10-3. Excerpt from Main Tables of Light List

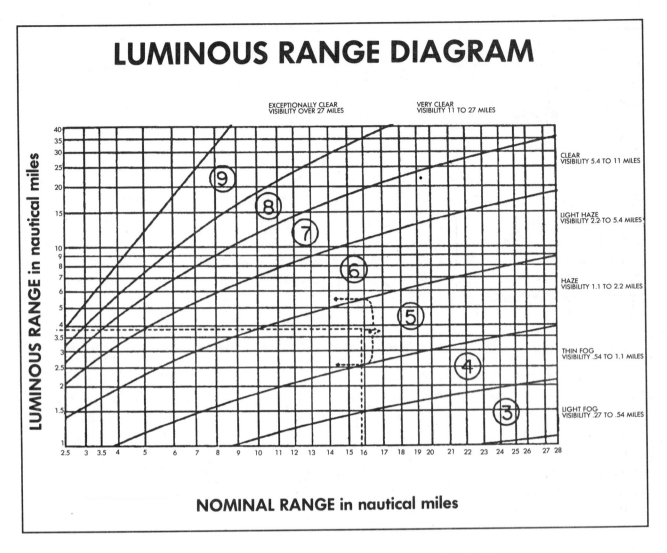

Fig. 10-4. Luminous Range Diagram from Light List.

mates of the height of eye aboard the vessel and the height of the object from the *Light List,* calculate the geographic range, gr. *Finally,* the estimate of the actual range is the *smaller* of the luminous range or the geographic range. In the above example, the luminous range (7 miles) was smaller than the geographic range (15.4 miles), so the luminous range would be the best estimate of the distance at which the Buzzards Bay entrance light could be seen.

As an aside, David Burch writing in the book *Emergency Navigation,* offers the following simple approximation to the luminous range,

$$lr \quad = \quad \frac{v\,(N)+1}{10},$$

where lr = luminous range (nautical miles),
     v = visibility (nautical miles), and
     N = nominal range (nautical miles).

Using this formula, the approximate luminous range in the above example would be 1 + 2.2 (22)/10 or approximately 6 nautical miles, slightly less than found from Figure 10-4.

Other useful information contained in the *Light List* applicable to radio navigation is discussed in Chapter 9.

NOTICE TO MARINERS

Nautical charts and publications are kept up-to-date through use of the Notice to Mariners, prepared jointly by the National Ocean

Service and the US Coast Guard. The notice is published weekly, and is available free of charge from the Defense Mapping Agency Hydrographic/Topographic Center (DMAHTC) through the Office of Distribution Services (IMA), Defense Mapping Agency, Washington, DC 20315.

This pamphlet contains the latest information on navigational safety, changes in aids to navigation, channels, and chart information over a broad area useful to the ocean going and coastal vessel alike. The *Coast Pilots* are kept current through the navigator's incorporating into them the information supplied by the weekly Notice to Mariners.

ANMS

ANMS is an acronym that stands for *Automated Notices to Mariners System.* Anyone having a personal computer with a modem can dial up this system (contact DMA for details and the latest access numbers) and, after entering a user identification number (available on request from DMA), access the system. The system is very easy to use ("user friendly" in the jargon) and can print out chart corrections, *Light List* revisions, Broadcast Warnings, and other important corrections. (By the time you read this, the *US Coast Pilot* and a related publication, *Sailing Directions,* will also be available through ANMS.)

One very nice feature of ANMS is that it can provide *all* of the corrections to each chart *from the date of issue.* This eliminates the possibility of missing an important correction because you neglected to enter a given mailing. Additionally, changes/corrections are *first* input to ANMS before the *Notices to Mariners* are printed, so with ANMS you can get information sooner.

LOCAL NOTICE TO MARINERS

The Commander of the local US Coast Guard district issues the Local Notice to Mariners--also on a weekly basis. There is no charge for this publication, which may be obtained upon request to the local Coast Guard District Com-

mander. The Local Notice to Mariners contains the very latest navigational safety information pertinent to all craft within the area of the district. Notices of marine regattas and other important marine events are also announced through the Local Notice to Mariners.

KEY TO ABBREVIATIONS USED IN LNM

One of the most important purposes of the Local Notice to Mariners (LNM) is the dissemination of information on changes to aids to navigation. In this process, some districts use the abbreviations listed below to convey this information:

BY	-Buoy
CH	-Channel
DBD	-Dayboard
DBN	-Daybeacon
DISC	-Discontinued
EMER CHAR	-Emergency Characteristics
FOG SIG INOP	-Sound Signal Inoperative
IMP CHAR	-Aid not displaying characteristics as advertised in *Light List* or Chart.
LB	-Lighted Buoy
LBB	-Lighted Bell Buoy
LGB	-Lighted Gong Buoy
LHB	-Lighted Horn Buoy
LNB	-Large Navigational Buoy
LWB	-Lighted Whistle Buoy
LLNR/LLP	-Light List Number/Light List Page
NM	-Nautical Miles
OP CONSTSLY	-Signal is on throughout 24 hours
RBN	-Radiobeacon
RED INT	-Aid operating at a lesser range/intensity than stated in *Light List* .
REMOVED	-Old structure located and removed
REMAINS	-Structure remains in area, possibly still standing, and the search for the structure was unsuccessful or search is yet to be made.
TEMP	-Temporarily Discontinued
TRLB	-Temporarily replaced by a lighted buoy
TRSB	-Temporarily replaced by a smaller buoy
TRUB	-Temporarily replaced by an unlighted buoy
UNKNOWN	-Failed to locate structure during a search of the area
W/P	-Watching properly

BROADCAST WARNINGS

Finally, the Coast Guard transmits *broadcast warnings* (monitor channel 16) that provide information too urgent to be left to a weekly publication.

ADVICE YOU SHOULD HEED

Although most commercial vessels regularly receive Notices to Mariners (and LNMs), the number of subscriptions to these publications is very much smaller than the number of registered vessels. This proves the sad truth that many mariners are either unaware of these publications or believe that the information isn't worth the effort of reading and updating charts and other publications.

Failure to pay attention to these important changes is akin to playing the marine equivalent of Russian Roulette. You may be lucky, the steel post on which the daymark was secured that was knocked down by a tow (and duly reported by the Coast Guard in a *Broadcast Warning*) may not penetrate your hull. And the entrance buoy that you depend on for navigation may not have been blown off station by last week's storm. (In fact, the Brenton Reef Light on which you have taken bearings throughout the course will probably be history by the time you read this.) But to assume that everything is as represented in any of these charts or publications, particularly when operating in unfamiliar waters, is to take an uncalculated risk.

For example, the cumulative total changes to nautical chart 13218, May 1987, (the "real-life" counterpart of the 1210-Tr chart) as of this writing amounts to four single spaced large pages of computer output as obtained from the ANMS system. These updates include changes to buoys (existence, color, location), lights (characteristics, and nominal ranges), descriptions of new safety zones, and the addition of eight wrecks or obstructions (several described as dangerous). An excerpt from this computer run is reproduced in Figure 10-5. Wouldn't you like to have this information?

NON-U. S. GOVERNMENT SOURCES

In addition to the publications discussed above, a number of commercial firms publish cruising guides and related materials that are useful to take along. The commercial guides often emphasize services available at various marinas and provide interesting historical information about the areas covered. Many cruising areas are interesting from the perspective of the tourist, and it is handy to have a guide that includes this information. For example, Penikese Island (located in Buzzards Bay and referred to elsewhere in this text) was at one time a leper colony, gunnery and bombing range for military aircraft, and a type of reform school for troubled youths. Although this information is not essential for navigation, it does provide interesting reading.

Some of these guides also contain information on tidal and other currents, tide tables, a Nautical Almanac, or other material available from the government.

Additionally, there are a number of cruising guides available from other governments, such as Canada or Great Britain, that are useful. The english publication, *Ocean Passages For the World*, is viewed as a compact classic. A trip to your nearest source of nautical publications is definitely in order.

```
                    AUTOMATED NOTICE TO MARINER            2/18/90
                   CHART CORRECTION QUERY SYSTEM
                 EXTRACT ALL CORRECTIONS TO SELECTED CHARTS
                      THRU CURRENT NTM  9/90
```

```
S   13218 29Ed. 5/09/87 NEW EDITION                              40/87
                                    (NOS; 19/87 CG1; FED REG 7/31/87)
            Change      Color of buoy to green and
                        red bands (topmost band green)
                            41deg 24min 41sec N  70deg 45min 52sec W

            Add         "RESTRICTED AREA 334.78
                        (see note A)" bound by
                        purple composite line joining
                            41deg 20min 29sec N  71deg 19min 52sec W
                            41deg 20min 29sec N  71deg 18min 32sec W
                            41deg 18min 57sec N  71deg 18min 32sec W
                            41deg 18min 57sec N  71deg 19min 52sec W


    13218 29Ed. 5/09/87 LAST NM 40/87      (21/87 CG1; USCG LL)  43/87
            Change      Color of buoys, each to green
                            "3"
                            41deg 29min 30sec N  71deg 13min 55sec W
                            "7"
                            41deg 34min 39sec N  71deg 13min 23sec W
                            "7"
                            41deg 28min 18sec N  71deg 22min 20sec W


    13218 29Ed. 5/09/87 LAST NM 43/87            (23/87 CG1)     44/87
            Change      Color of buoy "WH" to
                        red and white stripes
                            41deg 29min 23sec N  71deg 04min 12sec W
                        and add ball topmark

S   13218 29Ed. 5/09/87 LAST NM 44/87        (25, 26/87 CG1)     48/87
            Change      Color or buoys, each to green
                            "3"
                            41deg 09min 20sec N  71deg 32min 29sec W
                            "9"
                            41deg 33min 06sec N  70deg 54min 30sec W


    13218 29Ed. 5/09/87 LAST NM 48/87        (32, 36/87 CG1)     49/87
            Delete      Buoys "A"
                            41deg 26min 00sec N  71deg 16min 54sec W
                            "CC"
                            41deg 27min 42sec N  71deg 18min 36sec W
                            "SR"
                            41deg 26min 26sec N  71deg 13min 30sec W

            Add         Buoy "SR", red and white stripes,
                        ball topmark, Mo(A), WHISTLE
                            41deg 25min 45sec N  71deg 13min 23sec W

    13218 29Ed. 5/09/87 LAST NM 49/87            (36/87 CG1)     52/87
            Delete      Buoy "CC"
                            41deg 25min 42sec N  71deg 18min 36sec W
                        (See 49/87-13218)
```

Fig. 10-5. Excerpt of ANMS Output.

REFERENCES

The principal references are to the relevant *Light List* and *U. S. Coast Pilot.* Additional references include:

Borton, M. C. *ET AL, The Complete Boating Guide to Rhode Island & Massachusetts*, Embassy Marine Publishing, Essex, CT., 1989

Burch, D. *Emergency Navigation,* International Marine Publishing Co., Camden, ME, 1986, p205.

Holland, F. R. *America's Lighthouses, An Illustrated History*, Dover Publications Inc., New York, NY, 1988.

Chapter 11

Fuel and Voyage Planning

Few things are as frustrating as hearing the familiar rhythmic hum of the vessel's engine(s) interrupted by a "deafening" silence and realizing that the vessel has run out of fuel. Add some other elements to the scenario, such as deteriorating weather and an adverse current setting the vessel towards shoal waters or a busy shipping channel, and inconvenience quickly turns to potential disaster. Perhaps most disturbing is the fact that, in most cases of fuel exhaustion, it is operator error rather than mechanical malfunction that is the assignable cause. Neglecting to verify the amount of fuel in the tanks before setting out for a "demonstration ride around the harbor," a decision not to buy fuel at the last marina visited because of high prices or lack of the proper credit card, a failure to allow for foul currents or poor weather, neglecting to top the tanks in order to avoid a long waiting line at the fuel dock, etc., all sound like feeble excuses while drifting under a hot sun and waiting for an expensive tow.

Accurate statistics on the frequency of running out of fuel for pleasure craft are not available--in part because out-of-fuel vessels are often towed in by friends or good samaritans and not reported to the Coast Guard. But, in the opinion of most experts, incidents of fuel exhaustion are surprisingly common. Aircraft also run out of fuel, despite explicit regulations on the amount of fuel to be carried. According to available statistics, in an average year more than 200 aircraft are destroyed and 30 people are lost in fuel exhaustion accidents. In 1977, one of the worst years for this type of accident, one of the worst years for this type of accident,

55 persons were killed, and 60 seriously injured. These accidents are not limited to recreational pilots. Commercial aircraft and airliners also are involved in fuel exhaustion accidents, albeit less frequently. On 25 January, 1990, Avianca Flight 52 inbound to New York from Bogota, Colombia, crashed, killing 72 persons. Although the National Transportation Safety Board (NTSB) had not completed its investigation by the time this text was written, preliminary evidence points to fuel exhaustion as the probable cause of this accident. Earlier in 1978, a United Airlines DC-8 crashed near Portland, Oregon, after running out of fuel, killing 10 of 189 persons on board.

One of the reasons for discussing aircraft-related fuel incidents in a text on marine navigation is that aircraft manufacturers and pilots have developed systematic approaches to fuel planning and management that are equally useful to the mariner. Several of these techniques are discussed in this chapter, and illustrated with actual fuel consumption data for vessels.

The material in this chapter presents a systematic view of fuel planning and management for vessel operators. Development of fuel consumption curves and related material is complemented by practical tips on this important subject.

BEGINNINGS:
A FUEL CONSUMPTION CHART

Careful fuel planning and management should be an integral part of navigation. A basic

TABLE 11-1 ILLUSTRATIVE SPEED CURVE FOR VESSEL AVENTURA		
THROTTLE SETTING (RPM)	SPEED THRU THE WATER STW (KNOTS)	VESSEL: AVENTURA TEST CONDITIONS
1000	1.0	DATA ARE FOR VESSEL AT "CRUISE
1250	2.0	WEIGHT," FULL FUEL AND WATER TANKS.
1500	3.5	THE HULL CONDITION IS CLEAN AND
1750	5.0	JUST REPAINTED. OTHER LOADING DATA
2000	7.0	ARE AS FOLLOWS: 4 ADULTS, 150 LBS.
2250	8.0	BAGGAGE. WIND AT TIME OF TEST WAS
2500	9.0	LESS THAN 15 KNOTS, AND SEAS LESS
2750	9.5	THAN 2 FEET.
3000	10.0	

TABLE 11-2

RELATIONSHIP BETWEEN RPM AND FUEL CONSUMPTION

THROTTLE SETTING (RPM)	FUEL CONSUMPTION RATE (GPH)
1000	0.33
1250	0.80
1500	1.80
1750	3.30
2000	5.00
2250	6.70
2500	9.00
2750	11.90
3000	16.00

First, the fuel consumption chart includes the relationship between the engine throttle setting in revolutions per minute (RPM) and the vessel's speed through the water (STW) in knots, the familiar *speed curve* for the vessel discussed in Chapter 5. An illustrative speed curve for a semi-displacement hull vessel, *Aventura*, is shown in Table 11-1. (The source of these data is given in the references at the end of this chapter.)

Second, the fuel consumption chart includes data on the relationship between engine RPM and fuel consumption rate, measured in gallons per hour (GPH). Table 11-2 shows these data for the same vessel.

input to the fuel planning process is the vessel's *fuel consumption chart or curve*. This curve ties together the vessel's speed curve with engine fuel consumption information.

Data from these two sources are combined into a *fuel planning worksheet*, shown in Table 11-3. (Sources and methods for obtaining these data are discussed later in this chapter.) The fuel-planning worksheet presents basic data on the throttle setting (RPM), speed through the water (STW), and the fuel consumption rate (GPH). In Table 11-3 no current (either fair or foul) is assumed; so the speed of advance (SOA) is numerically equal to the STW at any throttle setting. The other columns are discussed below.

To facilitate following the calculations in this chapter, several significant figures are retained for each entry in the tables. However, the reader should bear in mind that fuel consump-

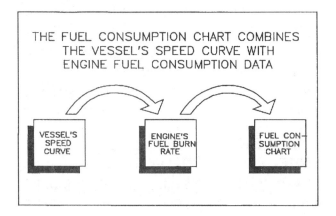

THE FUEL CONSUMPTION CHART COMBINES THE VESSEL'S SPEED CURVE WITH ENGINE FUEL CONSUMPTION DATA

VESSEL'S SPEED CURVE → ENGINE'S FUEL BURN RATE → FUEL CONSUMPTION CHART

TABLE 11-3

ILLUSTRATIVE FUEL PLANNING WORKSHEET

VESSEL: AVENTURA   FUEL CAPACITY: 200 GALLONS

FOUL CURRENT: 0 KNOTS

THROTTLE SETTING (RPM)	SPEED THRU THE WATER STW (KNOTS)	SPEED OF ADVANCE SOA (KNOTS)	FUEL CONSUMPTION RATE (GPH)	FUEL EFFICIENCY (MPG)	ESTIMATED RANGE IN NAUTICAL MILES WITH FUEL RESERVE		ESTIMATED ENDURANCE IN HOURS WITH FUEL RESERVE	
					10%	20%	10%	20%
1000	1.0	1.00	0.33	3.03	545	485	545	485
1250	2.0	2.00	0.80	2.50	450	400	225	200
1500	3.5	3.50	1.80	1.94	350	311	100	89
1750	5.0	5.00	3.30	1.52	273	242	55	48
2000	7.0	7.00	5.00	1.40	252	224	36	32
2250	8.0	8.00	6.70	1.19	215	191	27	24
2500	9.0	9.00	9.00	1.00	180	160	20	18
2750	9.5	9.50	11.90	0.80	144	128	15	13
3000	10.0	10.00	16.00	0.63	113	100	11	10

tion data are seldom exact-error margins of ±10% or even larger should be attached to these figures. This injunction is particularly applicable to manufacturer's test data--not because of any deliberate attempt to inflate performance statistics, but rather because these data are often developed under "ideal" test conditions. Therefore, it is appropriate to round off actual fuel-planning calculations to within this margin.

--Fuel Efficiency, Range, and Endurance

Before discussing the sources of these data it is instructive to see the uses of such information. From these basic data, it is possible to calculate other quantities that are important in fuel planning. One important measure is the *fuel efficiency*, defined as the distance the vessel can travel on each gallon of fuel. It is measured in nautical miles per gallon (MPG) and is calculated as the speed of advance (knots) divided by the fuel consumption rate in GPH. Thus, for example, referring to Table 11-3 at 2000 RPM the SOA is 7 knots and the fuel consumption is 5 GPH. Therefore, the fuel efficiency is 7/5 or

1.4 MPG. Fuel efficiency figures at this and other throttle settings are given in the fifth column of Table 11-3.

Another important fuel planning factor is the *range* of the vessel. The *range* is the distance in nautical miles that a vessel can travel with the fuel available. The range depends upon the throttle setting. In Table 11-3, the fuel capacity of the vessel is given as 200 gallons, and this capacity could be used for range estimates. More typically, a contingency factor of 10%, 20%, or more is assumed to allow for unusable and "reserve" fuel as discussed below. Thus, if a 10% fuel reserve is assumed, the fuel capacity is reduced by this amount [0.1 (200) or 20 gallons in this example] leaving 180 gallons "voyage" or "enroute" fuel. The estimated range is calculated by multiplying the enroute fuel (gallons) by the fuel efficiency (MPG). To continue the above example, the range of this vessel at a throttle setting of 2000 RPM is the enroute fuel (180 gallons) times the fuel efficiency (1.4 MPG) or 252 nautical miles, assuming a 10% fuel reserve.

Finally, the vessel's fuel *endurance* is the length of time in hours that the vessel can be operated at a given throttle setting until the enroute fuel is exhausted. The endurance is given by the enroute fuel (total fuel less reserve) divided by the fuel consumption rate. The endurance of this vessel at a throttle setting of 2,000 RPM is the enroute fuel (180 gallons) divided by the fuel consumption rate (5 GPH) or 36 hours. Table 11-3 displays these calculations for both a 10% and 20% fuel reserve at various power settings. The reader should repeat the calculations shown in Table 11-3 to ensure familiarity with the various terms and how these can be calculated.

WHY FUEL RESERVES?

In the above numerical examples, the term *fuel reserve* was used. The fuel reserve is just that--a reserve or set-aside to allow for contingencies or unforseen circumstances that could arise in a voyage. Illustrative contingencies could include greater fuel-burn rates than reckoned

in the fuel consumption curve, the necessity to divert to an alternate destination due to weather, an unanticipated requirement to tow another vessel, adverse currents, and the need to stand off an inlet until bar conditions improve. There are no hard-and-fast rules for setting fuel reserves. For a voyage in familiar waters where currents are generally predictable, enroute fueling opportunities are abundant, seas are calm and the weather outlook is good, a reserve of only 10% might be sufficiently prudent. In less ideal conditions, a larger reserve would be warranted. Reserve margins of 20%, 30%, or even 50% might be justified in more adverse circumstances.

Many mariners were taught a simple rule for fuel planning, use one-third of the fuel on the outbound voyage, one-third for the return, and keep one-third in reserve. Aircraft pilots operating under Part 91 of the Federal Aviation Regulations (FARs) under instrument flight rules (IFR) are required under FAR 91.23 to

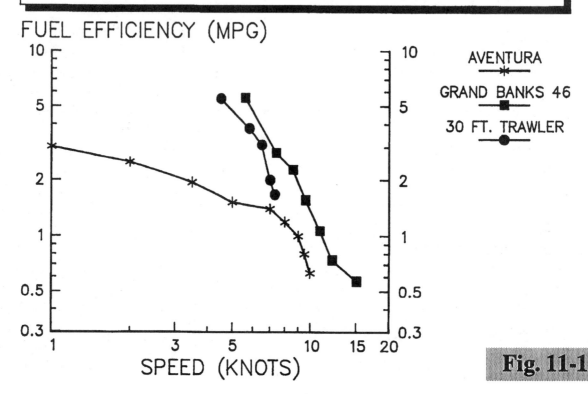

Fig. 11-1

carry sufficient fuel (considering weather reports and forecasts, and actual weather conditions) to complete the flight to the airport of intended landing, fly from that airport to an alternate airport, and fly after that for 45 minutes at normal cruising speed. These rules or guidelines are offered for perspective only, the navigator is responsible for selecting the most appropriate fuel reserve, considering the circumstances of the voyage.

FUEL EFFICIENCY VERSUS SPEED

These simple calculations displayed in Table 11-3 provide useful information for fuel planning decisions. In particular, these calculations show that--for this vessel--*increases* in the throttle setting (and hence speed) are associated with *decreases* in fuel efficiency and range. In this example, depending upon the throttle setting and, therefore, how fast the vessel is operated, the range (assuming a 10% reserve) can vary by more than a factor of five from only 113 nautical miles at a speed of 10 knots to 545 nautical miles at a speed of 1 knot. For the example given in Table 11-3, a throttle setting of 1,000 RPM maximizes both range and endurance. That is, there is no other throttle setting for which the range or endurance is higher.

In general, however, throttle settings for maximum range and maximum endurance are different. The relationship between fuel efficiency and throttle setting shown in Table 11-3 is broadly characteristic of displacement or semi-displacement hull vessels. Figure 11-1 shows fuel efficiency versus speed curves for a small but representative sample of displacement hull or semi-displacement hull vessels including trawlers or trawler-yachts. (The data for the Grand Banks 46 are taken from an article in *Boating* magazine.) Recall that a vessel with a displacement hull achieves its buoyancy by displacing a volume of water equal to the vessel weight (as loaded). The maximum speed, or hull speed, for a displacement vessel in knots is approximately equal to 1.35 times (the theoretical number is 1.34) the square root of the water line length in feet. For example, the hull speed of a vessel with a 25 ft. length at the water line would be approximately 1.35 (5) or 6.8 knots. Examples of displacement hull vessels include sailboats, motor sailers, many trawlers, and most merchant vessels. The constant, 1.35, is only approximate and depends upon the hull design. Values between 1.25 and 1.5 are reported for displacement hull vessels. As can be seen, in each case, extra speed is attained only at the expense of decreased fuel efficiency (and range) for these vessels.

It should be stressed that the hull speed serves as a physical limit in the case of a true displacement-hull vessel. Installation of a more powerful engine, or adding a second engine to vessels with this hull design will not result in speeds appreciably greater than the hull speed. The additional power simply creates a larger bow wave, causes the stern to sink deeper in it's wake, and sharply increases fuel consumption. In general, the normal cruising speed for a displacement-hull vessel is slightly lower (say, 10% or so) than the theoretical hull speed.

Adding a second engine to a displacement-hull vessel confers many benefits (chiefly increased reliability and maneuverability), but speed and fuel efficiency are not among these. In fact, the twin-engine version of a displacement-hull vessel will burn almost twice the fuel of the single-engine version and be only slightly faster. Range, therefore, will be decreased compared to the single-screw version.

For vessels with hulls that can get on plane, it is often found that fuel efficiency first decreases as speeds are increased within the displacement range and then *increases* at speeds above "hull speed" when the vessel comes "unstuck" and water drag is reduced. In these cases there is more than one speed with increased range. Figure 11-2 shows fuel efficiency curves for a sample of vessels with planing hulls as taken from various issues of *Boating* magazine given in the references. In each case, there is a secondary power setting for increased fuel economy that is above hull speed. But substantial boat-to-boat differences are evident--even in this small sample--so that it is difficult to provide useful rules-of-thumb. Nonetheless, it is common for fuel efficiency to increase above planing speeds. As speed is increased still further, drag forces again increase and fuel efficiency falls off.

The top speed of a planing vessel is determined by the hull design, propulsion, and planing angle. Installation of larger engines in a planing vessel will increase the top speed (for a fixed hull design), but not in direct proportion to the increase in horsepower. Several theoretical and empirical equations have been proposed for the speed horsepower relationship (see the references at the end of the chapter). Although these differ somewhat, most indicate that the top speed varies with horsepower raised to an exponent between approximately 0.33 to 0.55--that is, if the engine horsepower were to double, the top speed would increase by only 25% to 50%. The attainment of significantly faster speeds for planing hulls depends upon hull design and powerplant selection jointly. None the less, unlike the situation with displacement-hull vessels, adding power to a planing-hull vessel can increase the top speed.

At the other end of the speed range, planing hull vessels can be operated at displacement speeds. Operation at these lower speeds often (but not always, see Figure 11-2) results in increased fuel efficiency. Advocates of planing hull cruisers for long distance voyages are quick to point this out. However, for vessels of comparable length and overall size, a vessel with a planing hull will generally be less fuel efficient than a "similar" one with a displacement hull,

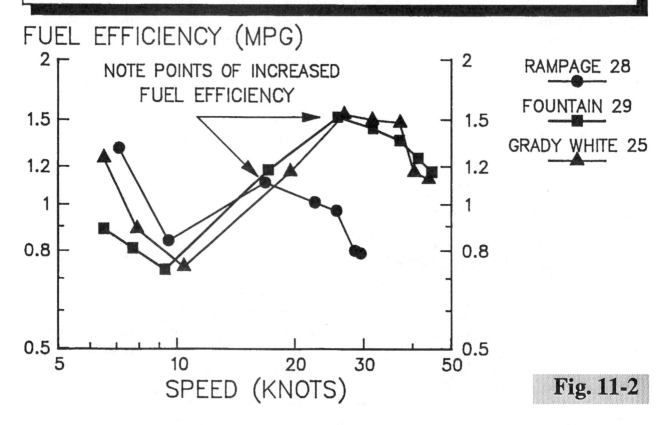

VESSELS WITH PLANING HULLS MAY INCREASE FUEL EFFICIENCY WHEN "ON PLANE." BOAT-SPECIFIC DIFFERENCES ARE IMPORTANT

FUEL EFFICIENCY (MPG)

NOTE POINTS OF INCREASED FUEL EFFICIENCY

SPEED (KNOTS)

RAMPAGE 28
FOUNTAIN 29
GRADY WHITE 25

Fig. 11-2

The difference in fuel efficiency between the two vessels, which could range from 20% to 40%, is the "penalty" paid for the flexibility of being able to get on plane and attain higher speeds. There is little doubt that the full displacement vessel is optimal for long distance cruising.

Incidentally skippers who habitually run turbocharged engine equipped vessels at displacement speeds should check with the vessel or engine manufacturer to determine the proper procedures to ensure long engine life at these speeds. One source recommends that turbocharged engines be run up to 1800 RPM periodically during a voyage to avoid engine damage.

References given at the end of this chapter provide a theoretical discussion of fuel consumption for displacement and planing hull vessels.

SOURCES OF FUEL CONSUMPTION INFORMATION

There are numerous sources of fuel-consumption information of the kind displayed in Table 11-3. Vessel owner's manuals often provide these data. Additionally, several periodicals, such as *Boating* magazine, offer compilations of test data for newer vessels. Finally, these data can be measured directly.

Measurement of fuel consumption can be accomplished in a variety of ways. Commercial fuel flow meters, sometimes integrated into microprocessor-based "fuel management systems" are useful, but are an expensive means for measurement. A simpler, although less accurate method is to fill the tank, run the vessel at a constant RPM for say, half an hour, and then measure the amount of fuel it takes to refill the tank to its original level. This process can be repeated at other throttle settings to produce data such as are shown in Table 11-2.

Even if data are available from manufacturer's literature or periodicals, it makes sense to check (audit) some of the data points to ensure that these are appropriate for the vessel. The accuracy of this "audit" is one of the factors that should be used in determining a safe reserve. If, for example, the fuel consumption for a vessel was 10% higher than published data indicate, the curve should be adjusted by this amount and/or an adequate reserve included.

Unless the vessel is equipped with a fuel flow meter, it is tedious and time consuming to check fuel consumption data for *each* possible throttle setting. A practical compromise would be to check only key points in the chart, such as the maximum range RPM, the normal cruise RPM, and the maximum RPM.

TABLE 11-4

FACTORS THAT AFFECT FUEL EFFICIENCY

---VESSEL HULL DESIGN
---CONDITION OF HULL
---ENGINE TYPE, HORSEPOWER, AND CONDITION
---ENGINE THROTTLE SETTING (RPM)
---WEIGHT (LOAD) AND WEIGHT DISTRIBUTION (BALANCE)
---TRIM SETTINGS
---FAIR OR FOUL CURRENTS
---WIND AND SEA CONDITIONS
---ABILITY OF HELMSMAN TO MAINTAIN COURSE

TABLE 11-5

TIME-THROTTLE SETTING TRADEOFFS ILLUSTRATED

VESSEL:	AVENTURA
FUEL:	200 GALLONS ON BOARD
DISTANCE:	120 NAUTICAL MILES
CURRENT:	0 FOUL CURRENTS ARE NEGATIVE

THROTTLE SETTING (RPM)	STW (KNOTS)	SOA (KNOTS)	FUEL CONSUMPTION RATE (GPH)	REQUIRED TRIP DURATION (HOURS)	TRIP FUEL REQUIRED (GALLONS)	FUEL REMAINING AT DESTINATION (GALLONS)	TIME TO FUEL EXHAUSTION AT DESTINATION (HOURS)	RESERVE RANGE AT DESTINATION (HOURS)
1000	1.0	1.00	0.33	120.0	40	160	486.1	486
1250	2.0	2.00	0.80	60.0	48	152	190.0	380
1500	3.5	3.50	1.80	34.3	62	138	76.8	269
1750	5.0	5.00	3.30	24.0	79	121	36.6	183
2000	7.0	7.00	5.00	17.1	86	114	22.9	160
2250	8.0	8.00	6.70	15.0	101	100	14.9	119
2500	9.0	9.00	9.00	13.3	120	80	8.9	80
2750	9.5	9.50	11.90	12.6	150	50	4.2	40
3000	10.0	10.00	16.00	12.0	192	8	0.5	5

NOTE: EFFECTS OF CURRENT NOT CONSIDERED IN THIS RUN

FACTORS THAT AFFECT FUEL EFFICIENCY

It is clear that hull design, powerplants, and throttle setting are important determinants of fuel efficiency and range. Table 11-4 shows several other factors that are also important. Some of these are discussed below.

Many of these factors are self-evident, such as vessel hull design, condition of hull, throttle setting (RPM), engine tuning, and engine horsepower.

The condition of the hull can affect the relationship between RPM and speed (and hence fuel efficiency) quite significantly. A rough and time honored rule-of-thumb recommended in older texts was to reduce the speed corresponding to any RPM by approximately 1% for each month since the vessel was out of dry dock. Rather than use this approximation, it is preferable to periodically recalibrate the speed curve and update the fuel consumption table.

The weight of the vessel (and how this weight is distributed) can also affect the speed curve. Devotees of so-called predicted log races (where even seconds matter) make corrections to the speed curve to account for the change in the vessel's weight as fuel is burned. Adjustments to the speed curve to reflect fuel burn are generally not significant for most fuel planning purposes, however.

The installation and positioning of trim tabs also affects the vessel's speed curve and fuel economy. Ensure that the trim tabs (if installed) are set to the correct position when the speed curve is determined.

Some of the factors listed in Table 11-4 are more subtle, such as vessel trim and the ability of the person at the helm to maintain course. Environmental conditions such as wind and sea conditions or currents are also important. The effect of currents is discussed below. Winds affect powerboats as well as sailing craft--in part by direct action (e.g., increased drag or leeway) and also because winds can induce fair or foul currents. Finally, sea conditions are important. It is found for large and small craft alike that SOAs decrease as wave heights increase--even if the same throttle setting is maintained. Additionally, it is often necessary to reduce engine RPM's or alter course when wave heights increase in order to ensure a more comfortable "ride." Some of these effects--such as RPM, hull design, and engine variables--are considered explicitly in the fuel-consumption chart. But other factors, such as trim, sea state, and prevailing winds are not. For this as well as other reasons noted above, a prudent planner makes allowance for these contingencies and maintains an adequate fuel reserve.

ENROUTE TIME-THROTTLE SETTING TRADEOFFS

Returning to the example given in Table 11-3, this section shows how these data can be used in a practical manner for improved fuel management and voyage planning. The fact that, with displacement hull vessels, high cruising ranges can only be achieved at low speeds does not mean that low speeds are always desirable. Not all voyages are long enough to require great range, and sometimes fuel stops can be found even on long voyages. The fuel consumption chart provides essential information for speed-range "tradeoff analysis."

One way to make use of the information given in the fuel consumption chart is to reformat it as shown in Table 11-5. In this example, a trip of 120 M.'s length is being planned. For purposes of this illustration, the possibility of intermediate fuel stops is not considered. Table 11-5 repeats the data in Table 11-3 to show the time required to reach the destination and the estimated fuel, time, and cruising distance remaining when the destination is reached. This fuel remaining must include fuel for entry into the harbor, additional maneuvering, and a contingency for foul currents, adverse weather or sea conditions, waiting outside an inlet for favorable passage conditions, diversions enroute, etc. Note first that at a throttle setting of 1000 RPM the fuel remaining at the destination is maximized--only approximately 40 gallons enroute fuel is consumed. To see this, note that the SOA (assuming no current) is 1 knot, so it would take 120 hours (120 M/1 MPH) for the trip as shown in column 5 of Table 11-5. The fuel required for this trip equals the trip time (120 hours) multiplied by the fuel consumption rate (0.33 GPH) or approximately 40 gallons as shown in column 6 of Table 11-5. Assuming full tanks (200 gallons) at the start of the trip, this would leave (200-40) 160 gallons remaining in the tanks, as shown in column 7 of Table 11-5. This remaining fuel (160 gallons) would allow the vessel to cruise at 1000 RPM for 160/0.33 or approximately 486 hours, and to travel an additional (486 hrs) (1 MPH) = 486 miles as shown in columns 8 and 9 of Table 11-5.

But the speed (1 knot)[1] at this throttle setting is so slow that 120 hours would be required for the trip! Alternatively at a throttle setting of 3000 RPM corresponding to a STW of 10 knots, the 120 M. trip will take only 12 hours, but fuel consumption is so high (192 gallons) that the tanks will be virtually dry upon arrival, leaving no margin for error. Compared to this plan, a compromise throttle setting of, say 2250 RPM, would add only 3 hours to the trip but would increase the estimated fuel on board at the destination to nearly 100 gallons--enough to travel nearly 120 additional miles at this throttle setting.

---

[1] Data used in this illustration are taken from the original source. Generally, however, the STW at the lowest feasible throttle setting (the so-called "clutch speed") is greater than 1 knot--often 5 or 6 knots.

The choice between throttle settings of 2250 RPM and 3000 RPM is, in reality, no choice at all. It would be sheer folly to attempt this voyage at 3000 RPM without a fuel stop. And, even if a fuel stop were feasible along the route of this voyage, the additional time required for the fuel diversion, queuing at the fuel dock, fueling, and return to the original track would have to be added to the voyage time at a throttle setting at 3000 RPM for a valid portal-to-portal time comparison. If the delay occasioned by the fuel stop were, for example, 1-1/2 hours, the total time difference would shrink to 1-1/2 hours (13.5 hours compared to 15 hours). As this example clearly shows, there is generally little purpose in running displacement-hull vessels at maximum speed.

The appropriate choice of RPM depends upon many factors (e.g., how much reserve is deemed prudent, time schedules, etc.), but the value of a systematic analysis of time/throttle setting tradeoffs should be clear. All that is required for this analysis is the vessel's basic fuel consumption chart and a few additional computations.

EFFECT OF CURRENT

Currents can be very important to fuel planning, and information on current set and drift should be considered if available. As is noted in Chapters 5 and 7, currents may alter the required course to maintain a desired track, and the fair or foul component of the current can either increase or decrease the estimated SOA relative to the STW.

Currents are important to fuel planning for two principal reasons:

(i) Currents can increase or decrease the range attainable at any throttle setting (RPM). Fair (i.e., following) currents increase the range, foul (head) currents decrease the range.

(ii) Currents can alter the "optimal" throttle setting for maximum range. Foul currents increase the optimal power setting.

These points are illustrated in Table 11-6, which builds upon the data given in Table 11-3 except that a 2-knot foul current is assumed.

TABLE 11-6

ILLUSTRATIVE FUEL PLANNING WORKSHEET

VESSEL: AVENTURA
FUEL CAPACITY: 200 GALLONS
FOUL CURRENT: 2.00 KNOTS

THROTTLE SETTING (RPM)	SPEED THRU THE WATER STW (KNOTS)	SPEED OF ADVANCE SOA (KNOTS)	FUEL CONSUMPTION RATE (GPH)	FUEL EFFICIENCY (MPG)	ESTIMATED RANGE IN NAUTICAL MILES WITH FUEL RESERVE		ESTIMATED ENDURANCE IN HOURS WITH FUEL RESERVE	
					10%	20%	10%	20%
1000	1.0	-1.00	0.33	UNDEFINED	INFEASIBLE	INFEASIBLE	545	485
1250	2.0	0.00	0.80	0.00	INFEASIBLE	INFEASIBLE	225	200
1500	3.5	1.50	1.80	0.83	150	133	100	89
1750	5.0	3.00	3.30	0.91	164	145	55	48
2000	7.0	5.00	5.00	1.00	180	160	36	32
2250	8.0	6.00	6.70	0.90	161	143	27	24
2500	9.0	7.00	9.00	0.78	140	124	20	18
2750	9.5	7.50	11.90	0.63	113	101	15	13
3000	10.0	8.00	16.00	0.50	90	80	11	10

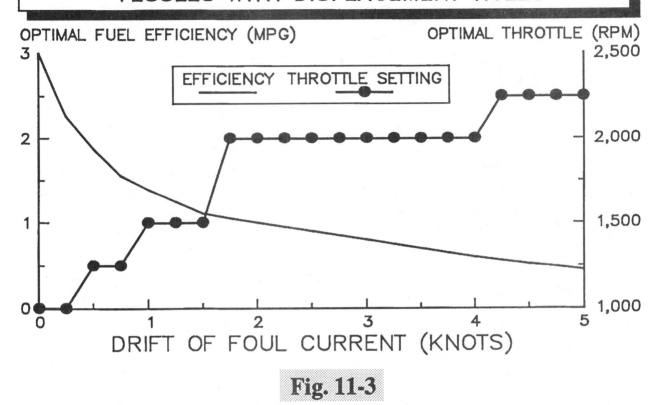

HOW OPTIMAL THROTTLE SETTING AND RESULTING FUEL EFFICIENCY VARY WITH FOUL CURRENTS FOR VESSELS WITH DISPLACEMENT HULLS

Fig. 11-3

The SOA is 2 knots less than the STW in this instance, but the calculations are otherwise identical to those in Table 11-3.

For example, consider a throttle setting of 1750 RPM. The STW at this RPM is 5 knots, but because a 2-knot foul current is assumed, the SOA is only 3 knots. Fuel consumption at this RPM is 3.3 GPH; so the fuel efficiency at this throttle setting is 3/3.3 or 0.91 MPG (shown in Table 11-6) rather than the 5/3.3 (1.52 MPG) shown in Table 11-3. The range with 10% fuel reserve is 180 times 0.91 or 164 miles, rather than 273 miles, a nearly 40% reduction. Obviously, a 2-knot foul current rules out operation at throttle settings less than 1500 RPM (2-knot STW) if a positive SOA is desired. But, in this instance, unlike that for the zero current calculations, the maximum range does not occur at the lowest feasible RPM nor are the throttle

settings identical for maximum range and maximum endurance. As shown in Table 11-6, the throttle setting that maximizes the range is 2000 RPM. In general, it can be shown that fuel consumption curves typical of displacement vessels, foul currents increase the RPM for maximum range. Table 11-7 and Figure 11-3 show how the optimal throttle setting and resulting fuel efficiency vary with the strength (drift) of the foul current.

Table 11-7 shows the results of varying the current from 5 knots fair to 5 knots foul. For each case the optimal RPM is determined as well as the resulting fuel efficiency and range. Although these calculations are tedious, they are not complex and are readily programmed into scientific calculators or micro computers. Once completed, the results of these calculations are easy to interpret and use.

TABLE 11-7.

**OPTIMAL POWER SETTINGS AND ASSOCIATED INFORMATION
AS A FUNCTION OF THE DRIFT OF THE ASSUMED CURRENT.**

CURRENT DESCRIPTION	DRIFT (KNOTS)	OPTIMAL THROTTLE SETTING (RPM)	OPTIMAL STW (KNOTS)	OPTIMAL SOA (KNOTS)	OPTIMAL FUEL EFFICIENCY (MPG)	OPTIMAL RANGE WITH 10% RESERVE (MILES)
FAIR	5.00	1000	1.0	6.00	18.18	3273
FAIR	4.00	1000	1.0	5.00	15.15	2727
FAIR	3.00	1000	1.0	4.00	12.12	2182
FAIR	2.00	1000	1.0	3.00	9.09	1636
FAIR	1.00	1000	1.0	2.00	6.06	1091
NONE	0.00	1000	1.0	1.00	3.03	545
FOUL	-0.25	1000	1.0	0.75	2.27	409
FOUL	-0.50	1250	2.0	1.50	1.88	338
FOUL	-0.75	1250	2.0	1.25	1.56	281
FOUL	-1.00	1500	3.5	2.50	1.39	250
FOUL	-1.25	1500	3.5	2.25	1.25	225
FOUL	-1.50	1500	3.5	2.00	1.11	200
FOUL	-1.75	2000	7.0	5.25	1.05	189
FOUL	-2.00	2000	7.0	5.00	1.00	180
FOUL	-2.25	2000	7.0	4.75	0.95	171
FOUL	-2.50	2000	7.0	4.50	0.90	162
FOUL	-2.75	2000	7.0	4.25	0.85	153
FOUL	-3.00	2000	7.0	4.00	0.80	144
FOUL	-3.25	2000	7.0	3.75	0.75	135
FOUL	-3.50	2000	7.0	3.50	0.70	126
FOUL	-3.75	2000	7.0	3.25	0.65	117
FOUL	-4.00	2000	7.0	3.00	0.60	108
FOUL	-4.25	2250	8.0	3.75	0.56	101
FOUL	-4.50	2250	8.0	3.50	0.52	94
FOUL	-4.75	2250	8.0	3.25	0.49	87
FOUL	-5.00	2250	8.0	3.00	0.45	81

Note that, in this example, even a small adverse current can substantially decrease the maximum range; a 1-knot adverse current reduces the maximum range by more than 50%. It is useful to make these calculations for each vessel to be operated because the results will differ from vessel-to-vessel. This example however, shows that current effects can be substantial--particularly for displacement vessels. Many mariners have a qualitative understanding of the effect of an adverse current on the vessel's range, but have not made the types of calculations shown above, and so lack a quantitative understanding. In one incident, for example, a small cabin cruiser ran out of fuel in the middle of the channel of the Delaware River, near Philadelphia, Pennsylvania. Fortunately, a Coast Guard Auxiliary patrol vessel was in the immediate vicinity and managed to get a line on and tow the disabled cabin cruiser out of the path of an oncoming tanker. When asked how it came to be that the cabin cruiser had run out of fuel, the distraught skipper responded, "I don't understand it, I filled the tanks yesterday morning and travelled down to the Delaware Bay and back--a trip I've made before without needing

TABLE 11-8

TIME-THROTTLE SETTING TRADEOFFS ILLUSTRATED

VESSEL: AVENTURA
FUEL: 200 GALLONS ON BOARD
DISTANCE: 120 NAUTICAL MILES
CURRENT: 2.00

THROTTLE SETTING (RPM)	STW (KNOTS)	SOA (KNOTS)	FUEL CONSUMPTION RATE (GPH)	REQUIRED TRIP DURATION (HOURS)	TRIP FUEL REQUIRED (GALLONS)	FUEL REMAINING AT DESTINATION (GALLONS)	TIME TO FUEL EXHAUSTION AT DESTINATION (HOURS)	RESERVE RANGE AT DESTINATION (HOURS)
1000	1.0	-1.00	0.33	N/A	N/A	N/A	N/A	N/A
1250	2.0	0.00	0.80	N/A	N/A	N/A	N/A	N/A
1500	3.5	1.50	1.80	80.0	144	156	31.1	47
1750	5.0	3.00	3.30	40.0	132	68	20.6	62
2000	7.0	5.00	5.00	24.0	120	80	16.0	80
2250	8.0	6.00	6.70	20.0	134	66	9.9	59
2500	9.0	7.00	9.00	17.1	154	46	5.1	36
2750	9.5	7.50	11.90	16.0	190	10	0.8	6
3000	10.0	8.00	16.00	15.0	240	-40	-2.5	-20

fuel enroute." Reconstruction of the details of the voyage showed that, on this occasion, the run down and back on the river was timed unfortunately--the cruiser had foul currents on both legs. (See Chapter 7 for a discussion of how to select starting times to avoid this situation.) After the fact range calculations for this vessel indicated that the effective range given a 2 knot foul current was reduced by 50% in comparison to the "no current" condition. Additionally, because the trip was longer, the skipper ran at a higher than customary throttle setting to complete the voyage during the daylight hours. As it was, the skipper nearly made it, the cruiser was only a few miles from home port when the engine quit. This skipper now has fuel consumption charts (of the type shown in Tables 11-3 and 11-6) pasted into the vessel's log!

Current considerations are also important to the kinds of tradeoffs considered in Table 11-6. Table 11-8, for example, shows similar calculations to those displayed in Table 11-5, except that a foul current of 2 knots is assumed. The range of throttle-setting options is more re-

stricted--1000 RPM and 1250 RPM are not feasible, and a 3000 RPM throttle setting guarantees fuel exhaustion before the destination is reached. The attractiveness of operation at 2250 RPM (a possible compromise) is reduced; enroute time has been increased from 15 hours to 20 hours and the cruising reserve decreased from nearly 120 miles to 60 miles--a substantial effect from what is arguably a modest current. Figure 11-4 shows this graphically.

RADIUS OF ACTION AND RELATED CONCEPTS

(This section is more technical and can be omitted without any loss of continuity. This material is not covered in the Student Study Guide or the final examination.) Aircraft pilots employ two other fuel planning concepts that are also relevant to the mariner, the *radius of action* and the *point of no return*. Before defining these terms, it is useful to imagine an "out and back" voyage from a port of origin without the possibility of refueling enroute--for example, on an offshore fishing trip from the coast of New Jersey to the Hudson Canyon.

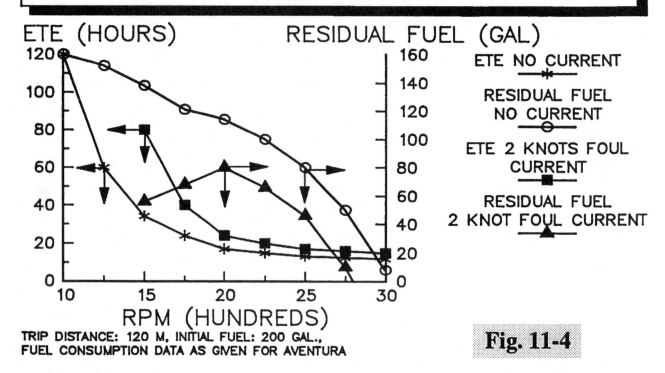

ASSUMED CURRENTS CAN SUBSTANTIALLY AFFECT SPEED–FUEL CONSUMPTION TRADEOFFS FOR DISPLACEMENT OR SEMIDISPLACEMENT HULL VESSELS

TRIP DISTANCE: 120 M, INITIAL FUEL: 200 GAL., FUEL CONSUMPTION DATA AS GIVEN FOR AVENTURA

Fig. 11-4

The *radius of action* is the greatest distance (out) that may be travelled and still leave sufficient fuel aboard to return to the port of origin without touching the fuel reserve. The point of no return is the point beyond which there is not sufficient fuel to return using the entire fuel reserve. Mathematically, the radius of action, RA, is given by the equation,

$$RA = F(1-R)/G([1/SOAo] + [1/SOAr])$$

where,

RA = radius of action (nautical miles),
F = fuel capacity (gallons),
R = fuel reserve (fraction),
G = fuel consumption rate (gallons per hour),
SOAo = speed of advance out (knots), and
SOAr = speed of advance on return leg (knots).

The *distance to the point of no return*, Dponr, is calculated using the same equation given above, except that the reserve, R, is set equal to

zero for this computation. (In the special case where there is no current and the SOAo and SOAr are each equal to the STW, the radius of action is equal to the range divided by two.)

To illustrate, suppose that the vessel *Aventura* (for which fuel consumption and capacity data are given in Table 11-3) is taken on a trip and a throttle setting of 2250 RPM is selected. The STW corresponding to this throttle setting is 8.0 knots (see Table 11-3). Suppose also that current sailing calculations employing estimated set and drift (discussed in Chapter 7) indicate that the best estimate of the SOA on the "out" leg is 7.1 knots, and on the return is 7.3 knots. (Both could well be beneath the STW in the case of a beam current.) The fuel consumption rate at this throttle setting, G, is 6.7 GPH (see Table 11-3). Assume that a 20% fuel reserve (R = 0.2) is desired. The radius of action at this throttle setting calculated from the above equation is,

RA = 200(1-0.2)/6.7([1/7.1]+[1/7.3]),

VOYAGE PLANNING WORKSHEET

REMARKS ON VOYAGE PLAN:

GENERAL INFORMATION:

CHECK ITEMS

DATE: _____   CHARTS REQD: _____   NAV. GEAR: _____
NAVIGATOR: _____   COAST PILOT: _____   TIMEPIECE: _____
VESSEL: _____   LIGHT LIST: _____   FUEL/RPM TABLE: _____
     TIDE TABLES: _____   PILOT CHARTS: _____

TIME START: _____   FOB (GAL): _____

DETAILED LEG PLAN:

LEG	FROM	TO	INTENDED TRACK (TRUE)	LEG DISTANCE (M)	POWER SETTING (RPM)	ESTIMATED STW (KNOTS)	CURRENT SET DRIFT	TRUE COURSE	VARIATION	MAGNETIC COURSE	DEVIATION	COMPASS COURSE	ESTIMATED SOA (KNOTS)	ETE HH:MM	ETA HH:MM	EST. FUEL CONSUMPTION (GAL)	EST. FUEL REMAINING (GAL)

TABLE 11-9   VOYAGE PLANNING WORKSHEET

TABLE 11-10

TIPS FOR IMPROVED FUEL MANAGEMENT

CATEGORY	DESCRIPTION
GENERAL PLANNING	-- Develop a fuel use versus throttle setting (RPM) curve for your vessel.
	-- Consider voyage routing or timing options to minimize exposure to foul currents or adverse weather conditions.
	-- Study publications to learn the locations along a proposed route where fuel is available.
	-- Use formal fuel planning and allow adequate reserve margins.
	-- Consider speed versus fuel consumption tradeoffs.
WHILE UNDERWAY	-- Do not trust fuel gauges--verify fuel levels before and during voyage.
	-- Maintain a "HOWGOZIT" chart, or
	-- Maintain a fuel log and be prepared to divert to alternate destinations.
MAINTENANCE AND RELATED	-- Keep engines tuned.
	-- Clean bottom periodically.
	-- Fill up tanks after each trip to minimize condensation problems.
VESSEL EQUIPMENT	-- Consider installation of crossfeeds in multiple tank/engine setups.
	-- Consider installation of fuel management system.
	-- Consider installation of vessel trim tabs.

or approximately 86 nautical miles. The point of no return in this numerical example would be 20% larger, or equal to approximately 119 nautical miles.

Both the radius of action and the point of no return vary with the throttle setting. This is because G, and STW (hence SOAo and SOAr) vary with the throttle setting.

Computations of the radius of action and point of no return are also useful for trips where the origin and destination differ--for example, on a trip from Florida to the Bahamas. For any distance out less than the point of no return, the vessel has sufficient fuel to return to Florida if a diversion is required. Beyond the point of no return the vessel is "committed" (at least in terms of available fuel) to continue to the Bahamas. This voyage to the Bahamas also serves as an example where the SOAo and SOAr would both be less than the STW, because the Gulf Stream would be a beam current on both the out and return legs. Normally, the point of no return would be calculated in advance as part of the pre-voyage planning. It serves as a convenient memory aid to enter the point of no return into the loran as one of the enroute waypoints. Obviously, if the estimated set and drift differ appreciably from those assumed in the plan, it is appropriate to recompute the point of no return.

INTEGRATION OF FUEL PLANNING INTO VOYAGE PLANNING

The above concepts are readily integrated into general voyage planning. Table 11-9, for example, shows a voyage planning worksheet that contains entries relevant to fuel planning (e.g., RPM, STW, SOA, fuel consumption rate, fuel required and remaining for each leg) as well as the TVMDC course entries and current sailing entries. Checkpoints (the ends of the trip legs) can be defined, not only for navigational convenience (e.g., where courses change), but also as "option points" where diversions for additional fuel stops can be considered. Re-

member the old adage that "The only time there is too much fuel aboard is when the vessel is on fire"!

IS ALL THIS REALLY NECESSARY?

The above fuel planning examples may seem unnecessarily elaborate. It is important to note that--for "short" voyages with frequent opportunities to refuel--some computational shortcuts can be taken. Just as the detail of DR plots, frequency of fixes, etc., can be adjusted to circumstances, so, too, can the detail of the fuel planning calculations. At a minimum, however, the vessel operator should determine that the fuel on board is sufficient for the voyage and provide a "reasonable" reserve.

ADDITIONAL TIPS FOR IMPROVED FUEL MANAGEMENT

Table 11-10 lists 14 experience-proven suggestions for improved fuel management that should be considered by the prudent mariner. These are grouped under four broad headings: general planning, while underway, maintenance and related, and vessel equipment.

--General Planning

Those suggestions in the "general planning" category summarize the material presented in this chapter and are not discussed further.

--While Underway

The "while underway" category includes the suggestion to verify fuel gauges before and during a voyage. Gauges (and other components of the system) can fail and, moreover, the complex (rounded) shape of some fuel tanks may make the gauge calibration inaccurate, particularly at low fuel levels. Many tanks can be checked by inserting a stick in the fuel filler cap. Calibrate the reading on this dipstick by adding measured quantities of fuel and marking the stick accordingly. These measurements are most valid while the vessel is stationary; so it is necessary to stop the vessel briefly during a voyage to ensure maximum accuracy. Keep an accurate log showing RPM and length of time the vessel is operated at each RPM as an additional check on fuel burn.

--The "HOWGOZIT" Chart

A simple means for keeping track of the vessel's fuel status is to maintain a "Howgozit" (a corruption of "How goes it") chart. Figure 11-5 illustrates such a chart. It is constructed as follows.

First, do conventional fuel planning for the intended voyage to ascertain the appropriate throttle setting etc. Suppose, for example, that a trip of 150 miles is planned, and that a fuel load of 200 gallons is available at the start of the voyage. In this example it is assumed that the vessel *Aventura* is used, for which basic fuel consumption data are given in Table 11-3.

Second, construct a graph with total gallons remaining on the y or vertical axis, and miles to go on the x or horizontal axis, as shown in Figure

11-5. Using a straight edge or plotter, draw a line starting in the upper left hand corner (200 gallons on board, 150 miles to go) of the graph to the lower right hand corner of the graph (0 gallons on board, 0 miles to go). Identify this as the "dry tanks" line. Next, specify the desired fuel reserve, say 20%, and calculate the remaining fuel on board at the end of the trip if this reserve is maintained. In this example, the reserve fuel is (0.2) (200) or 40 gallons. Draw another straight line on the "Howgozit" graph from the upper left hand corner (200 gallons on board, 150 miles to go) to the reserve fuel (40 gallons) at the destination (0 miles to go). Label this the 20% reserve line.

Once the "Howgozit" chart is prepared, keep track of the remaining fuel and distance to go while underway. For example, you might note the fuel remaining from inspection of the gauges or from a fuel totalizer (an instrument that is coupled to the fuel flow meter and notes

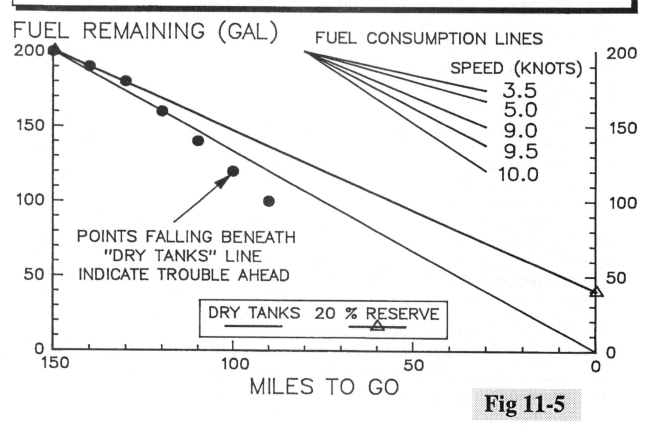

"HOWGOZIT" CHART FOR EXAMPLE VOYAGE

FUEL REMAINING (GAL)

FUEL CONSUMPTION LINES

SPEED (KNOTS)
3.5
5.0
9.0
9.5
10.0

POINTS FALLING BENEATH "DRY TANKS" LINE INDICATE TROUBLE AHEAD

DRY TANKS   20 % RESERVE

MILES TO GO

Fig 11-5

the total fuel consumed on the voyage) at selected DR positions, fixes (even better), and/or at the end of the various legs of the journey. Plot these data as you go. In order to ensure that you have sufficient fuel to complete the voyage, it is clear that the plotted points must always stay above the "dry tanks" line, and to ensure the desired fuel reserve at the destination, you must stay above the "20% reserve" line. If all points remain above both lines, the fuel will be adequate to reach the destination. However, if the plotted points dip beneath these lines (as these do in Figure 11-5), you have the makings of a problem because, at the fuel consumption rates experienced thus far in the journey, the vessel will run out of fuel before reaching the destination. Now, early in the voyage, something needs to be done. One solution might be to divert to an alternate marina where fuel is available. (Identification of suitable alternates where fuel is available is an important part of the preplanning process.) Another solution is to change the throttle setting so as to increase fuel efficiency. (Generally, with a displacement hull vessel, this amounts to slowing down.) In the example shown, the fuel remaining is 100 gallons with 90 miles to go. If it is desired to regain the 20% fuel reserve (40 gallons remaining at the destination), then no more than 60 gallons of fuel can be consumed during the remaining 90 miles, a fuel efficiency of 90/60 or 1.5 MPG. Reference to Table 11-3 shows that, theoretically at least, operating at a throttle setting of 1750 RPM (equivalent to a STW of 5 knots) or lower should leave you sitting at the dock with a 20% fuel reserve. If this solution were chosen, you would continue to maintain the "Howgozit" chart and monitor the vessel's fuel status. If the plotted points did not rise closer to the "dry tanks" line or, even better, the 20% reserve line, its time to rethink options. (The calculations, for example, might be in error because of the presence of an unallowed for foul current.)

As an alternative to having to calculate a feasible throttle setting as you go, it is relatively easy to superimpose the vessel's fuel consump-tion data on the "Howgozit" chart directly. This idea can be implemented if a series of "fuel consumption lines" are drawn, as shown in the upper right hand corner of Figure 11-5. Separate lines are drawn for each throttle setting, with the slope of the line equal to the fuel consumed per mile (reciprocal of the fuel efficiency) at that throttle setting or STW. For example, at a throttle setting of 1750 RPM, the vessel's STW (Table 11-3) is 5 knots, and the fuel consumption rate is 3.3 GPH. Therefore, the vessel will consume approximately 3.3/5, or 0.66 gallons per mile. To draw this "5 knot line," pick an uncluttered part of the chart and draw a line with this slope. Suppose that you start, as shown on Figure 11-5, at the point 200 gallons, 80 miles to go. Pick a distance, say 50 miles, sufficient to provide a clear indication of the slope. If a vessel traversed 50 miles at this throttle setting, it would consume 0.66 gallons per mile times 50 miles, or 33 gallons. Starting with 200 gallons, the fuel remaining would be 200 - 33, or 167 gallons. Draw the fuel consumption line from the original point (200 gallons, 80 miles to go) to the point (167 gallons, 30 miles to go), and label this with the speed (5 knots). Repeat this procedure for each of the other throttle settings to produce the fuel consumption lines shown in Figure 11-5. Although this might sound like a tedious effort, in practice it is quick to do. Moreover, once done, it radically simplifies enroute decision making. Whether or not you go to the trouble of drawing in the fuel consumption lines, it is important to use the "Howgozit" chart enroute.

Once drawn, the use of the fuel consumption lines is very simple. Just take a paraline plotter and align one end with the last solid dot in Figure 11-5, corresponding to the vessel's actual fuel state and distance to go. Next, take the other end of the paraline plotter and align it with the desired reserve at the destination. Now roll the paraline plotter up to the speed lines above, taking care not to change the alignment, and read directly the speed necessary to reach the final destination.

--Other Suggestions

The suggestions under the "maintenance and related" heading are self-evident for the most part. Topping off the tanks after each trip minimizes the chance that moisture in the airspace above the fuel in the tank condenses and (since water is heavier than fuel) settles at the bottom of the tank where it could be drawn into the engine.

The suggestions under vessel equipment are also self-explanatory, but some remarks are appropriate for vessels equipped with more than one fuel tank. Installation of crossfeeds (i.e., interconnections among fuel tanks and the engines) enable the vessel to be kept in better trim. They also enable any tank with "bad fuel" or a clogged line to be by-passed to maintain fuel flow to the engine(s). Some especially careful mariners will not take on an entire load of fuel from one source to minimize the possibility of contaminated fuel in all tanks. This consideration is particularly important at some foreign ports of call.

--Additional Perspective on Voyage Planning: The Seaman's Eye

When the mariner has learned navigation skills thoroughly, he or she will know when use of the formal techniques (such as plotting, making detailed float plans such as are shown in Table 11-9, or detailed fuel projections) is necessary and when departures from these formal processes are appropriate and can be made safely.

In familiar areas, such as on a particularly frequented embayment or sound, river or coastal area, where the charted hazards, aids to navigation, currents, tides, and other essential navigational information are well known, it may be sufficient only to keep the chart handy for marking positions when desired (at the approach of a fog bank or other period of restricted visibility, for example) but not carry on a DR plot or take frequent fixes.

Such a time may be when proceeding from the dock out to a rendezvous point at the beginning of a boating outing. Informal navigation is appropriate under these circumstances and is termed navigation by *Seaman's Eye*. Its proper and safe use comes only after the mariner has learned the navigation skills and techniques sufficiently and has gained sufficient experience to make sound judgments regarding the use of the various techniques available for navigation of the vessel.

Thus, Seaman's Eye navigation is applied after sufficient knowledge of the area is obtained through study of the available charts, Tide Tables, Current Tables, Coast Pilots, and other navigation publications and combined with local knowledge of the area. A thorough mastery of the navigational skills and techniques offered in the material in this textbook should provide a firm foundation for the navigator to know when to apply Seaman's Eye.

REFERENCES

Beebe, R. *Voyaging Under Power,* Seven Seas Press Inc., Newport, RI, 1984.

Berrien, A. D. "Boat Test No. 437: Grand Banks Motor Yacht," *Boating,* February 1987, pp. 93 et seq.

Collins, R. L. "Out of Gas; Accidents Caused By Running the Tanks Dry are Among the Most Avoidable of Mishaps," *Flying,* Vol. 112, No. 9, September 1985, pp. 25, et seq.

Kinney, F. S. *Skene's Elements of Yacht Design,* Eighth Ed., Dodd, Mead & Company, New York, NY, 1981.

Laudeman, W. J. "The Speed/RPM chart Revisited," *The Navigator,* Fall, 1986, p 16.

Lord, L. *Naval Architecture of Planing Hulls,* Third Ed., Cornell Maritime Press Inc., Cambridge, MD, 1963.

Lyon, T. C. *Practical Air Navigation, Eleventh Ed.,* Jeppesen, Denver, CO., 1972, pp. 136 et seq.

McFadden, R. D. "Toll at 72 in L. I. Air Crash; 89 Survive, Investigators Say the Colombian Plane May Have Run Out of Fuel," *New York Times,* VOL CXXXIX, No. 48,128, 27 January 1990, p 1, contd. on p 30.

Pike, D. *Motor Sailers,* David McKay Company, Inc. New York, NY 1976.

Rains, J., and P. Miller *Passagemaking Handbook A Guide for Delivery Skippers and Boat Owners,* Seven Seas Press, Camden, ME, 1989.

Shufeldt, H. H. and K. E. Newcomer *The Calculator Afloat,* Naval Institute Press, Annapolis, MD, 1980, pp 188 et seq.

Stapleton, S. *Stapleton's Powerboat Bible,* Hearst Marine Books, New York, NY, 1989.

Stearns, B. "Boat Test No. 423: Rampage 28 Sportsman," *Boating,* September, 1986, p 94.

Stearns, B. "Boat Test No. 443: Grady-White Trophy Pro 25," *Boating,* February, 1987, p 132.

Stearns, B. "Boat Test No. 458: Fountain 8.8 Meter Center Console," *Boating,* May, 1987, p 110.

Teale, J. *Designing Small Craft,* David McKay Company, Inc., New York, NY, 1977.

Weems, P. V. H. *Marine Navigation,* D. Van Nostrand Company, Inc., New York, NY, 1940.

Chapter 12

REFLECTIONS

aving reached this point in the course, you should have a working knowledge of the essential tools, techniques, and theory of coastal navigation. This chapter is written to go beyond technique to share insights on the practice and/or art of navigation. It presents ten experience-proven principles[1] of navigation practice for your consideration. There are no homework questions or problems in this chapter to slave over, simply points to ponder. None the less, this is one of the most important chapters in the ACN text.

Each of the principles discussed below is illustrated with examples--many taken from the vast literature on navigation, some from personal experience of the writer and other Auxiliarists. The examples all involve navigational errors, some with disastrous consequences, others with happy endings. These examples are not intended to frighten, but rather to instruct. Santayana's famous remark to the effect that those who fail to understand history are condemned to repeat it is equally applicable to the practice of navigation.

It has been said that the sea is a cruel mistress, totally unforgiving of error. Although there is some truth to this statement, there is also exaggeration. Careful study of marine mishaps indicates that isolated navigation errors are seldom the sole probable cause of an accident. Typically, *many* adverse factors are required

before error turns from mere embarrassment to disaster. Although it may be prudent to believe otherwise, an *isolated* navigational error is often of little or no consequence. In open ocean, far removed from navigational hazards, an error may be virtually inconsequential. Even in more restricted waters an error may not be critical if promptly detected and corrected. An error in taking or plotting a fix, for example, can be revealed by a comparison of a fix with the DR position, or from consistency checks with collateral information (e.g., depth soundings, additional bearings). Even if the fix error is not immediately discovered and causes the navigator to change course towards potentially dangerous waters, such as reefs, there is the possibility that the reefs can be seen visually and course altered to safer waters, unless night or storms also conspire to reduce visibility or mask the noise of breaking waves. In the famous case of the *Titanic,* for example, it has been argued that only an unfortunate conspiracy of timing was responsible for the disaster. Had the iceberg been seen just a few seconds earlier, the vessel could have turned to avoid collision. Had the berg been seen a few seconds later, the *Titanic* would have hit head on, and emerged with a bashed-in bow--seriously damaged--but with most of the water-tight compartments intact and passengers and crew still alive.

So it is that boating is a generally safe activity. Moreover, available statistics indicate that

---

[1]It was tempting to title this chapter, "The Ten Commandments," but these ideas are not etched in stone, and are still evolving.

FIGURE 12-1. FATALITY RATES ARE ON THE DECLINE FOR BOATING ACCIDENTS IN THE UNITED STATES.

ANNUAL FATALITY RATE PER 100,000 VESSELS

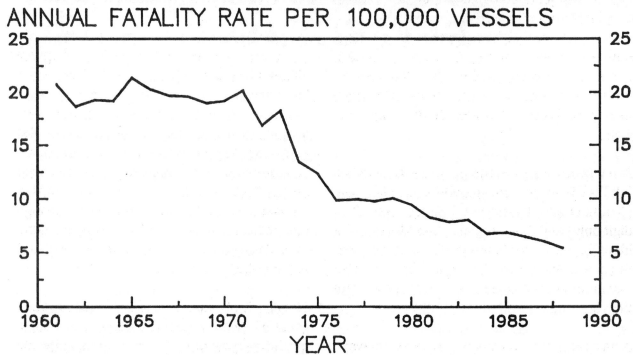

ESTIMATES FROM "BOATING STATISTICS 1988," SEE REFERENCES.

fatality rates (per 100,000 recreational vessels) are on the decline as shown in Figure 12-1. To note these trends lends valuable perspective, but it is also important to stress that *any* accidents or fatalities are, in some sense, *intolerable*. Statistics indicate, for most boating and aircraft accidents as a group, that it is *human error rather than equipment malfunction that is the probable cause*. For example, according to recent U.S. Coast Guard estimates published in *Boating Statistics 1988*, operator error was a contributing factor in 71% of the boating fatalities where fault could be determined. This statement is not intended as an indictment--rather as a challenge to increase professionalism.

Navigation errors *per se* generally account for only a small percentage of the recreational boating accidents in the United States. For example, according to *Boating Statistics 1988*, navigation error was judged to be the principal cause for reported accidents involving 236 of 8,981 (2.6%) recreational vessels[2] in 1988. Again, this statistic is furnished to lend useful perspective, and not to suggest that even such a low rate is "acceptable."

This chapter is organized into a series of *maxims or principles* that are useful to study and explore in search of wisdom.

_____

[2]It is estimated that only approximately 10% of boating accidents are reported to the Coast Guard. However, most serious accidents involving extensive damage, injuries, and/or fatalities are included in this sample.

Principle 1:

Pay Attention to Detail

Professional navigation is as much an attitude of mind as an art or science. In this regard, it is important to heed to advice of the late Frances W. Wright to practice "constant vigilance." This is particularly true with respect to the everyday details or computations that many mariners take for granted. A casual attitude can lead otherwise competent navigators to commit the most amazing blunders. Consider the following examples.

* A navigator tuned in the Brenton Reef (RBn 295) RDF station but dialed in 291 kilohertz (Nobska Point) by mistake (an error in the last digit only) and failed to verify the Morse code identifier or to plot the bearing and discover the error. Misled by the "false" bearing, the navigator altered course and nearly grounded the vessel on a reef.

* A navigator using loran with provision for waypoints and a course deviation indicator (CDI), allowed the vessel to drift off course to the left. On realizing that the CDI indicated a course correction to the right, the navigator put the helm over to return the ship to the intended track to reach the waypoint without plotting the vessel's position or realizing that a direct return to track put the vessel in shoal waters.

* Captain John M. Waters, Jr., in his book, *Rescue at Sea,* writes of a B-29 that was forced to ditch 200 miles away from its intended island destination because the navigator, in adjusting the true course for magnetic variation had subtracted, rather than added. This simple arithmetic mistake cost the lives of several people and an aircraft.

* Cameron Bright, writing in the magazine *Ocean Navigator,* describes a routine delivery of the cutter *Acadia* from West Palm Beach to New York. One storm-tossed night on this voyage near Cape Hatteras, the navigator finally realized that the reason for the increasing discrep-

ancy between DR and loran positions was accounted for by essentially the same arithmetic error noted above in adjusting for variation. In this episode, fate took a kinder hand, and the only damage was a bruised ego.

* In another story from the pages of *Ocean Navigator,* the third mate on the bulk freighter *Mavro Vetranick* sighted Pulaski light in the Dry Tortugas too close on the starboard beam. The mate adjusted the course on the autopilot to compensate but, unfortunately, turned the autopilot dial in the wrong direction before immediately retiring to the chart table to check the SATNAV receiver. The mate did not stay on deck to verify that the correct course change resulted and, instead of turning away from the reef, the vessel turned towards the reef and subsequently grounded!

* The late Sir Francis Chichester (a superb navigator of both aircraft and vessels) was most candid in his book, *Gipsy Moth Circles the World,* to reveal that on occasion he consulted the wrong page of the *Nautical Almanac,* and that he had left behind the required tables for celestial navigation when he originally set out on a round-the-world voyage!

* John Milligan, in his book, *The Amateur Pilot,* recounts the story of a participant in the *Transpac* race who made an error in misidentifying the *Molokai* light as the *Makapuu* light, a navigation error that caused the yacht to lose the race. The navigator had carefully timed the 10-sec light but failed to note that the *Molokai* light is flashing while the *Makapuu* light is occulting!

* While cruising near the Newfoundland port of Grand Bank, a navigator prepared to enter ASF corrections to a loran as published in the Canadian Coast Guard Publication, *Radio Aids to Marine Navigation.* The instructions indicated that the tabulated correction was to be *subtracted.* For example, if the published entry were -0.9 usec and the navigator incorrectly

entered -0.9 usec, rather than -(-0.9) = +0.9 usec in the loran with the result that the "corrected" loran position became less accurate than the original position.

• Richard Cahill, in his excellent book, *Strandings And Their Causes,* describes a 1979 accident to the tanker *Messiniaki Frontis* near the island of Crete. Enroute to a planned anchorage, the mate took a visual bearing on Megalonisi Light, and completed the fix with a radar range on this same light. The variable range marker (VRM) was not used for this purpose. Instead, the range was interpolated from the FRMs. Unfortunately, the range setting on the radar had inadvertently been switched to a 3 mile range from a 6 mile range, with the result that the estimated range was in error by a factor of two and, therefore, the fix was in error. No attempt was made to obtain another visual bearing on other lights in the area, and so the position error went undetected. Shortly thereafter, the vessel went aground.

None of these errors are profound--all appear quite "foolish" in the harsh glare of hindsight. All could happen to anyone reading (or, let's admit it, writing) this book. All were preventable by the simple expedient of rechecking calculations, seeking to validate estimates by other means, or taking a little more time to think. The key quality necessary to prevent, or at least reduce the likelihood of, these errors is to realize that small details are important and deserve attention. The U. S. Coast Guard uses the phrase *"sweat chart"* to describe a conning chart used for harbor approaches. This is a particularly apt term because it reinforces the concept of constant vigilance.

Another relevant aspect of the constant vigilance theme is the need to maintain a proper lookout. "Improper lookout" was the largest single cause of recreational boating accidents in 1988, according to *Boating Statistics.* An improper lookout was held as an assignable cause for accidents involving 2,469 out of 8,981 vessels (27.4%) in that year. A proper lookout is required by the Navigation Rules and good common sense besides.

Principle 2:
Practice is Essential and Can Also Be Fun

Upon completion of this course, the average student is well equipped to begin to learn the art of coastal navigation. However, experience, though essential, is not necessarily the best teacher. Twenty years of subsequent experience may simply amount to one year, repeated twenty times. Many students first eagerly begin to apply the tools and techniques taught in the course. In familiar waters, and during periods of good visibility and calm seas (which the beginning navigator wisely insists on), the techniques are first diligently practiced. Soon it becomes apparent that not all the formal techniques are necessary --at least under the circumstances of these relatively simple voyages. Fuel reserves, first laboriously calculated, are soon found to be more than adequate in home waters. DR plots, originally laid out in meticulous fashion, are often found to be "unnecessary." Lights are first carefully timed for positive identification, but then the local lights become familiar, and the stop watch left ashore. Other potentially unsafe habits evolve, justified first as expedient shortcuts, then later dignified with the appellation, *seaman's eye.* The navigator becomes preoccupied with other new and, no doubt, essential knowledge--tasks generally grouped under the rubric of seamanship. In short, experience in this benign environment can convince the beginning navigator that much of the material painfully learned in the course is merely "theoretical"--nice to know, but not really required for day-to-day boating/sailing.

Studies by the *Federal Aviation Administration* (FAA) indicate that many aircraft pilots go through the same degenerative process. Knowledge (at least that knowledge required to pass the airman written examinations) is actually lost at a fairly rapid rate. Unless the airman works to gain additional ratings, there is a real need to stay in practice to maintain/regain knowledge.

For this reason, among others, the FAA insists on periodic retraining for all licensed pilots.

In a benign environment, without equipment failure and in familiar waters in periods of good visibility, this loss of skills and/or knowledge may not be critical. However, lack of practice and diligence can take its toll; isolated thunderstorms may break out during the "dog days" of late summer, shutting down visibility and kicking up substantial waves in otherwise familiar waters. Or a pleasant fishing trip off the coast of Maine or portions of California turns into a real challenge as fog sets in, along with the realization that the bottom is not the familiar soft mud of the Chesapeake Bay, but rather sharp rocks, interrupted with pinnacles. Grounding in these waters does not simply call for volunteers to get wet pushing the vessel off a silty bottom, but rather may lead to a nasty gash in the hull and thoughts of "Mayday."

Nor is the gradual attrition of skills limited to "amateur" navigators. Full-time paid navigators also need to work to ensure that skills do not go rusty. A recent article in the pages of *Ocean Navigator* tells of the 672 ft. Venezuelan tanker, *Lagoven,* that went aground 60 miles outside the vessel's proper shipping channel on Cultivator shoal while enroute to Boston, MA. This vessel departed Venezuela in early February of 1987 with a full load of 14.5 million gallons of No. 6 fuel oil. After some early difficulties, including the loss of a SATNAV receiver off Savannah and the loss of one of two radar sets, the problems began in earnest. Bad weather, and an inability to obtain RDF fixes forced the vessel to rely on DR throughout most of the voyage. However, according to the *Ocean Navigator* article included in the references, the ship should have passed in range of the Highland Light RDF beacon and the Nantucket LNB beacon. Moreover, prior to grounding, there was an interval of clear weather when celestial sights should have been taken to fix the ship's position. Some celestial sights were attempted, but the worksheets containing the calculations were later described

the ship's agent as a "joke." Although a definitive investigation was not conducted, this appears to be a case of navigation error. It is noteworthy that the Captain was relieved of duty upon entry to Boston Harbor.

The provisional explanation for this near-disaster (the vessel was able to be refloated without a spill) is that the captain and officers were simply out of practice with the appropriate navigational techniques (here celestial as a backup) necessary for the voyage. "Use it or lose it," is an apt expression.

The requirement to stay current with navigational technique applies to all aboard who will handle the vessel, not simply the primary navigator. Captain John O. Coote (Royal Navy) recounts the following anecdote in his interesting and well-written book, *Yacht Navigation--My Way*: "Sailing *Roundabout* back from Copenhagen after the One-Ton Cup in 1966 I left a guest artist on the tiller after clearing the roads off Copenhagen. Around 0500 I awoke to realize that we were hard aground and in thick fog. There had not been a single entry in the log or on the chart for four hours, so it was anyone's guess where we had fetched up. We backed off and sailed a reciprocal course until we picked up an identifiable navigational landmark, but it was a creepy feeling."

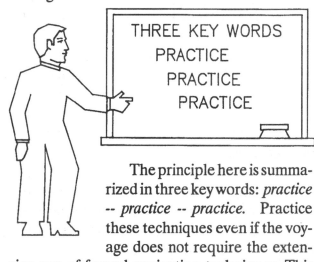

THREE KEY WORDS
PRACTICE
PRACTICE
PRACTICE

The principle here is summarized in three key words: *practice -- practice -- practice.* Practice these techniques even if the voyage does not require the extensive use of formal navigation techniques. This practice does not have to amount to unremitting drudgery, donning the nautical equivalent of a hair shirt. Try making a game of it. For example, divide the voyage into legs, and have various crew members act as navigators for each of the legs. Each "navigator" uses all available information to calculate an estimated time of arrival (ETA) at the checkpoint that marks the end of their leg. The navigator closest to the actual time past the checkpoint wins dinner, or is excused from cleaning the dishes, washing down the vessel, or some other "grunt" task.

Another "game" (in vessels appropriately configured) is for the navigator to con the vessel from the navigator's station only, without being able to come on deck for visual observations. "Fog" or other limitation to visibility is simulated in excellent weather by having the lookouts report sightings only within a fixed distance of the vessel, e.g., one mile or one-half mile. The navigator's task is to reach an identifiable object, such as a buoy, from these limited data. The measure of success is the actual distance away from the buoy when the navigator indicates that the buoy has been reached. Variations on these ideas are literally endless. For example, certain electronic aids can be presumed inoperative and the display covered by a cardboard or rubber inset. (Aircraft pilots, at least those with instrument ratings, are well familiar with this idea, called "partial panel" work.) Or perhaps all the electronics can be presumed disabled and navigation conducted only by DR and visual fixes.

In the Coast Guard Auxiliary boat crew program, vessel operators-in-training have to pass a task called "night ops." Here one vessel, the search and rescue target, goes out at night and *simulates* a distress transmission. (The word "Mayday" is *never* used in this simulation and the phrase "this is a drill," repeated once, begins and ends each transmission.) The search and rescue unit (SRU), conned by the apprentice operator, tries to find the "lost" vessel. The operator of the SRU asks a series of questions of the "lost" vessel by radio to narrow down the area to be searched-- "Can you see any bridge over the river?"; "What color is the light on the buoy?";

"When did you leave your home port, and in what direction?" are illustrative questions. (Auxiliary Qualification Examiners, those entrusted with examining and certifying the skills of the prospective operator, can tell a great deal about the applicant's navigational skills merely from the questions asked!) This training exercise provides invaluable experience in night navigation and decision making, and is regarded as the highlight of the on-the-water training program by many Auxiliarists.

The obvious point of this practice in ideal conditions is to prepare the navigator to cope with less than ideal conditions when these arise. Good habits are formed, and equally important, the navigator becomes more alert to the possibility of error.

Boating is supposed to be fun, and it is not suggested here that *every* portion of *every* voyage has to be regarded solely as a training exercise. None the less, every voyage offers at least *some* opportunity for a learning experience, and the navigator should strive to perfect skills for at least a part of the voyage. In particular, the navigator should attempt to learn from his or her inevitable mistakes. For example, when a fix and DR position do not coincide, the navigator should attempt to rationalize this difference. Calculate the apparent current set and drift (using the methods of Chapter 7) and test the plausibility of this estimate from the data in the Tidal Current Tables or Charts (Chapter 8). Perhaps the DR was in error, or the navigator made the mistake of drawing the current vector from the fix to the DR (rather than the reverse). Perhaps the navigator failed to calculate the DR position corresponding to the exact time of the fix, or made an error in the 60D=ST formula. Tracking down the error is itself a learning opportunity.

The navigator should stay within the proven limits of his/her skills and the capabilities and equipment of the vessel--a point discussed below. But voyages should also be planned with the idea of pushing and stretching these limits. An excellent way to do this is to crew with more experienced navigators to learn their "tricks of the trade." Even crewing with less-experienced navigators can be instructive. It's appropriate to close this section with the apocryphal story of a famous navigator once asked the secret of his success: "Not making mistakes" was the tongue-in-cheek reply. This led to the inevitable follow-up question: "How did you learn to avoid making mistakes?" The elegant answer was: "By making mistakes!"

Principle 3:
Do Not Rely On Any One Technique for Determining the Vessel's Position

Many navigators would consider this the one cardinal rule of successful navigation. Indeed, there are scattered reminders of this point throughout the text. Simply stated, this principle urges the navigator to use all available information in fixing the vessel's position rather than to rely on any one measurement, method, or technique. For example, a loran fix can be cross-checked by radar, RDF, or visual bearings. Even depth information can be useful in assessing the plausibility of the loran fix.

The essential idea here is to use the various methods as cross checks on each other to increase the confidence of the navigator in the vessel's position. Excluding power failures, which can prevent any electrical system from functioning properly, the possible errors among the principal methods of fixing position are largely independent. Therefore, having several pieces of evidence all pointing to the same conclusion increases its reliability. Professor R. V. Jones, one of the key figures in British scientific intelligence during World War II, writing on the use of deception in hoaxes, explains the principle as follows:

"The ease of detecting counterfeits is much greater when different channels of examination are used simultaneously. This is why telephonic hoaxes are so easy -there is no accompanying visual appearance to be counterfeited. Metal strips were most successful (so called "chaff" or "window") when only radar, and that of one frequency, was employed. Conversely, the most successful naval mines were those which would only detonate when several different kinds of signal, magnetic, hydrodynamic, and acoustic, were received simultaneously. A decoy which simulates all these signals is getting very like a ship. From these considerations incidentally, we can draw a rather important conclusion about the detection of targets in defense and attack: that as many different physical means of detection as possible should be used in parallel. It may, therefore, be better in some circumstances to develop two or three independent means of detection, instead of putting the same total effort into the development of one alone."

Though obviously ventured in a different context than the practice of navigation, the point is equally valid here. The navigator is not necessarily the victim of intentional deception by another, but rather of self-deception.

The advice to use as many systems of position fixing as possible is particularly apt in these days of the "electronic revolution" in navigation instruments. The nautical literature abounds with examples of problems caused by over-reliance on one method of navigation.

It was noted in Chapter 9 that use of RDF for homing must include some additional means (perhaps an RDF cross bearing from a different station) for determining the distance of the vessel from the RDF station. In that chapter, the case of the collision of the liner, *Olympic*, with the Nantucket lightship in 1934 was briefly related. The *Olympic* homed in on the lightship's radio signal, without regard for the distance to the lightship, with disastrous results. Nor is this an isolated example. A relief lightship to the *Ambrose* lightship (on the approaches to New York Harbor) was rammed in 1960 by the freighter *Green Bay*. Closer to the waters covered by the 1210-Tr chart, the Texaco tanker *Lightburne* ran aground on rocks just beneath the Block Island Southeast Lighthouse on 10 February, 1939. The tanker had been using the RDF station at this light for navigation and misjudged the distance off. The wreck remains today, another memorial to the dangers of homing without position fixing. The wreck of the *Lightburne* is not shown on the 1210-Tr chart, but can be found on chart number 13218 (the "real-life" counterpart to the 1210-Tr) at L: 41° 04.3'N, Lo: 71° 32.3'W. Many other similar stories of sinkings and near misses abound, all prompted by the same mental error.

Incidentally, it may occasionally happen that there is no other convenient RDF station in the area that can be used to monitor the vessel's progress in homing towards an RDF station. If safe water exists in the vicinity of the vessel's track, an old aviator's trick may be helpful. Turn 90° to the right or left of course to put the station at a relative bearing of 090 or 270. Note the time and maintain this new compass course until the relative bearing of the station changes a few degrees (say 5 or 10 degrees). Record the time run, T (in minutes), note the number of degrees change in relative bearing, X, and turn again to resume homing. The approximate distance, y (in nautical miles), to the RDF station is given by the simple equation $y = ST/X$, where S is the vessel's speed through the water (in knots), T is the "dogleg" length (in minutes) and X is the bearing change in degrees. For example, a vessel making 10 knots altered course 90° to starboard for 20 minutes, during which the relative bearing changed 5 degrees. The approximate distance

to the RDF station is $y = (10)(20)/5 = 40M$. This approximate formula is easy to remember and remarkably accurate.[3]

Relying on one method of navigation can actually create two types of problems. Perhaps the most obvious problem is if the method chosen is flawed in some respect, and the navigator, unaware of the problem, is misled. Again, the pages of the *Ocean Navigator* and other nautical magazines are filled with examples of this error. One correspondent writes of undetected loran problems that led to the grounding of the 48-foot sloop *Victory,* near Conception Island in Exhuma Sound, in the 1985 race from Miami to Montego Bay, Jamaica. Although lights in this area are few and far between, visual LOPs apparently were not attempted and the crew sailed on unaware of the problem until striking the reef. There is also another problem caused by over-reliance on one method of navigation. This is caused when the one method chosen fails catastrophically, e.g., a loran outage caused by a power failure or surge as an engine is started. Losing the one tool in use creates chaos, as neglected DR tracks are hastily reconstructed.

It is particularly important to seek confirmatory evidence in connection with the location of floating aids to navigation. Buoys in US waters are, in fact, on station the vast majority of the time. But collisions, storms, and particularly ice can lead to buoys being sunk, damaged, or off station. Major as well as minor buoys can be off station. In early October of 1986, for example, the Nantucket Large Navigation Buoy (LNB), which is an important aid located south of the

---

[3]See Figure 12 - 2 for a diagram of the situation. By design, angle Y (in degrees) should be 90 degrees. In Figure 12-2 the angle Y is deliberately shown to be slightly greater than 90 degrees to show the effects of possible helm error on the results. The correct formula for distance y can be derived from elementary trigonometry to be $y = ST \sin Y/(60 \sin X)$, compared to the approximation $y = ST/X$. For values of the angle X from 0 to 20 degrees, and angles Y from 70 to 110 degrees the error of this approximation varies from 2.6% to 11.4%, being smallest as Y approaches 90 degrees. In the example in the text, if the actual turn angle were 95 degrees rather than 90 degrees, the correct distance would be 38.1 M rather than 40 M.

Nantucket Shoals, broke free of its mooring chain and drifted out to sea still flashing its light, transmitting its RDF broadcast, and returning a racon signal. Thus, RDF and radar navigation as well is visual observations could have been in error over the time period from the buoy's escape until it was located and towed back by the Coast Guard buoy tender *Evergreen.* Fortunately in this case, alert navigators of commercial vessels noted the discrepancy and reported it to the Coast Guard.

In earlier chapters, mention has been made of the utility of the depth sounder in checking positions determined by other methods. Although there are many circumstances (e.g., in areas where the depth is nearly constant over a broad area, or where dangerous reefs rise abruptly off the ocean floor) where a depth sounder cannot be used directly to fix or estimate the vessel's position, depth information can sometimes be quite useful in confirming a fix determined by other methods. Mention of the text, *Strandings And Their Causes,* has already been made. This invaluable compilation of case studies of large ship groundings lists numerous examples of groundings that were either caused by negligence in the use of, or failure to use the depth sounder. Specific accidents cited in this text involve the tanker *Argo Merchant* in December, 1976, the tanker *Messiniaki Frontis* in February, 1979, the liberty ship *Valiant Effort,* in January, 1959, the tanker *Hindsia,* in January, 1965, the liberty ship *Bobara,* in January, 1955, the steamship *Cornwood,* in November, 1957, the tanker *Cristos Bitas,* in October, 1978, the tanker *Transhuron,* in September 1974, and the freighter *Bel Hudson*, in May, 1970. A careful study of these cases shows conclusively the value of the depth sounder.

A professional navigator uses all available means--radar, loran, RDF, piloting, depth information, and maintains a DR plot to fix and navigate the vessel. In truth, these means are complementary and mutually reinforcing, rather than competitive.

Principle 4:
Be Alert to Anomalies
Many professional navigators seem to develop a "sixth" sense about the well-being of the

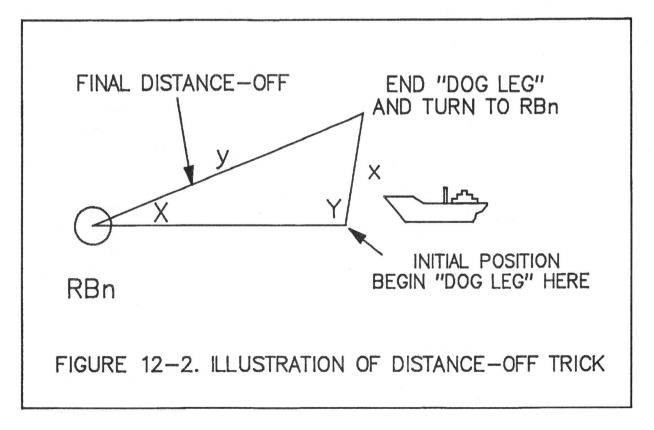

FIGURE 12-2. ILLUSTRATION OF DISTANCE-OFF TRICK

vessel. An experienced navigator asleep in a comfortable bunk may waken if the vessel's motion changes -- such changes could come about from wind shifts, changes in sea conditions, or an inattentive helmsman who allows the vessel to slowly drift off course.

The clues to changed conditions or problems may be quite subtle. The famous Sherlock Holmes story of the dog that did not bark in the night reminds us that negative information can also be important. A marine VHF radio that is silent, when normally abuzz with clatter, may indicate that someone has altered the squelch setting, the vessel has departed normally crowded sea lanes, or be the first indication of a power failure. A light that is not seen may be the first indication that the vessel is not where it is supposed to be or that the visibility is deteriorating.

In addition to being concerned about the failure to observe something *expected,* the sight or sound of something *unexpected* could be cause for alarm. For example, John Rousmaniere quotes Hewitt Schlereth as noting that the naked eye has sufficient resolving power to enable the mariner to count individual trees on a shoreline from a distance off of 1 M., count windows in waterfront houses at 2 M., and see the junction line between land and water at 3 M. Using these rules of thumb,[4] if a vessel's intended track were to pass no closer than 4 M to shore but windows could be counted on waterfront houses, the alert navigator should investigate further.

In the days before inertial navigation systems became common, an aviator broke out "on top" of the clouds after flying some distance over the ocean by reference to instruments alone to find that the sun was on the right, rather than on the left where it should have been if the aircraft were on course. This was the first clue to a compass failure. Because the failure was gradual in this case, the pilot had kept resetting the directional gyro to the compass and the directional gyro was similarly useless.

To the uninitiated, such a "sixth" sense may seem almost mystical. In truth, this "sixth" sense has more pedestrian origins and, with a little care and planning, can be developed by any navigator. The "unseen" light provided a clue only because the navigator took the trouble to estimate the range at which the light could be seen (using methods discussed in Chapter 10) and either drew a circle of visibility on the chart and made a note to look for the light when the vessel was supposedly within this arc of visibility. The pilot who identified the compass error simply exploited the common knowledge that the sun rises in the east and sets in the west. The navigator who counted windows and wisely fixed the vessel's position and altered course also exploited elementary knowledge.

Good weather and sea conditions and the availability of ATONs in abundance lower the level of cockpit tension, but can lull the navigator into a state of complacency. For example, after completing a difficult landfall a navigator left the helmsman at the wheel of a trawler with instructions to maintain course so as to keep the bow pointed at a distant lighthouse visible on the bow with the vessel's heading 270 degrees. After going below for coffee, a well-thumbed copy of the appropriate light list, and a few minutes of conversation, the navigator returned topside to bring coffee to the helmsman. A quick glance showed the lighthouse, apparently larger now over the bow. To the casual navigator all was well, an occasion to swap lies with the helmsman over coffee. A more alert navigator would check the vessel's compass heading upon returning topside. A heading significantly greater (smaller) than 270 degrees would indicate a current setting the vessel to the south (north) of the original

---

[4]Many other simple rules of thumb have also been suggested (see e.g., USPS), some slightly at variance with the above. Those given here are illustrative, rather than exhaustive. The reader is encouraged to develop his/her own personal rules of thumb by observation (see Principle 2).

track. In effect, this vessel is "homing" (using visual means) rather than "tracking"--a distinction made in Chapter 9 in connection with RDF. Perhaps this distinction is of no great consequence--but it could be if there were unsafe water to the south (north). In any event, an alert navigator gains potentially valuable information from a simple glance at the compass.

Sound and kinesthesia (motion sense) can also furnish important clues to the navigator. After many hours operating the same vessel the navigator develops a clear, although intuitive sense of the relation between speed, power setting, and trim that goes beyond the mere ability to identify a rough-running engine. Slight changes in trim and/or bottom condition affect the speed curve (Chapter 5) and (absent a speedometer) may be a clue to the reason for a discrepancy between the DR position and a fix that cannot be accounted for by current alone. In operating powerboats in conditions of restricted visibility it is often useful to periodically slow down or stop the vessel and shut off the engine. In the silence that follows it is sometimes possible to hear the sound of diaphones or other sound clues (let's hope not the sound of breaking surf!) that would otherwise be masked by the noise of the engine. (Slowing down may be important for other reasons as well as noted below.)

Principle 5:
Emphasize Routine in Times of Stress

Now and again, the tapes or transcripts of communications between commercial aircraft pilots and air traffic controllers are made public after an accident or near-accident. The startling thing to most non-pilots is the high degree of professionalism and calm decision-making revealed in these communications. To many this appears almost "heroic," and well it may be. But it is also the product of extensive conditioning. Pilots are systematically trained (in actual aircraft and sophisticated simulators) to cope with all manner of emergencies. This training alone lends an element of the routine to emergencies. Equally important, however, is the programmed method of instruction for dealing with emergencies. Pilots are taught early and often in their careers to use checklists. There are checklists used in the preflight inspection, checklists used in starting engines, pre-takeoff checklists, cruise checklists, etc. There are also various emergency checklists--often neatly categorized as fire, engine out, landing gear inoperative, etc. Reading out the items in this checklist and following the concise instructions is not only an orderly way of problem solving that lowers the likelihood of omission of critical items, but also serves to lower the likelihood of panic among the aircrew. In short, these checklists act to "routinize" emergencies, to place these in the context of the familiar.

Mariners can benefit from this same approach. For example, Marvin Creamer (an accomplished "bare bones" blue water navigator), writing in *Ocean Navigator,* makes the point that DR is both possible and necessary during storms. He cites several "positive aspects" to attempts at storm navigation: assists in prompt post-storm location; helps focus minds of personnel and combat lethargy; increases confidence of crew in navigator/skipper; provides practice in heavy-weather navigation; and helps to pass away time. All too frequently, the drama of a "crisis event" distracts the navigator from necessary tasks. In storms, particularly severe storms, seamanship, rather than navigation may be the most immediate priority. However, assuming that the vessel survives the storm, it is essential to know the vessel's position and proximity to dangerous waters. This task will be vastly simplified if a simple record of estimated speeds and courses was maintained. Such a record may not be exact for a variety of reasons--speeds may be very approximate (particularly for a sailing vessel running in a storm under bare poles), and leeway only a guess--but even an approximate DR record is better than no information.

So get in the habit of using checklists. Start out with obvious checklists, such as the pre-underway checks, cruise checks, approaching

GET IN THE HABIT OF USING CHECKLISTS.

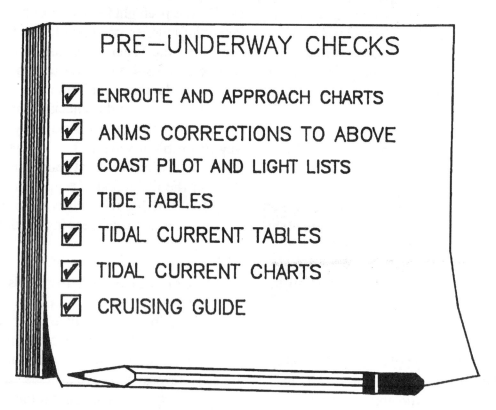

PRE—UNDERWAY CHECKS

- ☑ ENROUTE AND APPROACH CHARTS
- ☑ ANMS CORRECTIONS TO ABOVE
- ☑ COAST PILOT AND LIGHT LISTS
- ☑ TIDE TABLES
- ☑ TIDAL CURRENT TABLES
- ☑ TIDAL CURRENT CHARTS
- ☑ CRUISING GUIDE

rough weather checks, and the like. Put experience to work by gradually developing and revising these checklists for maximum utility on your vessel. And remember that checklists are particularly useful in emergency situations because it is precisely in time of emergency that important items are most likely to be overlooked.

Principle 6:
Slow Down or Stop the Vessel If Necessary and Circumstances Permit

Sometimes a crisis is self-induced to a degree. It may be a crisis to be unsure of your position when approaching a reef-strewn harbor at 20 knots. At this speed the vessel will travel over 333 yards in 30 seconds, roughly the length of time that it has taken you to read two or three paragraphs of this text. But part of this crisis is self-induced and can be removed by the simple expedient of slowing down or stopping. (Obviously, there are circumstances where stopping is ill-advised, such as in the middle of running a tough inlet.)

It was noted in Chapter 9 that any confusion in interpreting a relative motion plot (RMP) from radar observations can be eliminated if you stop. After stopping, aside from the effects of possible drift, the radar plot appears much the same as if a true motion device were used. *This comment is not intended to relieve the mariner of any obligation under the navigation rules, such as the responsibility of the stand-on vessel (if defined) to maintain course and speed.*

Slowing down or stopping may be prudent or necessary in circumstances of reduced visibility. And it should be considered whenever the vessel is in hazardous waters and you are unsure of your position. Leaving the vessel running will just get you to the scene of the accident faster!

Slowing down may also be prudent even if you know generally where you are, but can use extra time to think, identify buoys or lights, and/or take more frequent position fixes. In a harbor with a complex and/or unfamiliar approach, for

FIGURE 12-3. RECREATIONAL BOATING ACCIDENTS BY OPERATION AT THE TIME OF ACCIDENT: DRIFTING AND/ OR ANCHORED VESSELS ARE STILL AT RISK.

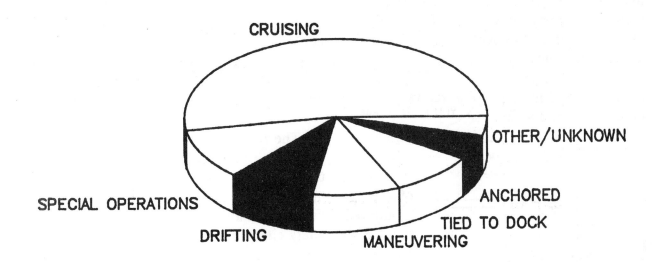

CRUISING

OTHER/UNKNOWN

ANCHORED

SPECIAL OPERATIONS

TIED TO DOCK

DRIFTING

MANEUVERING

ESTIMATES FROM "BOATING STATISTICS, 1988" SEE REFERENCES

example, proceeding at a slower speed provides the navigator time to "catch up" with the physical progress of a vessel. It is not unusual for three or more minutes to be required to take bearings and plot a fix.[5] At 20 knots the vessel will be 1 M or approximately 2,000 yards "beyond" the fix by the time it is plotted; at 5 knots only 500 yards.

If circumstances permit (e.g., absence of rocks, shoals, bars, crab or lobster pots, etc.) it may be advisable to move a shallow-draft vessel out of the main channel to avoid traffic conflicts with deep-draft vessels.

If you elect to drift or anchor, remember that, while this gives you valuable time to assess your situation, it confers no immunity from acci-

dents. It is still important to stay alert and maintain a proper lookout. As Figure 12-3 shows the majority of recreational boating accidents (72.4%) occur while vessels are cruising, engaged in special operations (e.g., waterskiing, towing, being towed), or maneuvering, but an appreciable fraction (14.6%) occur while drifting or at anchor.

When it comes to stopping, vessels have an extraordinary advantage over aircraft. Stopping gives you time to think, and to use other means of fixing the vessel's position. Stopping gives you silence to listen. Stopping allows you time to regain command. Remember the immortal phrase given in Mixter's *Primer of Navigation,* "the anchor is part of the navigator's equipment!"

---

[5]According to the *Admiralty Manual of Navigation,* this process should take no more than 2 minutes, and "a practised navigator should be able to complete the task in 60 seconds." However, it is believed that the figure given in the text is more representative for recreational boaters.

Principle 7:

Preplan As Much As Possible

George S. Morrison, in discussing the planning for the so-called Culebra Cut, one of the most difficult ports of the Panama Canal is quoted as saying: "It was a piece of work that reminds me of what a teacher said to me when I was at Exeter over forty years ago, that if he had five minutes in which to solve a problem he would spend three deciding the best way to do it." So it is with the practice of navigation. Time spent in planning the details of a voyage is time well spent. Simply put, if you fail to plan you plan to fail.

SIMPLY PUT, IF YOU FAIL TO PLAN YOU PLAN TO FAIL

Search and rescue experience indicates that too many mariners neglect to plan fuel needs adequately. They behave as though they were driving automobiles in easy range of the next service station. On the water, refueling opportunities are often more limited. Moreover, other factors combine to make fuel consumption per nautical mile quite variable--unplanned for currents, a diversion to assist a disabled vessel, etc. For these reasons, formal fuel planning, as discussed in Chapter 11, is important. Fuel planning should not be limited to "before the fact" calculations. A mariner should know the vessel's fuel state and safe cruising radius at all times, together with feasible alternate destinations where fuel is available. A few minutes time spent with the U.S. Coast Pilot, or equivalent cruising guide are all that is required to identify these alternates.

Preplanning is particularly important for approaches to unfamiliar harbors. Of course, the relevant charts and reference publications should be aboard, but it is even easier if the navigator summarizes this information as extra chart annotations, or as separate lists. (For example, a list of which ATONs have horns, gongs, or other sound-producing devices would be a handy reference in circumstances of reduced visibility.) The mere act of writing this information down increases the navigator's retention. Precalculated turning bearings (even if buoys are available) on what are expected to be prominent visible landmarks save work during the actual approach when time may be at a premium.

The mariner should devote some time to thinking through possible *contingencies* during the voyage planning process. For example, the mariner might plan to make a landfall by offsetting the intended aim point so as to arrive definitely either north or south of the harbor entrance (a trick of long ago and present-day navigators alike) and to turn one way or the other to follow a particular depth contour to the main channel. However, this plan is certain to need revision if the depth sounder becomes inoperative enroute. Time spent in the comfort of your den or office thinking about how to handle this contingency and the precalculation of alternate check points based upon visual fixes is likely to be much more productive than the same time spent at the navigator's station of a pitching vessel.

As noted in earlier chapters of this text, it is impossible to plan out everything in advance-- unanticipated events can and do arise. However, planning can go a long way towards reducing the likelihood and/or consequences of an unpleasant surprise. Arrival at the proper time to take advantage of a slack or favorable current (Chapter 8), the on-board availability of the appropriate large-scale nautical charts for alternate destinations, adequate fuel margins (Chapter 11), distance of visibility arcs (Chapter 10) scribed on charts, and an array of prominent preidentified fix objects, for example, will not be happenstance events if a little care is exercised in the planning phase of a voyage. Moreover, the

Figure 12-4. The destroyers *S. P. Lee* (right) and *Nicholas* (left) seen against the rock-strewn coast. Photograph originally appeared in *Tragedy at Honda,* and is reproduced with the kind permission of the Lockwood family.

development of contingency plans gives the navigator a real edge in the battle with panic when trouble develops. It's much more calming (to the navigator and crew alike) to be able to say "let's put plan B into operation," rather than "this sure doesn't look like Kansas, Toto. Any ideas?" Planning, like checklists, serves to make contingencies routine.

Principle 8:
Be Open to Data or Information at Variance With Your Understanding of the Situation

Robert Jervis, a political scientist writing on misperception in international politics, writes that "actors tend to perceive what they expect." Humans often tend to form fixed ideas based upon limited information. Once formed, these ideas are often difficult to displace and contrary evidence may be dismissed as incorrect or overlooked entirely.

The same phenomenon also occurs with navigators. In this context, the fixed idea might be the appropriateness of a particular method of navigation (compared to alternatives), or even the accuracy of a particular position estimate developed by this method. Often these ideas are soundly based--it is generally true, for example, that a visual fix taken on positively identified fixed ATONs is likely to be more accurate than one based solely on RDF bearings. The danger arises when alternative and conflicting information is simply rejected out of hand without more careful examination.

Errors of this type have occurred on numerous occasions in the history of navigation. Perhaps the most dramatic example of this error occurred on the night of 8 September 1923 when nine navy destroyers ran aground and seven were stranded/sunk off the coast of California.

In brief, the story is as follows. The destroyers were part of a navy training exercise involving a high-speed endurance test run down the coast of California from San Francisco to San

Figure 12-5. Port side of the destroyers *Young* (middle distance) and *Chauncey* (foreground). The *Woodbury* (309) can be seen in the distance. Photograph originally appeared in *Tragedy at Honda,* and is reproduced with the kind permission of the Lockwood family.

Diego. The lead destroyer had three experienced navigators aboard, one fresh from teaching navigation at the U.S. Naval Academy.

During the run, a careful DR track was maintained, predicated on the assumption of a 20 knot speed. RDF was then a new system and, in the opinion of the many mariners, unproven. None the less, RDF bearings were obtained from a shore station.[6] These bearings gave LOPs that were inconsistent with the lead destroyer's (the *Delphy*) DR course, indicating that the squadron was not making good the estimated SOA and/or the squadron was closer to the shore than planned.

An anticipated sighting of a light at Point Arguello was not observed, and so no visual LOPs or running fixes were obtained from this source. Visibility was sharply reduced by fog.

Given this situation, a prudent mariner should have reduced speed to try to sort things out and, in this case, to obtain soundings that might confirm or reject the DR position. (One of the destroyers, the *Thompson,* did just that but, as this was the last destroyer in the column, this did not help the others.) This was not done by the lead ship, in part because of the demands of the training exercise to maintain speed. In any event, a further RDF bearing was taken which also in-

---

[6] As a point of historical interest, RDFs operated slightly differently during the early days. Then mariners radioed in to a shore-based direction finding (DF) station, which would report the bearing of the ship. Thus, if each of the destroyers were to independently request DF bearings, frequency congestion could result. With today's systems many users can simultaneously take bearings on an RDF signal, (see Chapter 9).

Figure 12-6. Another photograph of *Chauncey* (296) at right
and *Woodbury* (309) at left on what is now known as Woodbury Rock.
The mast of the *Fuller* (297) can be seen projecting above Woodbury Rock.
Photograph courtesy of the Lockwood family.

dicated that the squadron was well north of its DR position at the entrance to the Santa Barbara channel. Despite this evidence, the navigators in the lead destroyer clung to the idea that the DR was correct and that the RDF bearings were erroneous. Indeed, it was assumed that a *reciprocal* bearing was obtained. The squadron altered course to an easterly heading and, one-by-one in sequence, crashed onto the rocks appropriately named "the Devil's Jaw" well north of the DR position. Figures 12-4, 12-5, and 12-6 show photographs taken after the disaster. Remarkably, although nine vessels were sunk or damaged, only 23 sailors of the 800 at risk were killed. The full version of this abbreviated story can be found in the excellent (but unfortunately out-of-print) book, *Tragedy at Honda,* listed among the references.

There are many lessons to be learned from this tragedy--e.g., some navigators on the following destroyers had a very different appreciation of the situation yet did not question the order to alter course to the east, etc. But those errors that stand out in this context are the reluctance and ultimately failure of the lead navigation team to consider information at variance with their preconceived DR-based estimate of position (Principle 8), their unwillingness to seek additional depth information (Principle 3), or to slow down to sort things out (Principle 6).

Many observers have drawn the analogy between navigation and solving a puzzle. The pieces of the puzzle are the various bits of information, or misinformation, and the navigator has to assemble these into a coherent picture. Its comforting when the pieces fit....but this principle reminds us that it is equally important if they don't.

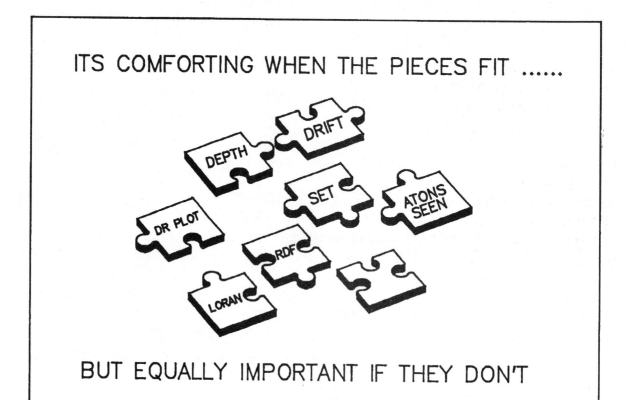

ITS COMFORTING WHEN THE PIECES FIT ......

DRIFT
DEPTH
SET
ATONS SEEN
DR PLOT
RDF
LORAN

BUT EQUALLY IMPORTANT IF THEY DON'T

Principle 9::
Know and Operate Within Your Limits

In commercial aviation, the concept of *limits* and standards for safe operation are well developed and codified. For example, there are explicit regulatory limits on:

(i) the aircraft: Commercial aircraft have *minimum equipment lists* which determine exactly what equipment must be *on-board and operational* before a flight is permitted.

(ii) the pilot: Pilots are likewise subject to a variety of explicit limits/requirements. Pilots without an instrument rating, for example, cannot legally undertake a flight unless the weather conditions along the route of flight satisfy certain constraints in terms of ceiling and visibility. Additionally, the pilot must satisfy recent experience and retraining requirements.

(iii) destination weather: In addition to requirements on the demonstrated proficiency of the pilot, each type of instrument approach to a destination airport has unique weather minimums. So-called *precision approaches* to an airport enable the pilot to descend lower and operate in lower visibility than do nonprecision approaches to the same airport. And even for the same type of instrument approach (e.g., ADF) the weather minimums may vary from airport to airport. Finally, the legal weather minimums for a particular instrument approach become more stringent if components of the landing system are inoperative.

Recreational boaters are not federally licensed and have much greater flexibility of operation. None the less, the concept of self-imposed limits is valuable. It is obviously foolish, for example, to deliberately undertake an ocean voyage without at least a working knowledge of celestial navigation and the appropriate tools, reference publications, and nautical charts. (This notwithstanding the story published in one of the otherwise fine boating magazines of a major ocean crossing in which the navigator brought books and embarked on a "crash" on-the-job self-training program in celestial navigation!) Some harbors may require extensive local knowledge for safe operation, while others have easy and well-marked approaches. Some harbors may be easy to enter during conditions of daylight and good visibility, but tricky at night or in fog. In this latter example, a prudent mariner would plan to arrive at the harbor during times of good visibility and either divert to an alternate destination or anchor out if this proved impossible.

A prudent navigator gives thought to these and other factors in deciding whether or when to attempt a particular voyage. Table 12–1 provides a candidate list of factors to consider in establishing personal limits to operation. There is no attempt to spell out detailed "go/no-go" rules. This is left to the discretion of the navigator. However, it is suggested that the navigator think carefully about establishing personal limits for these and other relevant factors. Over time, these limits are likely to change. As the navigator gains experience, local knowledge, or skippers a better-equipped vessel, these personal limits can be modified or stretched.

One of the "personal minimums" often overlooked by mariners and aircraft pilots alike is fatigue. Persons can suffer two overlapping types of fatigue, *acute skill fatigue,* or *chronic fatigue.* Acute skill fatigue is that diminution of acuity resulting from task repetition during an extended voyage. Symptoms include lassitude,

---

TABLE 12-1
A SUGGESTED LIST OF FACTORS TO
CONSIDER FOR SETTING PERSONAL LIMITS

1. General knowledge and recent experience of navigator and crew.

2. Local knowledge of navigator and crew.

3. Navigation equipment (including up-to-date and corrected nautical charts and navigation reference publications) and communications gear aboard.

4. Enroute and destination weather (visibility and sea conditions) and daylight/ darkness at ETA.

5. Features of destination harbor and enroute:
   - hazards to navigation
   - availability of ATONs.

6. Availability and characteristics of nearby alternate destinations.

7. Health and fatigue status of navigator/crew.

8. General seaworthiness and type/size/speed of vessel.

an inability to concentrate, and an aversion to further activity. Fatigue leads to degradation of skills, increased reaction time, and impaired judgment. Fatigue is not often explicitly cited as a cause of vessel or aircraft accidents, in part because data may be lacking and/or the effects of fatigue are difficult to quantify.[7] None the less it is generally recognized that a well-rested crew is important. Fatigue was one of the causes listed in the crash of a Learjet on final approach to Byrd Field in Richmond, VA, on 6 May 1980. At the time of the accident, the pilot had been awake for 20 hours, and the copilot for 18 hours. The crash came after the pilots misjudged the approach.

Navigators should set personal fatigue standards as part of their personal limits.

Principle 10:
Maintain A DR Plot

Arguably the need to maintain an accurate DR plot falls under several principles enumerated above. But, to lend emphasis to this important task, it is made a separate principle.

Were this text written as few as ten years ago, it would probably not have been necessary to underscore the need for DR plotting. However, the "electronic revolution" with its proliferation of ever more lightweight, lower cost and more powerful navigation tools such as loran, radar, electronic charting, and integrated navigation packages, has rendered DR all but obsolete in the minds of many navigators.

Electronic navigation is fast, accurate, convenient, and powerful. Electronic systems have coverage in many parts of the world, and (with the elimination of the "mid-continent" loran gap) soon will completely cover all U.S. waters. The ground system reliability of the principal electronic navigation aids that require external signals (e.g., loran, RDF) is very high, typically exceeding 99.9% of the scheduled on-air hours.

Yet, for these systems to function, the shipboard components must also work correctly. As noted in many places in this text, the marine environment is notoriously hostile (or at least unkind) to electronics and power supplies alike. Barely a month goes by without one or more articles appearing in the boating press reporting instances of shipboard failures of electronic components on recreational, commercial, and naval vessels alike. Fuses blow, antennas are knocked down, green water breaks over the bow and saturates the supposedly waterproof loran, and batteries or alternators fail. G. R. Kane, for example, in his interesting book, *Instant Navigation*, writes of a racing yacht lost on a Cuban shoal after a loran failure which occurred after starting the engine to recharge the batteries. This was an unpleasant event, to be sure, and one with critical consequences because the navigator apparently did not maintain a DR track or record of fixes.

Redundancy is a partial solution to the availability/reliability problems of electronic systems. Carry extra fuses, bulbs, an emergency antenna, and even complete systems--such as a portable, rechargeable, self-contained, battery-powered loran and/or RDF. But this solution is expensive and, in any event, still imperfect.

A cheaper and ultimately more satisfactory solution to the problem is to maintain a DR plot and update this by frequent visual fixes as discussed in Chapters 5 and 6 of this text. Unless the mariner is voyaging near home port in well-known waters and the actual and forecast weather is benign, a DR plot should be maintained--and updated as new data become available.

---

[7]Search and rescue planners do make an approximate allowance for fatigue of search crews by a factor to reduce the effective range of detection. Also, the Coast Guard has explicit fatigue standards for crews.

As the story of the tragedy at Honda illustrates, DR positions can still be in error. But these are undoubtedly superior to no position at all. Remember the proverb that in the land of the blind, the one-eyed man is king.

Concluding Comments

Probably most readers of this text will never elect to make navigation a profession, in the sense of a paying occupation. But all readers of this text have the opportunity to become a *professional navigator* in the sense of developing a professional attitude and professional calibre skills and judgment. Graduation from high school, college, or university is often called commencement, because this marks the point when the graduate commences to gain experience, maturity, and insight--in a word "wisdom." Go forth, learn, enjoy, stay humble (remember it is arrogant to sail *to* a destination and appropriately humble to sail *towards* a destination[8]), continue to study (the chapter references are a good starting point), write and tell us of your experiences. Better still, join the United States Coast Guard Auxiliary and consider writing the next edition of this book!

---

[8]Read the excellent book on the Gulf Stream listed in the references for the origin of this advice.

REFERENCES

Alden, J. D. *Flush Decks and Four Pipes*, United States Naval Institute, Annapolis, MD, 1965.

Anon. "A Spin of the Dial," *Ocean Navigator*, No. 30, January/February 1990, pp. 67-68.

Anon. "Nantucket LNB Goes Adrift,"*Ocean Navigator*, No. 11, January/February 1987, p. 12.

Bachand, R. G. *Northeast Lights: Lighthouses and Lightships Rhode Island to Cape May New Jersey*, Sea Sports Publications, Norwalk, CT, 1989.

Bloomfield, H. V. L. *The Compact History of the United States Coast Guard*, Hawthorn Books, New York, NY, 1966.

Bright, C. "A Confusing Night Off Cape Hatteras," *Ocean Navigator*, No. 14, July/August 1987, pp. 6, 44.

Cahill, R. A. *Strandings and Their Causes*, Fairplay Publications, London, UK, 1985.

Chichester, Sir F. *Gipsy Moth Circles the World*, Coward-McCann, Inc., New York, NY, 1967.

Coote, J. O. *Yacht Navigation -- My Way*, W. W. Norton and Company, New York, NY, 1988.

Creamer, M. "Dead Reckoning During the Onslaught,"*Ocean Navigator*, January/February 1986, p. 39.

Hadaway, R. B. "Course Zero Nine Five," *United States Naval Institute Proceedings*, Vol. 83, Jan 1957, pp 40-48.

Haines, T. B. "Retrospective," *AOPA Pilot*, Vol. 33, No. 2, February 1990, p. 102.

Hall, G. E. "The Correct Use of Corrections," *Ocean Navigator*, No. 23, January/February 1989, pp. 15-16.

Howell, S. "Aground in the Bahamas,"*Ocean Navigator*, July/August 1985, pp. 8 - 10.

Jervis, R. "Hypotheses on Misperception," *World Politics*, Vol. 20, No. 3, 1968, pp. 454 - 479.

Jones, R. V. "The Theory of Practical Joking -- Its Relevance to Physics,"*Bulletin of the Institute of Physics*, June 1967, p. 7.

Kane, G. R. *Instant Navigation*, Second Edition, Associated Marine, San Mateo, CA, 1984.

Lockwood, C. A., and H. C. Adamson. *Tragedy at Honda*, Chilton Company, Philadelphia, PA, 1960.

Lord, W. *A Night To Remember*, Bantam Books, New York, NY, August 1988, p. 135.

MacLeish, W. H. *The Gulf Stream*, Houghton Mifflin Co., Boston, MA, 1989.

McCullough, D. *The Path Between the Seas*, Simon and Schuster, New York, NY, 1977.

Mixter, G. W. (McClench, D., Ed.), *Primer of Navigation*, Fifth Edition, Van Nostrand Reinhold Co., New York, NY, 1967.

Mueller, W. "7 Out at Pt. Honda," *Sea Classics*, Special Edition, Spring 1980, pp. 40 *et seq.*

Quinn, W. P., *Shipwrecks Along the Atlantic Coast*, Parnassus Imprints, Orleans, MA, 1988.

Rousmaniere, J. *The Annapolis Book of Seamanship, New Revised Edition,* Simon and Schuster, NY, 1989, p. 264.

United States Department of Transportation, United States Coast Guard. *Boating Statistics 1988,* COMDTPUB P16754.1, Washington, DC, June 1989.

United States Department of Transportation, United States Coast Guard. *Shiphandling,* D 42601-0, U.S. Coast Guard Institute, Oklahoma City, OK, 1988.

United States Power Squadrons. *The Advanced Piloting Course,* USPS, 1986, PAP-85/86 Appendix SM B-2.

Walsh, G. "Poor Navigation Leads to Disaster," *Ocean Navigator,* No. 13, May/June 1987, pp. 5 - 6.

Waters, J. M., Jr. *Rescue at Sea,* Second Edition, Naval Institute Press, Annapolis, MD, 1989.

Wright, F. W. *Celestial Navigation,* Cornell Maritime Press, Centreville, MD, 1982.

Appendix A

Glossary

Attached is a glossary of nautical terms for convenient reference. Many, but not all, of these terms are used in this *Advanced Coastal Navigation* text or on the 1210-Tr chart.. These definitions are brief of necessity. The reader is referred to the appropriate chapter in the text and the associated references for a more complete discussion. Certain of these definitions have been taken from the *Light List*, the *Tide Tables* and *Bowditch*. Consult Appendix B for any abbreviations.

This glossary serves as more than simply a convenient source for definitions of words used in the text. Definitions are also included for some specialized terms of art (e.g., rate, phase coding, GDOP) that space and scope constraints prevented from being discussed at any length in the text.

Finally, many specialized terms that are used on nautical charts are included. The 1210-Tr chart is integral to this course, and it is appropriate to provide the technical definitions of many of the terms used on this chart. To many, the distinctions among such terms as rock awash, rock, and submerged rock may seem pedantic. But, these distinctions could be important to the navigator. As it is, aside from *Bowditch* (which, though excellent, is found to be intimidating by many beginning students of navigation), there is no single, generally accessible, and easily readable source for these specialized terms. It is hoped that the ACN student finds this a worthwhile source.

A

Abeam—At right angles to the keel of the boat, but not on the boat.

Aboard—On or within the boat.

Abreast—Side by side; by the side of.

Absolute Accuracy—Term often used in connection with loran system to mean the difference between the loran's estimate of position and the actual position. Also called geodetic accuracy. Within the coverage area, the absolute accuracy of loran-C is 0.25 NM or better.

Acquisition—The reception and identification of transmitted loran-C signals from master and selected secondaries to permit reliable measurement of TDs. The requisite signal-to-noise ratio for original signal acquisition is generally greater than for tracking (qv).

Additional Secondary Factors—Land path factors due to variation in the conductivity of the earth's surface that alter the speed of propagation of loran signals over land compared to over water. ASFs degrade the absolute accuracy of a loran system (unless compensated for) but do not affect the repeatable accuracy.

Adrift—Loose, not on moorings or towline.

Advanced LOP—A line of position which has been moved forward, parallel to itself, along a course line to obtain a line of position at a later time. If the same procedure is followed to move the line to an earlier time, the LOP is said to be retired.

Aft—The stern or back of the vessel.

Agger—See Double Tide.

Agonic Line—The imaginary line connecting points of zero variation.

Aground—A vessel touching or fast to the bottom.

Aid to Navigation (ATON or NAVAID)—Any device external to a vessel or aircraft specifically intended to assist navigators in determining their position or safe course, or to warn them of dangers or obstructions to navigation.

Alee—Away from the direction of the wind. Opposite of windward.

Align—To place objects in line.

Alternating Light—A rhythmic light showing light of alternating colors.

Amidships—The center of the boat with reference to its length or breath.

Anchor Alarm—Feature of many loran-C receivers that can be set to warn the user that the vessel has moved outside the swing circle of the anchor. This is also termed an anchor watch.

Anchor Rode—See Rode.

Anchor Scope—See Scope.

Anchorage—A place suitable for anchoring in relation to the wind, seas and bottom; and permitted by regulations.

Anchorage Mark—A navigation mark which indicates an anchorage area or defines its limits.

Angle of Cut—The smaller angular difference of two bearings or lines of position. See also crossing angle.

Annotation—Any marking on illustrative material for the purpose of clarification, such as numbers, letters, symbols, or signs.

Annual Inequality—Seasonal variation in the water level or current, more or less periodic, due chiefly to meteorological causes.

Apogean Tides or Tidal Currents—Tides of decreased range or currents of decreased speed occurring monthly as the result of the moon being in apogee (farthest from the earth).

Apogee—Point in the lunar cycle when the moon and the earth are furthest apart. Tides have decreased range when the moon is in apogee.

Arc Measure—The angle included between radii connecting the ends of an arc with the center of the circle of which it is a part.

Arc Of Visibility—The portion of the horizon over which a lighted aid to navigation is visible from seaward.

Armed Lead—A weight which has a hollowed bottom and is filled with tallow, grease, wax, chewing gum, or bedding compound to bring up a sample of the bottom.

Articulated Beacon—A beacon-like buoyant structure, tethered directly to the seabed and having no watch circle. Called articulated light or articulated daybeacon, as appropriate.

Assigned Position—The latitude and longitude position for an aid to navigation.

Astern—Direction of movement, opposite of ahead; toward a vessel's stern.

Athwartships—Across or at right angle to the centerline of a boat; rowboat seats are generally placed athwartships (thwarts).

Aural Null—A null detected by listening for a minimum or the complete absence of an audible signal. This null as received by a radio direction finder indicates that the plane of its loop antenna is perpendicular to the direction of the radio wave.

Automated Notices to Mariners System—Computer system that can be accessed by authorized users to obtain chart corrections and notices to mariners. Users need a teletype, computer terminal, or other device, and an access code available from DMA.

Autopilot—Device for automatic steering of a vessel. Depending upon the sophistication of the autopilot, these can be used to maintain a heading, or to interface with a loran or other electronic navigation system. Sometimes informally called "George" or "Iron Mike."

Axis Of Rotation—The imaginary line connecting the poles of the earth and on which the earth supposedly spins or rotates.

B

Back Range—A range observed astern, particularly one used as guidance for a craft moving away from the objects forming the range.

Bar—A ridge or mound of sand, gravel, or other unconsolidated material below the high water level, especially at the mouth of a river or estuary which may obstruct navigation.

Bare Poles—When a sailboat is underway with no sails set.

Bare Rock—A rock that extends above the mean high water datum in tidal areas or above the low water datum in the Great Lakes. See also rock awash, submerged rock.

Baseline—The segment of a great circle that joins the master and a secondary station in a loran chain.

Baseline Extension—The extension of the baseline beyond the two joined stations. Loran positions in baseline extension areas are problematic and ambiguous.

Bay—A recess in the shore, on an inlet of a sea or lake between two capes or headlands, that may vary greatly in size but is usually smaller than a gulf but larger than a cove.

Beacon—A lighted or unlighted fixed aid to navigation attached directly to the earth's surface. (Lights and daybeacons both constitute "beacons.")

Beam—The greatest width of the boat.

Beam Sea—Waves act directly on the vessel's sides (coming from abeam) and, in rough water, could roll some boats over on their side. Commonly known as "in the trough."

Bearing—The horizontal direction of a line of sight between two objects on the surface of the earth.

Beat—To sail to windward, generally in a series of tacks. Beating is one of the three points of sailing, also referred to as sailing "close-hauled" or "by the wind."

Bell—A sound signal producing bell tones by means of a hammer actuated by electricity or, on buoys, by sea motion.

Bifurcation—The point where a channel divides when proceeding from seaward. The place where two tributaries meet.

Bight—1. A long and gradual bend or recess in the coastline which forms a large open receding bay. 2. A bend in a river or mountain range.

Binnacle—A stand holding the steering compass.

Binocular--An optical instrument for use with both eyes simultaneously.

Blink—An indication that the master or secondary signals in a loran chain are out of tolerance and not to be used. Loran receivers have a blink alarm that warns the user that the indicated positions may not be reliable. Blink conditions warn that the signal power or TD is out-of-tolerance (OOT) and/or that an improper phase code or GRI is being transmitted.

Bluff—A headland or stretch of cliff having a broad nearly perpendicular face. See also cliff.

Boat—A fairly indefinite term. A waterborne vehicle smaller than a ship. One definition is a small craft carried aboard a ship. Submarines, however, are universally referred to as boats.

Bobbing a Light—Quickly lowering the height of eye several feet and then raising it again when a navigational light is first sighted to determine whether or not the observer is at the geographic range of the light. If he is, the light disappears when the eye is lowered and reappears when it is restored to its original position.

Bolt Holes—Safe places to anchor or moor in the event that the weather worsens or mechanical difficulties occur.

Boulder—A detached water-rounded stone more than 256 millimeters in diameter, i.e., roughly larger than a basketball. See also cobble.

Bow—The forward part of a boat.

Breakwater—Anything which breaks the force of the sea at a particular place, thus forming protection for vessels. Often an artificial embankment built to protect the entrance to a harbor, or to form an artificial harbor. See also jetty.

Bridge—1. An elevated structure extending across or over the deck of a vessel or part of such a structure. 2. A structure erected over a depression or an obstacle such as a body of water, railroad, etc. to provide a roadway for vehicles or pedestrians.

Broach—The turning of a boat parallel to the waves, subjecting it to possible capsizing.

Broad On The Beam—At right angles to the keel or centerline. Abeam (not aboard the vessel).

Broad On The Bow—A direction midway between abeam and dead ahead.

Broad On The Quarter—A direction midway between abeam and dead astern.

Broadcast Notice to Mariners—A radio broadcast designed to provide important marine information.

Building or House—One of these terms, as appropriate, is used on nautical charts when the entire structure is a landmark, rather than an individual feature of it.

Bulkhead—A transverse, vertical partition separating compartments.

Buoy—A floating object of defined shape and color, which is anchored at a given position and serves as an aid to navigation.

Buoy System—IALA Maritime Buoyage System B applies to buoys and beacons that indicate the lateral limits of navigable channels, obstructions, dangers such as wrecks, and other areas or features of importance to the mariner.

Burdened Vessel—That vessel which, according to the applicable Navigation Rules, must give way to another (privileged) vessel. The terms have been superseded by the terms "give-way" and "stand-on."

C

Cable Area—Area shown on charts transited by submarine cables. Formal anchorage restrictions may apply in cable areas.

Cairn—A mound of rough stones or concrete, particularly one serving or intended to serve as a *landmark*. The stones are customarily piled in a pyramidal or beehive shape.

Cape—A relatively extensive land area jutting seaward from a continent, or large island, which prominently marks a change in or interrupts notably the coastal trend.

Channel—1. That part of a body of water deep enough for navigation through an area otherwise not suitable. It is usually marked by a single or double line of buoys and sometimes by ranges. 2. The deepest part of a stream, bay, or strait, through which the main current flows. 3. A name given to large straits, for example, the English Channel.

Characteristic—The audible, visual, or electronic signal displayed by an aid to navigation to assist in the identification of an aid to navigation. Characteristic refers to lights, sound signals, racons, radiobeacons, and daybeacons.

Chart—A nautical map for use by mariners or aviators, which depicts features and displays information of interest to these groups..

Chart NO. 1—A booklet prepared by the National Ocean Survey which contains symbols and abbreviations that have been approved for use on nautical charts published by the U. S. Government. Past editions of this chart were in actual chart form.

Chart Scale—The number of distance units on the earth's surface represented by the same distance unit on the chart. Charts are typically partitioned on the basis of scale. Sailing charts have scales of 1:600,000 and greater. General charts have scales between 1:150,000 and 1:600,000. Coast charts have scales between 1:40,000 and 1:150,000. Harbor charts have scales larger than 1:40,000.

Chart Symbol—A character, letter, or similar graphic representation used on a chart to indicate some object, characteristic, etc. May be called map symbol when applied to any map.

Chimney—A relatively small, upright structure projecting above a building for the conveyance of smoke.

Clay—See mud.

Clear—To leave or pass safely, as to clear port or clear a shoal.

Clearing Bearing—British term for danger bearing.

Cliff—Land arising abruptly for a considerable distance above water or surrounding land. See also bluff.

Close Aboard—Not on, but near to, a vessel.

Close-hauled—Sailing with the boom hauled as close to the centerline of the vessel as is possible, thus sailing as much into the wind as is possible. Also known as beating, or "by the wind"; one of the three points of sailing.

Closest Point of Approach—The closest distance that a target will pass clear of the reference vessel. This distance is estimated from the relative motion plot. The estimated time that this occurs is called the time to closest point of approach (TCPA).

Clutter (Radar)—Unwanted radar echoes reflected from heavy rain, snow, waves, etc., which may obscure relatively large areas on the PPI—and thus targets of interest. Related terms: sea clutter, sea return, rain clutter.

Cobble—See stone.

Coastal Confluence Zone—A zone extending seaward 50 nautical miles from shore or to the 100 fathom curve, whichever is greater.

Coastal Navigation—Navigation in coastal (sometimes called pilot) waters, where the opportunity exists to determine or check the vessel's position by reference to navigational aids and observations (by either visual or electronic means) of the coast and its features.

Cocked Hat—Error triangle formed by lines of position that do not cross at a common point. So named because of the characteristic appearance of these lines in the vicinity of the fix. The size of the cocked hat is an indication of the precision of the fix--and is valuable information to the navigator. For this reason, conservative navigators term a position a fix only if at least three objects are used to determine the fix. Fixes determined only from two LOPs would be relegated to the status of estimated positions in this view.

Cockpit—An opening in the deck from which the boat is handled.

COLREGS, 72—The International Regulations for Preventing Collisions at Sea, 1972, commonly called the International Rules.

Coming About—The changing of course when close-hauled by swinging the bow through the eye of the wind and changing from one tack to another; reverse course or nearly so.

Commissioned—Specialized term of art to denote the action of placing a previously discontinued aid to navigation back in operation.

Compass Card—Part of a compass, the card is graduated in degrees, to conform with the magnetic meridian-referenced direction system inscribed with direction which remains constant; the vessel turns, not the card.

Compass Errors—Generic term used to describe all compass errors including variation, deviation, northerly turning error, acceleration error, heeling error. These are discussed at length in Chapter 2.

Compass Heading—The direction a vessel is heading at any one instant as shown by its compass.

Compass Point—One of 32 points of the compass equal to 11-1/4 degrees.

Compass Rose—The resulting figure when the complete 360° directional system is developed as a circle with each degree graduated upon it, and with the 000° indicated as true north. Also called true rose. This is printed on nautical charts for determining direction.

Composite Group-Flashing Light—A group-flashing light in which the flashes are combined in successive groups of different numbers of flashes.

Composite Group-Occulting Light—A light similar to a group-occulting light except that the successive groups in a period have different numbers of eclipses.

Conformal Projection—A map or chart projection which preserves correct angular relationships.

Contact—Any echo detected on the radarscope not evaluated as clutter or as a false echo. The term "contact" is used in a general sense, whereas "target" (q.v.) is used in a more particular sense to denote a contact about which more information (such as CPA, TCPA, course, or speed) is desired. Thus, radar targets would typically be plotted. Of course, the difference is not clear cut--one navigator's contact might be another's target.

Contour Lines—Lines that connect points of equal depth on a nautical chart.

Conventional Direction of Buoyage—The general direction taken by the mariner when approaching a harbor, river, estuary, or other waterway from seaward, or proceeding upstream or in the direction of the main stream of flood tide, or in the direction indicated in appropriate nautical documents (normally, following a clockwise direction around land masses).

Coriolis Force—The deflective effect of the earth's rotation on an object in motion which causes it to divert to the right in the northern hemisphere. (See rotary current.)

Correcting—Converting a compass heading or a magnetic heading to its equivalent true heading.

Course (C)—Course is the average heading and the horizontal direction in which a vessel is intended to be steered, expressed as the angular distance relative to north, usually from 000° at north, clockwise through 359° from the point of departure or start of the course to the point of arrival or other point of intended location.

Course Deviation Indicator—An indicator, shown on some lorans, that graphically displays whether or nor the vessel is on course and, if not, the direction to return to course.

Course LOP—An LOP situated approximately directly ahead or behind the vessel, so named because the LOP provides a good indication of the vessel's CMG.

Course Made Good (CMG)—This indicates the single resultant direction from a point of departure to a point of arrival at a given time. (Synonym: Track Made Good)

Course Of Advance (COA)—This indicates the direction of the *intended* path to be made good *over the ground*.

Course Over the Ground (COG)—This indicates the direction of the path *actually followed* by the vessel *over the ground,* usually an irregular line.

Cove—A small sheltered recess or indentation in a shore or coast, generally inside a large embayment.

Cross Rate (Cross Chain) Interference—Interference in the reception of radio signals from one loran chain caused by signals from another loran chain.

Cross Track Error—Distance between the vessel's actual position and the direct course between two waypoints.

Cross Track Error Alarm—Alarm that can be set on many loran-C receivers that warns the navigator if the vessel's cross track error exceeds some pre-specified value.

Crossing Angle—Generally, the angle between two LOPs which determine a fix. The closer this angle is to 90 degrees, the better the fix. Also used with loran LOPs.

Cupola—A small dome-shaped tower or turret rising from a building.

Current—Term used in two senses. It is used to refer either to the horizontal motion over the ground, including ocean current, tidal, and river currents, or more generally to these factors together with the effect of wind and seas, steering error of the helmsman, compass error, speed curve error, and other factors. (See Chapter 7.)

Current (alternate definition)—Generally, a horizontal movement of water. Currents may be classified as *tidal* and *nontidal*. Tidal currents are caused by gravitational interactions between the sun, moon, and earth and are a part of the same general movement of the sea that is manifested in the vertical rise and fall, called *tide*. Nontidal currents include the permanent currents in the general circulatory systems of the sea as well as temporary currents arising from more pronounced meteorological variability.

Current Correction Angle—The difference between the intended track and the calculated course to steer to compensate for the estimated current.

Current Difference—Difference between the time of slack water (or minimum current) or strength of current in any locality and the time of the corresponding phase of the tidal current at a reference station, for which predictions are given in the *Tidal Current Tables*.

Current Drift Angle—The difference in angle between the course steered and the resulting CMG in the presence of current.

Current Ellipse—A graphic representation of a rotary current in which the velocity of the current at different hours of the tidal cycle is represented by radius vectors and vectorial angles. The cycle is completed in one-half tidal day or in a whole tidal day according to whether the tidal current is of the semidiurnal or the diurnal type. A current of the mixed type will give a curve of two unequal loops each tidal day.

Current Sailing—The process of allowing for current in determining the predicted course made good, or in determining the effect of a current on the direction and speed of motion of a vessel.

D

Danger Bearing—The maximum or minimum bearing of a point for safe passage of an off-lying danger. As a vessel proceeds along a coast, the bearing of a fixed point on shore, such as a lighthouse, is measured frequently. As long as the bearing does not exceed the limit of the predetermined danger bearing, the vessel is on a safe course with respect to the hazard in question.

Danger Buoy—A buoy marking an isolated danger to navigation, such as a rock, shoal or sunken wreck.

Datum—The technical term for the baseline from which a chart's vertical measurements are made—heights of land or landmarks, or depths of water.

Daybeacon—A fixed NAVAID structure used in shallow waters upon which is placed one or more Daymarks.

Daylight Saving Time—A time used during the summer in some localities in which clocks are advanced one hour from the usual standard time.

Daymark—A signboard attached to a daybeacon to convey navigational information presenting one of several standard shapes (square, triangle, rectangle) and colors (red, green, orange, yellow, or black). Daymarks usually have reflective material indicating the shape, but may also be lighted.

Dead Ahead—A relative bearing of 000 degrees.

Dead Astern—Directly aft.

Dead In The Water—Adrift, floating with the current.

Dead Reckoning—The practice of estimating position by advancing a known position for courses and distances run. The effects of wind and current are not considered in determining a position by dead reckoning.

Dead Reckoning Plot—A DR plot is the charted movement of a vessel as determined by dead reckoning.

Dead Reckoning (DR) Position—A position determined by dead reckoning.

Deck—A permanent covering over a compartment, hull or any part thereof.

Demarcation Line—Boundary shown on nautical charts between areas where inland navigation rules and international navigation rules apply.

Departure—A known location (fix) from which a dead reckoning plot is initiated.

Depth Sounder—An electronic means of measuring water depth by sound waves.

Deviation—The effect of the vessel's magnetic fields upon a compass. Deviation is the difference between *the* direction that the compass actually points and the direction that the compass would point if there were no magnetic fields aboard the vessel.

Diaphone—A sound signal which produces sound by means of a slotted piston moved back and forth by compressed air. A "two-tone" diaphone produces two sequential tones with the second tone of lower pitch.

Dinghy—A small open boat. A dinghy is often used as a tender for a larger craft.

Direction (true)—The angle between the local true meridian and a line from the observer's position to an object or another location.

Direction of Relative Motion—Determined from the relative motion plot, this is the apparent course of the target as inferred from observations on the radar screen.

Directional Light—A light illuminating a sector or very narrow angle and intended to mark a direction to be followed.

Discontinued—To remove from operation (permanently or temporarily) a previously authorized aid to navigation.

Discrepancy—Failure of an aid to navigation to maintain a position or function as prescribed in the *Light List*.

Discrepancy Buoy—An easily transportable buoy used to temporarily replace an aid to navigation that is not watching properly.

Displacement—The weight of water displaced by a floating vessel, thus, a boat's weight.

Displacement Hull—A type of hull that plows through the water, displacing a weight of water equal to its own weight, even when more power is added. (See Chapter 11.)

Diurnal—Having a period or cycle of approximately one tidal day. Thus, the tide is said to be diurnal when only one high water and one low water occur during a tidal day, and the tidal current is said to be diurnal when there is a single flood and single ebb period in the tidal day. A rotary current is diurnal if it changes its direction through all points of the compass once each tidal day.

Diurnal Inequality—The difference in height of the two high waters or of the two low waters of each day; also the difference in speed between the two flood tidal currents or the two ebb tidal currents of each day. The difference changes with the declination of the moon and to a lesser extent with the declination of the sun.

Dividers—An instrument consisting of two pointed legs joined by a pivot, and used principally for measuring distances or coordinates. An instrument having one pointed leg and the other carrying a pen or pencil is called a drafting compass.

Dock—A protected water area in which vessels are moored. The term is often used to denote a pier or a wharf.

Dolphin—A minor aid to navigation structure consisting of a number of piles driven into the seabed or riverbed in a circular pattern and drawn together with wire rope.

Dome—A large, rounded, hemispherical structure rising above a building or a roof of the same shape.

Double Ebb—An ebb tidal current where, after ebb begins, the speed increases to a maximum called *first ebb;* it then decreases, reaching a *minimum ebb* near the middle of the ebb period (and at some places it may actually run in a flood direction for a short period); it then again ebbs to a maximum speed called *second ebb* after which it decreases to slack water.

Double Flood—A flood tidal current where, after flood begins, the speed increases to a maximum called *first flood;* it then decreases, reaching a *minimum flood* near the middle of the flood period (and at some places it may actually run in an ebb direction for a short period); it then again floods to a maximum speed called *second flood,* after which it decreases to slack water.

Double Tide—A double-headed tide; that is, a high water consisting of two maxima of nearly the same height separated by a relatively small depression, or a low water consisting of two minima separated by a relatively small eleva-

tion. Sometimes, it is called an *agger*.

Doubling the Angle on the Bow—A method of calculating a running fix by measuring the distance a vessel travels on a steady course while the relative bearing (right or left) of a fixed object doubles. The distance from the object at the time of the second bearing is equal to the distance run between bearings, neglecting drift.

Draft—The vertical depth from the bottom of the keel to the top of the water.

Drift—The speed in knots at which the current is moving. Drift may also be indicated in statute miles per hour in some areas, the Great Lakes, for example. This term is also commonly used to mean the speed at which a vessel deviates from the course steered due to the combined effects of external forces such as wind and current.

Drms—A term used to describe the statistical accuracy of a loran or other fix. Twice the Drms is the radius of a circle that should include the fix point with at least 95% certainty. The geodetic accuracy limit of the loran-C system within the designated coverage area is that 2Drms should be less than 0.25 nautical miles.

Drogue—Any device streamed astern to slow a vessel's speed, or to keep its stern to the waves in a following sea.

Drying Heights—Heights above chart sounding datum of those features which are periodically covered and exposed by the rise and fall of the tide.

Dual Rate Blanking—To provide continuous service from one loran-C chain to the next, some stations are dual rated (see dual rated). A dual-rated station is faced periodically with an impossible requirement to radiate two overlapping pulse groups at the same time. During the time of overlap, the subordinate (secondary) signal is blanked or suppressed.

Dual Rate Station—Term used to describe a master or secondary station in one loran-C chain that is also used as a master or secondary in another chain. The Dana, Indiana, loran transmitter is one example, serving as the zulu secondary in the 9960 (Northeast U.S.) chain as well as the master in the 8970 (Great Lakes) chain.

Dumping Ground—Area shown on charts where dumping took place (the practice is no longer permitted) and which may present a hazard to navigation.

Duration of Flood and Duration of Ebb—*Duration of flood* is the interval of time in which a tidal current is flooding, and the *duration of ebb* is the interval in which it is ebbing.

Duration of Rise and Duration of Fall—*Duration of rise* is the interval from low water to high water, and *duration of fall* is the interval from high water to low water.

Dutchman's Log—A buoyant object thrown overboard to determine the speed of a vessel. The time required for a known length of the vessel to pass the object (assumed to be dead in the water) is measured. Speed can be computed from the two known values of time and distance. The Dutchman's log can also be used to measure the drift of a current if a vessel can be held stationary (keep station) with respect to a fixed object.

E

Ebb Current—The movement of a tidal current away from shore or down a tidal river or estuary. In the mixed type of reversing tidal current, the terms *greater ebb* and *lesser ebb* are applied respectively to the ebb tidal currents of greater and lesser speed of each day. The terms *maximum ebb* and *minimum ebb* are applied to the maximum and minimum speeds of a current running continuously ebb, the speed alternately increasing and decreasing without coming to a slack or reversing.

Echo—Term used in radar to denote an object that reflects the radar beam, often used interchangeably with the terms return, target, blip, contact and pip. Properly speaking, however, there are subtle distinctions among these. See, for example, contact.

Eclipse—An interval of darkness between appearances of a light.

Electronic Bearing Line—An adjustable bearing line which appears as a spoke radiating from the center of the PPI. EBLs are used to measure the bearing of a target. Also called electronic bearing marker.

Electronic Bearing Marker—See electronic bearing line.

Electronic Chart—A device that can display a chartlike representation on a screen. Some electronic charts are very elaborate and allow the user to "zoom in" to examine an area at a larger scale. Depth contours, NAVAIDS, and other chart features can be displayed—even down to individual docks at certain locations. Electronic charts can interface with other shipboard electronics, such as a loran and display the vessel's current position, waypoints, and related information.

Emergency Light—A light of reduced intensity displayed by certain aids to navigation when the main light is extinguished.

Emergency Position Indicating Radio Beacon (EPIRB)—A device which emits a continuous radio signal alerting authorities to the existence of a distress situation and leading rescuers to the scene.

Endurance—The time in hours that the vessel can be operated at a given throttle setting until the enroute fuel is exhausted.

Enroute Fuel—Fuel intended for use in a voyage. Numerically the enroute fuel is the fuel on board minus an allowance for a fuel reserve. Also termed voyage fuel.

Ensign—A national or organizational flag flown aboard a vessel.

Equator—Great circle formed by passing a plane perpendicular to the axis of rotation of the earth.

Equatorial Tidal Currents—Tidal currents occurring semimonthly as the result of the moon being over the equator. At these times the tendency of the moon to produce a diurnal inequality in the tide is at a minimum.

Equatorial Tides—Tides occurring semimonthly as the result of the moon being over the equator. At these times the tendency of the moon to produce a diurnal inequality in the tide is at a minimum.

Establish—To place an authorized aid to navigation in operation for the first time.

Estimated Position (EP)—An improved position based upon the DR position and which may include, among other things, factoring in the effects of wind and current, a single line of position, or all of the above.

Extinguished—A lighted aid to navigation which fails to show a light characteristic.

Existence Doubtful—Term used principally on charts to indicate the possible existence of a rock, shoal, or other obstruction, for which the actual existence has not been established.

F

Fair Current—Current moving in the same direction as the vessel.

Fall Off—To turn the bow of the boat away from the direction of the oncoming wind.

Fast—Said of an object that is secured to another.

Fathom—A nautical measure of length, six feet, used for measuring water depth and length of anchor rode.

Fix—A known position determined by passing close aboard an object of known position or determined by the intersection of two or more lines of position (LOPs) adjusted to a common time, determined from terrestrial, electronic, and/or celestial data (see Chapter 6). The accuracy, or quality of a fix, is of great importance, especially in coastal waters, and is dependent on a number of factors.

Fixed ATON—An aid to navigation placed on a fixed structure such as a light house, tower, etc.

Fixed Bridge—A bridge that does not lift, swing, or otherwise open for vessel traffic.

Fixed Light—A light showing continuously and steadily, as opposed to a rhythmic light. (Do not confuse with "fixed" as used to differentiate from "floating.")

Fixed Range Markers—A series of concentric range rings displayed on a PPI. The spacing of these rings can be adjusted by a range switch, but all FRMs are fixed in relation to each other.

Flag Tower—A scaffold-like tower from which flags are displayed.

Flagpole—A single staff from which flags are displayed. The term is used when the pole is not attached to a building.

Flagstaff—A flagpole rising from a building.

Flash—A relatively brief appearance of a light, in comparison with the longer interval of darkness in the same character.

Flash Tube—An electronically controlled high-intensity discharge lamp with a very brief flash duration.

Flashing Light—A light in which the total duration of light in each period is clearly shorter than the total duration of darkness and in which the flashes of light are all of equal duration. (Commonly used for a single-flashing light which exhibits only single flashes which are repeated at regular intervals.)

Float Plan—A document that describes the route(s) and estimated time of arrival of a particular voyage. The float plan generally includes a description of the vessel, radio and safety equipment carried, planned stops, names of passengers, and other pertinent information.

Floating Aid To Navigation—A buoy, secured in its assigned position by a mooring.

Flood Current—The movement of a tidal current toward the shore or up a tidal river or estuary. In the mixed type of reversing current, the terms *greater flood* and *lesser flood* are applied respectively to the flood currents of greater and lesser speed of each day. The terms *maximum flood* and *minimum flood* are applied to the maximum and minimum speeds of a flood current, the speed of which alternately increases and decreases without coming to a slack or reversing.

Fluxgate Compass—A compass that senses the earth's magnetic field electronically, rather than with magnets. Fluxgate compasses can interface with other shipboard electronics such as radar or loran.

Flying Bridge—An added set of controls above the level of the normal control station for better visibility. Usually open but may have a collapsible top for shade.

Fog Detector—An electronic device used to automatically determine conditions of visibility which warrant the turning on and off of a sound signal or additional light signals.

Fog Signal—See Sound Signal.

Following Sea—Sea in which the waves move in a direction approximately the same as the vessel's heading. Opposite of head sea.

Fore-and-Aft—In a line parallel to the keel.

Forward—Toward the bow of the boat.

Fouled—Any piece of equipment that is jammed or entangled, or dirty.

Foul Current—Current moving in the opposite direction to the vessel.

Foul Ground—An area unsuitable for anchoring due to being strewn with rocks, boulders, coral, or obstructions. Foul grounds are often shown on nautical charts.

Founder—When a vessel fills with water and sinks.

Freeboard—The minimum vertical distance from the surface of the water to the gunwale cap.

Frequency—The rate at which a cycle is repeated.

Fuel Consumption Chart—Chart or graph that relates the engine throttle setting, speed through the water, and the fuel burn rate in gallons per hour.

Fuel Efficiency—The distance that a vessel can travel on each gallon of fuel. Fuel efficiency is a function of the throttle setting and several other factors discussed in Chapter 11.

Fuel Reserve—A quantity of fuel set aside for possible contingencies.

G

Gear—A general term for ropes, blocks, tackle and other equipment.

Geometric Dilution of Precision (GDOP)—Term used to include all geometric factors (gradient, crossing angle) that degrade the accuracy of position fixes from externally referenced navigation systems, such as loran-C. GDOP can be calculated from an equation which summarizes these effects in one single number.

Gimbals—A pair of rings pivoted on axes at right angles to each other so that one is free to swing within the other; a ship's compass, etc., will keep a horizontal position when suspended on gimbals.

Give-way Vessel—A term, from the Navigational Rules, used to describe the vessel which must yield in meeting, crossing, or overtaking situations.

Gong—A wave-actuated sound signal on buoys which uses a group of saucer-shaped bells to produce different tones.

GPS—Global Positioning System, an electronic navigation system using satellites for worldwide coverage. This is not discussed in the ACN text but is included in some of the references listed at the end of Chapter 9.

Gradient—The ratio of the spacing between adjacent loran TDs, as measured in nautical miles, yards, or feet, and the number of microseconds difference between these lines. Generally speaking, the smaller the gradient, the better the fix.

Graticule—The network of lines representing parallels and meridians on a map, chart, or plotting sheet.

Gravel—See stone.

Great Circle—The circle formed on the earth's surface when a plane is passed through the earth's center.

Great Diurnal Range—The difference in height between mean higher high water and mean lower low water. The expression may also be used in its contracted form, *diurnal range*.

Ground Swell—See Swells.

Ground Tackle—A collective term for the anchor and its associated gear.

Groundwave—A radio wave that travels near or along the earth's surface. Groundwave signals are used for the present loran system

Group Flashing Light—A navigational aid light which emits flashes in groups, specified in number, and repeated at regular intervals.

Group Occulting Light—An occulting light in which a group of eclipses, specified in number, is regularly repeated.

Group Repetition Interval—Length of time (in microseconds) between the start of one transmission from the master station in a loran-C chain and the start of the next. For convenience the GRI is usually divided by 10. Thus, for example, the 9960 GRI Northeast U. S. Chain has a group repitition interval of 99,600 microseconds.

Gudgeon—The eye supports for the rudder, mounted on the transom and designed to receive the pintles.

Gulf—That part of an ocean or sea extending into the land, usually larger than a bay.

Gulf Coast Low Water Datum—A chart datum. Specifically, the tidal datum formerly designated for the coastal waters of the Gulf Coast of the United States. It was defined as *mean lower low water* when the type of tide was mixed and *mean low water* when the type of tide was diurnal.

Gunwale—The upper edge of a boat's sides.

H

Hachures—Short marks on topographic maps or nautical charts to indicate the slope of the ground or the submarine bottom. These marks usually follow the direction of the slope.

Half-Tide Level—See *mean tide level*.

Hand-Bearing Compass—Portable compass (magnetic or electronic) that is used aboard ship for taking bearings.

Head Sea—Sea in which the waves move in a direction approximately opposite the vessel's heading. Opposite of following sea.

Heading (HDG)—The instantaneous direction of a vessel's bow. It is expressed as the angular distance relative to north, usually 000° at north, clockwise through 359°. Heading should not be confused with course. Heading is a constantly changing value as a vessel yaws back and forth across the course due to the effects of sea, wind, and steering error. Heading is expressed in degrees of either true, magnetic, or compass direction.

Heading Flash—An illuminated radial line on the PPI of a radarscope for indicating the reference ship's heading on the bearing dial. Also called heading marker.

Headway—The forward motion of a boat through the water. Opposite of sternway.

Heave To—To bring a vessel up in a position where it will maintain little or no headway, usually with the bow into the wind or nearly so. To stop.

Heavy Iron—Slang expression used to denote large ships.

Heel—To tip or lean to one side.

Helm—The wheel or tiller controlling the rudder.

High Frequency (HF)—A special frequency band used in long-distance communications.

High Water (HW)—The maximum height reached by a rising tide. The height may be due solely to the periodic tidal forces or it may have superimposed upon it the effects of prevailing meteorological conditions.

Higher High Water (HHW)—The higher of the two high waters of any tidal day.

Higher Low Water (HLW)—The higher of the two low waters of any tidal day.

Hole—A small bay (or channel), particularly in New England.

Homing—Process of moving towards a location by continually pointing the bow of the vessel in the direction of the station. In the absence of current, homing will lead to a ground track that is a straight line. With any current, however, the ground track will become curved, bowed in the direction of the prevailing current.

Hook—Something resembling a hook in shape, particularly, **a.** a spit or narrow cape of sand or gravel which turns landward at the outer end; or **b.** a sharp bend or curve, as in a stream.

Horn—A sound signal which uses electricity or compressed air to vibrate a disc diaphragm.

HOWGOZIT Chart—Chart that depicts the vessel's actual fuel quantity at various points in a voyage in comparison to the amount of fuel required to reach the destination with various levels of fuel reserves.

Hug—To remain close to, as to hug the shore.

Hull—The main body of a vessel.

Hull Speed—The maximum speed of a displacement vessel. It is limited by the length of the vessel and the shape of its underwater construction.

Hydraulic Current—A current in a channel caused by a difference in the surface level at the two ends. Such a current may be expected in a strait connecting two bodies of water in which the tides differ in time or range.

Hyperbolic Grid—Lattice of curved (hyperbolic) lines of position produced by a hyperbolic system.

Hyperbolic System—Navigation system, such as loran-C, that operates by measuring the time difference between signals transmitted by two or more transmitters.

I

Inclinometer—Device to measure the angle of roll of a vessel.

Index Diagram—An inset in a nautical chart where contiguous or related charts at different scales are noted.

Inoperative—Sound signal or electronic aid to navigation out of service due to a malfunction.

Interrupted Quick Light—A quick flashing light in which the rapid alternations are interrupted at regular intervals by eclipses of long duration.

Intrusion Alarm—Alarm that can be set on a radar to alert the radar operator that a target has penetrated a range ring.

Iron Genny—Slang expression to denote the engine of a sailboat.

Isogonic Lines—Lines on a chart connecting points of equal magnetic variation.

Isolated Danger Mark—A mark erected on, or moored above or very near, an isolated danger which has navigable water all around it.

Isophase Light—A rhythmic light in which all durations of light and darkness are equal. (Formerly called equal interval light.)

Isthmus—A narrow strip of land connecting two larger portions of land.

J

Jetty—A structure built out into the water to restrain or direct currents, usually to protect a river mouth or harbor entrance from silting, etc.

Junction—The point where a channel divides when proceeding seaward. The place where a tributary departs from the main stream.

K

Keel—The main structural member of a vessel running fore-and-aft; the backbone of a vessel.

Knot (kn sometimes kt)—A measure of speed equal to one nautical mile (6076 feet) per hour.

L

Landmark—A conspicuous artificial feature on land, other than an established aid to navigation which can be used as an aid to navigation. Sometimes also used in a less technical sense to include natural features as well as artificial features.

Large Navigational Buoy (LNB)—Buoys developed to replace lightships and are placed at points where it is impractical to build a lighthouse. The unmanned LNBs are 40 feet in diameter with light towers approximately 40 feet above the water. LNBs are equipped with lights, sound signals, radiobeacons, and racons. LNBs are painted red, not for lateral significance, but to improve visibility.

Lateral System—A system of aids to navigation in which characteristics of buoys and beacons indicate the sides of the channel or route relative to a conventional direction of buoyage (usually upstream).

Latitude—Distance north or south of the equator expressed in degrees from zero to ninety, north or south; i.e., L 073N.

Lead Line—A line used to measure the depth of the water.

Leading Lights—British terminology for range lights.

Ledge—On the sea floor, a rocky projection or outcrop.

Lee—The side sheltered from the wind; the direction toward which the wind is blowing.

Leeward—The direction away from the wind. Opposite of windward.

Leeway—The sideways movement of the boat caused by either wind or current.

Leg—That portion of a voyage track that can be represented by a single course line. A track could be composed of several legs.

Legend—A title or explanation on a chart, diagram, illustration.

Light—Lighthouses or beacons, fixed aids to navigation, or a vessel's navigation lights. On a vessel, lights are designed to help identify the size, direction of movement, status of the vessel, and sometimes the tasks being performed.

Light List—USCG Publication discussed in Chapter 10.

Light Sector—The arc over which a light is visible, described in degrees true, as observed from seaward towards the light. May be used to define distinctive color difference of two adjoining sectors, or an obscured sector.

Lighted Ice Buoy (LIB)—A lighted buoy without sound signal, and designed to withstand the forces of shifting and flowing ice. Used to replace a conventional buoy when that aid to navigation is endangered by ice.

Lighthouse—A lighted beacon of major importance.

Line of Position (LOP)—A line of bearing to a known origin or reference, upon which a vessel is assumed to be located (see Chapter 6, Line of Position). An LOP is determined by observation (visual bearing) or measurement (RDF, loran, radar, etc.). An LOP is assumed to be a straight line for visual bearings, or an arc of a circle (radar range), or part of some other curve such as hyperbola (loran). LOPs resulting from visual observations (magnetic bearings) are generally converted to true bearings prior to plotting on a chart.

Line of Sight—The straight line between two points. This line is in the direction of a great circle, but does not follow the curvature of the earth.

Local Notice to Mariners—A written document issued by each U. S. Coast Guard district to disseminate important information affecting aids to navigation, dredging, marine construction, special marine activities, and bridge construction on the waterways within that district.

Log—A daily record of a ship's progress or operations and messages sent or received on its radio. A device to measure a vessel's speed. To record a ship's progress in a journal.

Longitude—Distance east or west of the prime meridian expressed in degrees from zero to 180ᴵ east or west; i.e., Lo 123W.

Lookout Station (watchtower)—A tower atop a small house used for observation.

Loran—A contraction of long-range navigation, used to describe an electronic navigation system using a chain of transmitting stations that allows mariners (or aviators) to determine their position.

Loran-C LOP—Line of position as determined from reception of the loran master signal and that of one secondary. Loran-C LOPs at convenient intervals are plotted on NOAA charts. See also rate.

Loran Chain—Series of three to five transmitting stations consisting of a master station and two to four secondary stations used in the loran system.

Loran Linear Interpolator—A small inset diagram shown on loran overprinted charts that enables interpolation of time differences.

Loran Pulse—Basic "building block" of the transmitted loran signal. The loran pulse exhibits a characteristic (and well controlled) waveform which can be identified and timed by a receiver. The loran signal from a master station actually consists of nine pulses. The first eight pulses are spaced 1,000 microseconds apart, followed at an interval of 2,000 microseconds by the ninth pulse. Secondary stations transmit only eight pulses, each separated by 1,000 microseconds. Pulsed transmission saves on the power required for signal transmission and facilitates signal identification. Multiple pulse transmission is used rather than single pulse transmission to increase the average power of the loran signal.

Low Water (LW)—The minimum height reached by a falling tide. The height may be due solely to the periodic tidal forces or it may have superimposed upon it the effects of meteorological conditions. Use of the synonymous term, low tide, is discouraged.

Lower High Water (LHW)—The lower of the two high waters of any tidal day.

Lower Low Water (LLW)—The lower of the two low waters of any tidal day.

Loxodrome—Any line on the earth's surface (other than due east or due west) which cuts successive meridians of longitude at the same oblique angle. When extended, it spirals toward, but never reaches, one of the earth's poles.

Lubber's Line—A mark or permanent line on a compass which is used to read the compass heading of a vessel. When properly mounted it is parallel to the vessel's keel.

Luminous Range Diagram—A diagram used to convert the nominal range of a light to its luminous range under existing conditions. The ranges obtained are approximate.

Lunar Day—The duration of one rotation of the earth on its axis, with respect to the moon. Its average length is about 24 hours and 50 minutes.

M

Magnetic Compass—A magnet, balanced so that it can pivot freely in a horizontal plane; a sailor's most common and most reliable direction-indicating aid.

Magnetic Direction (M)—A direction relative to the earth's magnetic field and magnetic north. Magnetic courses are labeled with an "M," to signify "magnetic."

Magnetic Meridian—A system of "meridians" passing through the earth's magnetic poles. A compass aligns with these "meridians" if there is no local magnetic field on the vessel to cause deviation.

Maneuvering Board—A printed compass rose which is used together with parallel rulers and dividers to solve problems of the movement of vessels relative to each other such as those that arise when the vessels change position relative to each other. Used, for example, when another vessel is observed on a radar scope.

Marine Radiotelephone—VHF-FM radio; an important safety factor in emergencies.

Mark—A visual aid to navigation. Often called navigation mark, includes floating marks (buoys) and fixed marks (beacons).

Masking—Obscuration of an object. Radar masking (also radar shadow) refers to a phenomenon in which a target is obscured (masked) by virtue of its location behind another larger target—such as a mountain, structure, or other vessel. Visual masking can also occur.

Master Station—Essential component of a loran-C chain. This station broadcasts the signal that is used to identify the chain (the GRI) and is the common base against which all time differences are calculated.

Mean High Water (MHW)—The arithmetic mean of the high water heights observed over a specific 19-year cycle. For stations with shorter series, simultaneous observational comparisons are made with a primary control tide station in order to derive the equivalent of a 19-year value.

Mean Higher High Water (MHHW)—The arithmetic mean of the higher high water heights of a mixed tide observed over a specific 19-year cycle. Only the higher high water of each pair of high waters, or the only high water of a tidal day is included in the mean.

Mean Low Water (MLW)—A tidal datum. The arithmetic mean of the low water heights observed over a specific 19-year Metonic cycle (the National Tidal Datum Epoch). For stations with shorter series, simultaneous observational comparisons are made with a primary control tide station in order to derive the equivalent of a 19-year value.

Mean Low Water Springs (MLWS)—Frequently abbreviated *spring low water*. The arithmetic mean of the low water heights occurring at the time of the spring tides observed over a specific 19-year cycle.

Mean Lower Low Water (MLLW)—The arithmetic mean of the lower low water heights of a mixed tide observed over a specific 19-year cycle. Only the lower low water of each pair of low waters, or the only low water of a tidal day is included in the mean.

Mean Range of Tide—The difference in height between mean high water and mean low water.

Mean Sea Level (MSL)—The arithmetic mean of hourly water elevations observed over a specific 19-year cycle. Shorter series are specified in the name; e.g., monthly mean sea level and yearly mean sea level.

Mean Tide Level (MTL)—Also called half-tide level. A tidal datum midway between mean high water and mean low water.

Mercator Projection—The projection technique most commonly used in navigational charts; shapes and distances are increasingly distorted as you move into extreme northern and southern areas. This is a cylindrical projection ingeniously modified fuel by expanding the scale at increasing latitudes to preserve ship's direction, and angular relationships.

Meridian (Geographic Meridian)—A great circle of the earth passing through both the geographic poles and any given point on the earth's surface.

Meteorological Visibility—The greatest distance at which a black object of suitable dimension could be seen and recognized against the horizon sky by day, or, in the case of night observations, could be seen and recognized if the general illumination were raised to the normal daylight level.

Microsecond—One millionth of a second.

Midship—Approximately in the location equally distant from the bow and stern.

Mileage Number—A number assigned to aids to navigation which gives the distance in sailing miles along the river from a reference point to the aid to navigation. The number is used principally in the Mississippi River System.

Mixed Tide—Type of tide with a large inequality in the high and/or low water heights, with two high waters and two low waters usually occurring each tidal day. In strictness, all tides are mixed but the name is usually applied to the tides intermediate to those predominantly semidiurnal and those predominantly diurnal.

Most Probable Position—Vessel's probable position considering all available navigational information. Term is generally used when there is position uncertainty as a result of conflicting or ambiguous information.

Mud—A general term applied to mixtures of sediments in water. Where the grains are less than 0.002 millimeter in diameter, the mixture is called clay. Where the grains are between 0.002 and 0.0625 millimeter in diameter, the mixture is called silt. See also sand; stones; rock, definition 2.

Multiple Ranges—A group of two or more ranges, having one of the range marks in common.

Mushroom Anchor—A stockless anchor with a cast iron bowl at the end of the shank; used principally in large sizes for permanent moorings.

N

Nautical Chart—See Chart.

Nautical Mile (M)—One minute of latitude; approximately 6076 feet—about 1/8 longer than the statute mile of 5280 feet.

Nautical Slide Rule—Analog device for solving time-speed-distance calculations. In present manufacture these are typically circular slide rules with three separate scales graduated in units of time, speed, and distance.

Navigation—The art and science of conducting a boat safely from one point to another.

Navigation Rules—Regulations governing the movement of vessels in relation to each other, formerly "Rules of the Road."

Neap Tides or Tidal Currents—Tides of decreased range or tidal currents of decreased speed occurring semimonthly as the result of the moon being in quadrature. The *neap range* of the tide is the average semidiurnal range occurring at the time of neap tides.

Neck—1. A narrow isthmus, cape, or promontory. 2. The land between streams flowing into a sound or bay. 3. A narrow strip of land which connects a peninsula with the mainland. 4. A narrow body of water between two larger bodies.

North Geographic Pole—A reference for specifying a position on the earth's surface, at the north end of the earth's axis. Also called True North.

North Magnetic Pole—The central point of the north end of the earth's magnetic core to which a compass points when it is free of other influences.

North Up—Type of relative motion radar display with own ship at center. This is linked to a gyrocompass or fluxgate compass to display a continuous north-up picture on PPI.

Notch Filters—Filters in a loran receiver that are either fixed or capable of being tuned to reduce ("notch out") the effects of interfering signals. Some filters (termed "Pac-Man") filters can automatically seek and notch out interfering signals. Typical signals that can cause loran interference are listed in the *Loran-C Handbook*. The notch filters on a loran should be adjusted for the area of intended cruising to maximize the efficiency of the filtering.

Null—Position of minimum signal strength for directional antenna. This position occurs when the directional antenna is perpendicular to the radiated signal. The null is used to determine the relative bearing in an RDF set.

O

Oblate Spheroid—Sphere flattened at the poles, resembling a pumpkin.

Occulting Light—A light in which the total duration of light in each period is clearly longer than the total duration of darkness and in which the intervals of darkness (occultations) are all of equal duration. (Commonly used for single-occulting light which exhibits only single occultations which are repeated at regular intervals.)

Ocean Data Aquisition System (ODAS)—Certain very large buoys in deep water for the collection of oceanographic and meteorlogical information. All ODAS buoys are yellow in color and display a yellow light.

Off Shore Tower—Monitored light stations built on exposed marine sites to replace lightships.

Off Station—A floating aid to navigation not on its assigned position.

Omega—Electronic navigation system. This is not discussed in the ACN text. See references listed at the end of Chapter 9 for details.

On Plane—As more and more speed is gained, a boat feels as though it has "climbed out of its hole," and it rides up "on plane."

Ooze—A soft, slimy, organic sediment covering part of the ocean bottom.

Out of Tolerance—A condition in which a loran-C signal or time difference exceeds established tolerances. An out-of-tolerance (OOT) condition causes the secondary transmitter to blink.

Outfall—The discharge end of a narrow stream, sewer drain, etc.

Overboard—Over the side.

P

Palisades—A line of cliffs.

Paraline Plotter—Plotter that has a set of rollers attached to enable the device to be moved parallel to itself, and used for the same purpose as parallel rules.

Parallel of Latitude—Any of the imaginary lines parallel to the equator and representing latitude.

Parallel Rules—An instrument for transferring a line parallel to itself, used in chartwork for drawing and measuring courses or bearings.

Passing Light—A low intensity light which may be mounted on the structure of another light to enable the mariner to keep the latter light in sight when passing out of its beam during transit.

Pebble—See stone.

Pelorus—A sighting device, marked off in degrees, used to determine relative bearings.

Peninsula—A section of land nearly surrounded by water. Frequently, but not necessarily, a peninsula is connected to a larger body of land by a neck or isthmus.

Perigean Tides or Tidal Currents—Tides of increased range or tidal currents of increased speed occurring monthly as the result of the moon being in perigee or nearest the earth. The *perigean range* (Pn) of tide is the average semidiurnal range occurring at the time of perigean tides.

Perigee—Point in the lunar cycle when the moon and the earth are closest together. Tides have increased range when the moon is in perigee.

Period—The interval of time between the commencement of two identical successive cycles of the characteristic of the light or sound signal.

Personal Flotation Device (PFD)—A life preserver which, when properly used, will support a person in the water. Available in several sizes and types.

Phase Code Interval—That interval over which the phase code repeats itself. For the loran-C system, phase codes repeat every two GRIs.

Phase Coding—Not discussed in the text, this is a scheme of changing the phase of the pulses in a transmitted loran signal to minimize pulse-to-pulse sky-wave interference and to reject synchronous interfering signals. Master and secondary transmitters use different phase codes for signal identification.

Pier—A loading or mooring platform extending at an angle (usually a right angle) from the shore.

Pile—A wood, metal or concrete pole driven into the bottom. Craft may be made fast to a pile; it may be used to support a pier (see piling) or a float.

Piling—Support, protection for wharves, piers, etc.; constructed of piles (see pile).

Pilot Waters—Areas in which the services of a pilot are recommended or required. Also used in a more general sense to denote waters in which navigation is done using pilotage/piloting.

Piloting—Piloting is navigation involving frequent or continuous reference to charted landmarks, ATONs, or charted objects, and depth soundings.

Pivot Point—A point somewhat aft of the bow, somewhere forward of the midpoint. To an observer on board, a vessel appears to turn about its pivot point.

Plan Position Indicator (PPI)—The screen display of a radar, so named because it presents a plan view of the area scanned.

Planing—A boat is said to be planing when it is essentially moving over the top of the water.

Planing Hull—A type of hull with flat surfaces (not necessarily horizontal) which enable a vessel to climb up its bow wave and to glide across the water when it has attained sufficient speed (see bow wave).

Plotter—Device for drawing straight lines on a nautical chart, and measuring courses, bearings, and (with some plotters) distances.

Plotting Sheet—A blank chart, usually on the Mercator projection, showing only the graticule and a compass rose. The meridians are usually unlabeled by the publisher so that these can be appropriately labeled when the chart is used in any longitude. Plotting sheets are often used in lieu of charts when the vessel is "off-soundings" (in deep water).

Point—A tapering piece of land projecting into a body of water. It is generally less prominent than a cape.

Point of No Return—The point of no return is the point beyond which there is not sufficient fuel on board to return on an out-and-back journey using the entire fuel on board, including the reserve.

Point System—A nearly obsolete system of dividing a circle into 32 parts of 11-1/4 degrees each, for reference to direction; i.e., NNW (337°30').

Polyconic Projection—A map or chart projection in which the earth is projected on a series of cones concentric with the earth's axis and tangent to the sphere of the earth. Charts of the Great Lakes are typically based on the polyconic projection.

Port—The left side of a boat looking forward. A harbor.

Port Hand Mark—A buoy or beacon which is left to the port hand when proceeding in the "conventional direction of buoyage."

Position—On the earth this refers to the actual geographic location of a vessel defined by two parameters called coordinates. Those customarily used are latitude and longitude. Position may also be expressed as a bearing and distance from an *object,* the position of which is known.

Position Approximate—Term used on nautical charts to denote an inexact position. This term is used principally on charts to indicate that the position of a wreck, shoal, or other obstruction has not been accurately determined or does not remain fixed.

Position Doubtful—Of uncertain position. This term is used principally on charts to indicate that a wreck, shoal, or other obstruction, has been reported in various positions and not definitely determined.

Position Line—See line of position.

Predictable Accuracy—Term meaning the same as absolute accuracy.

Preferred Channel Mark—A lateral mark indicating a channel junction or bifurcation, or a wreck or other obstruction which, after consulting a chart, may be passed on either side.

Primary Aid To Navigation—An aid to navigation established for the purpose of making landfalls and coastwise passages from headland to headland.

Prime Meridian—The meridian from which longitude is measured both east and west; 0^l longitude. It passes through Greenwich, England, and divides the earth into Eastern and Western Hemispheres.

Privileged Vessel—A vessel which, according to the applicable Navigation Rule, has right-of-way (this term has been superseded by the term "stand-on").

Prohibited Area—An area shown on nautical charts within which navigation and/or anchoring is prohibited except as authorized by appropriate authority.

Prolate Spheroid—Sphere flattened at the equator, resembling a football.

Promontory—High land extending into a large body of water beyond the line of the coast. Called headland when the promontory is comparatively high and has a steep face.

Protractor—An instrument for measuring angles on a surface, such as a chart. Typically a protractor is constructed of transparent plastic and has a semicircular scale measured in degrees.

Pulse Repetition Frequency—The average number of pulses per unit of time.

Q

Quarter—The sides of a boat aft of amidships.

Quartering Sea—Sea coming on a boat's quarter.

Quay—A structure of solid construction along a shore or bank which provides berthing and cargo handling facilities for ships. A similar facility of open construction is call a wharf.

Quick Light—A light more than 50 but less than 80 flashes per minute. (Previously called quick flashing light.)

R

Race—A rapid current or a constricted channel in which such current flows.

Racon—Racons are devices placed on certain buoys or other ATONs to increase the likelihood of detection and aid identification. Racons, when triggered by pulses from a vessel's radar will transmit a coded reply that is displayed on the vessel's PPI. This reply identifies the racon station by exhibiting a series of dots and dashes which appear on the PPI emanating radially from the racon. All racons operate in the marine radar X-Band from 9,300 to 9,500 Mhz. Some "frequency agile" racons also operate in the 2,900 to 3,000 Mhz marine radar S-Band.

Radar—Self-contained navigation and collision avoidance system consisting of a shipboard transmitter and receiver. The transmitter transmits briefly, then shuts off to permit the receiver to "listen" for the reflected transmission or echo.

Radar Bearing—A bearing obtained with radar.

Radar Fix—A position fix determined by radar alone, or by radar in conjunction with some other method for determining a LOP. Conventionally, radar fixes can be determined by a radar range and bearing from an identified radar conspicuous object, by two ranges from two such objects, or by two bearings from two such objects.

Radar Range—1. A range (distance) obtained with radar. 2. The maximum distance at which a radar set is effective in detecting targets.

Radar Reflectors—Objects that reflect radar waves very well and which serve to increase the size or strength of the radar return. Some buoys, for example, are equipped with a radar reflector to increase the ease of detection and identification. Radar reflectors are also made to carry aboard fiberglass or wood vessels to increase the likelihood of detection by other radar-equipped vessels.

Radar Transfer Plotting Sheet—Plotting sheet similar to a maneuvering board used for plotting radar targets. This sheet is discussed in Chapter 9.

Radio Beacons—Transmitting stations used for RDF system. Marine radio beacons operate in the 285 to 325 kilohertz band. As of this writing there are two types of radio beacons, continuous and sequenced. See Chapter 9.

Radio Direction Errors—See Chapter 9, Figure 9-3 for definitions of these errors.

Radio Direction Finding—Older short-range radio navigation system consisting of a series of land-based stations broadcasting in the LF/MF band and on-board receivers with directional antennas. Use of the directional antenna enables relative bearings to be determined, and, by simple conversion, lines of position.

Radio Mast—A relatively short pole or slender structure for elevating radio antennas, usually found in groups.

Radio Navigation—Determining positions using radio waves of known characteristics emitted from known locations. Forms include LORAN-C, RDF, OMEGA, Satellite systems, etc.

Radio Tower—A tall pole or structure for elevating radio antennas.

Radiobeacon—An electronic aid to navigation.

Radius of Action—The greatest distance (in an out-and-back voyage) that the vessel can travel and still leave sufficient fuel to return without drawing down the fuel reserve.

Rake—The slant of a ship's funnels, bow, or stern. The fore-and-aft slant of a vessel's mast.

Range—The distance in nautical miles that the vessel can travel with the available fuel on board. The range may or may not include an allowance for a fuel reserve. Range is a function of throttle setting and other factors discussed in Chapter 11.

Range Lights—Two lights associated to form a range which often, but not necessarily, indicates a channel centerline. The front range light is the lower of the two, and nearer to the mariner using the range. The rear range light is higher and further from the mariner.

Range of Tide—The difference in height between consecutive high and low waters, the *mean range* is the difference in height between mean high water and mean low water. Where the type of tide is diurnal the mean range is the same as the diurnal range.

Range Ring—Circular line on PPI (either fixed or variable) denoting a particular distance from the observer.

Ranges—A pair of ATONs placed a suitable distance apart, with the far daymark mounted higher than the near one. When the range marks are in line, the vessel is in the channel. Ranges can also be established by any charted objects.

Rate—Generic term sometimes used to describe a loran-C LOP. Nautical charts, for example, will identify the "rates" shown, e.g., 9960 W, 9960 X, 9960 Y, 9960 Z, 7980 W, etc.

Reach—The comparatively straight segment of a river or channel between two bends.

Real Time Method—An alternative radar plotting method, not discussed in this text, that provides a rapid means of plotting radar targets. Readers interested in radar plotting are well advised to study this method.

Rebuilt—A fixed aid to navigation, previously destroyed, which has been restored as an aid to navigation.

Reciprocal Bearing or Course—A bearing or course that differs from the original by 180 degrees.

Reciprocal Direction—Corresponding but reversed direction.

Red Sector—A sector of the circle of visibility of a navigational light in which a red light is exhibited. Such sectors are designated by their limiting bearings, as observed at some point other than the light. Red sectors are often located such that they warn of danger to vessels.

Reef—An offshore consolidated rock hazard to navigation at a depth of 16 fathoms (30 meters) or less. Also used as a term for a low rocky or coral area some of which is above water.

Reference Station—A tide or current station for which independent daily predictions are given in the *Tide Tables* and *Tidal Current Tables,* and from which corresponding predictions are obtained for subordinate stations by means of differences and ratios.

Regulatory Marks—A white and orange aid to navigation with no lateral significance. Used to indicate a special meaning to the mariner, such as danger, restricted operations, or exclusion area.

Relative (R)—See Relative Direction.

Relative Direction (Bearing)—A direction relative to the fore-and-aft line of a vessel, expressed in degrees and labeled "R."

Relative Motion Plot—Typical plot prepared on a maneuvering board to determine the point of closest approach and time of closest approach of a radar target. See Chapter 9 for details.

Relighted—An extinguished aid to navigation returned to its advertised light characteristics.

Repeatable Accuracy—Term used with the loran system to measure the repeatability of the loran TDs or Lat/Lo at a fixed point. Repeatable accuracy is typically much greater than absolute accuracy.

Replaced—An aid to navigation previously off station, adrift, or missing, restored by another aid to navigation of the same type and characteristics.

Replaced (Temporarily)—An aid to navigation previously off station, adrift, or missing, restored by another aid to navigation of different type and/or characteristic.

Reset—A floating aid to navigation previously off station, adrift, or missing, returned to its assigned position (station).

Restricted Visibility—Any condition in which visibility is restricted by fog, mist, falling snow, heavy rainstorms, sandstorms, or other similar causes.

Reversing Current—A tidal current which flows alternately in approximately opposite directions with a slack water at each reversal of direction. Currents of this type usually occur in rivers and straits where the direction of flow is more or less restricted to certain channels.

Rhumb Line—A line that is formed that spirals around the globe toward the nearer pole when a direction (other than due east or due west) is specified on the surface of the earth, and followed for any distance, so that each subsequent meridian is crossed at the same angle relative to the direction of the pole. Also called loxodrome. This appears as a straight line on a Mercator chart.

Rhythmic Light—A light showing intermittently with a regular periodicity.

Right-of-Way—An obsolete term. Under the 1972 COLREGS, no vessel has the "right-of-way" in a meeting situation, and each is equally responsible for avoiding collision.

Riprap—Stones or broken rock thrown together without order to provide a revetment.

Road—A open anchorage affording less protection than a harbor. Some protection may be afforded by reefs, shoals, etc. Often used in the plural, e.g, Hampton Roads.

Rock Awash—A rock that becomes exposed, or nearly so, between chart sounding datum and mean high water. In the Great Lakes, the rock awash symbol is used on charts for rocks that are awash, or nearly so, at low water datum.

Rock—1. An isolated rocky formation or single large stone, usually one constituting a danger to navigation. It may be always submerged, always uncovered, or alternately covered and uncovered by the tide. A pinnacle is a sharp-pointed rock rising from the bottom. 2. The naturally occurring material that forms the firm, hard, and solid masses of the ocean floor. Also, rock is a collective term for masses of hard material generally not smaller than 256 millimeters.

Rode—An anchor line and/or chain.

Root Mean Square (RMS)—The square root of the arithmetical mean of the squares of a group of numbers.

Rotary Current—A tidal current that flows continually, with the direction of flow changing through all points of the compass during the tidal period. Rotary currents are usually found offshore where the direction of flow is not restricted by any barriers. The tendency for the rotation in direction has its origin in the Coriolis force and, unless modified by location conditions, the change is clockwise in the Northern Hemisphere and counterclockwise in the Southern.

Round of Bearings—A group of bearings observed simultaneously, or over a short period of time, such as would be used to determine a visual fix.

Rudder—A vertical plate or board which can be pivoted to steer a boat.

Running Fix (RFIX)—A fix obtained by means of two or more LOPs taken at different times and adjusted to a common time. This practice involves advancing or retiring LOPs as discussed in Chapter 6.

Running Lights—Lights required to be shown on boats underway between sundown and sunup; indicates location and orientation of vessel.

S

Sand—Sediment consisting of small but easily distinguishable separate grains between 0.0625 and 2.0 millimeters in diameter. It is called **very fine sand** if the grains are between 0.0625 and 0.125 millimeter in diameter, **fine sand** if between 0.125 and 0.25 millimeters, **medium sand** if between 0.25 and 0.50 millimeters, **coarse sand** if between 0.25 and 0.50 millimeters, and **very coarse sand** if between 1.0 and 2.0 millimeters. See also mud, stones, rock, definition 2.

SATNAV—Satellite navigation system, not discussed in the ACN text. See references listed at the end of Chapter 9 for details.

Scalar—A scalar is a quantity that has magnitude only—in contrast to a vector which has both quantity and direction. Velocity, for example, is a vector because, properly speaking, it has both quantity (e.g., 10 knots) and direction (e.g., 045 degrees). Throttle setting, measured in revolutions per minute for example, is a scalar quantity because it has magnitude only.

Scope—The ratio of the length of anchor line deployed to the depth of the water, including the distance from the vessel's bow to the wa-

ter—see Chapter 8.

Screw—A boat's propeller.

Sea Anchor—Any device used to reduce a boat's drift before the wind. Compare with DROGUE.

Sea Room—A safe distance from the shore or other hazards.

Seaman's Eye—Navigation by informal means made possible by thorough familiarity with the area of operations.

Seaworthy—A boat or a boat's gear able to meet the usual sea conditions.

Secondary Coding Delay—Interval in microseconds between the reception of a loran signal at the secondary station and the time when the secondary station transmits a signal in the loran navigation system. Secondary coding delays are published for each secondary station.

Secondary Station—One of the two to four other transmitters in the loran-C chain (designated W, X, Y, and Z) that transmits a signal, keyed in time to that of the master, used to compute a time difference. At one time, the secondary transmitter would transmit (after an interval known as the secondary coding delay) only on receipt of the master signal. Now, the secondary transmitters maintain their own time standard, but the time of transmission relative to the master signal is designed to be the same as before.

Sector—See Light Sector.

Secure—To make fast.

Semidiurnal—Having a period or cycle of approximately one-half of a tidal day. The predominating type of tide throughout the world is semidiurnal, with two high waters and two low waters each tidal day. The tidal current is said to be semidiurnal when there are two flood and two ebb periods each day.

Set—The direction *towards* which the current is flowing expressed in degrees. This term is also commonly used to mean the direction towards which a vessel is being deviated from an intended course by the combined effects of external force such as wind and current.

Sextant—Device for precise measurement of horizontal or vertical angles.

Ship—A larger vessel usually thought of as being

used for ocean travel. A vessel able to carry a "boat" on board.

Ship's Head Up—Type of relative motion radar display with own ship in center and instantaneous relative bearings of targets displayed.

Shoal—An offshore hazard to navigation at a depth of 16 fathoms (30 meters) or less, composed of unconsolidated material.

Shoal Water—Shallow water or water over a shoal.

Short Legs—Slang expression to denote a vessel with a limited fuel capacity in relation to its fuel consumption. Opposite: long legs.

Signal-to-Noise Ratio (SNR)—The ratio of the signal strength to that of the electronic noise of a signal. Loran coverage diagrams are calculated so that the SNR is at least 1:3, even though many receivers are capable of processing weaker signals. Signal to noise is sometimes expressed in decibels (DB). The SNR in decibels is mathematically equal to 20 log (SNR), so that an SNR of 1:3 works out to approximately -9.54.

Silt—See mud.

Siren—A sound signal which uses electricity or compressed air to actuate either a disc or a cup-shaped rotor.

Skeleton Tower—A tower, usually of steel, constructed of heavy corner members and various horizontal and diagonal bracing members.

Skywave—Not discussed in this text, skywave is an indirect radio wave that reflects off the ionosphere, rather than traveling a direct path from transmitter to receiver. Because these waves travel a different distance (in particular a longer distance), skywaves will give an erroneous TD reading in a loran receiver. The shape of the loran pulse and phase coding are used to attempt to minimize or eliminate the effects of skywave contamination.

Skywave Delay—The time interval between the arrival of the groundwave and the various skywave reflections. Typically, skywaves can arrive as early as 35 microseconds, or as late as 1,500 microseconds after the groundwave.

Slack Water—The state of a tidal current when its speed is near zero, especially the moment when a reversing current changes direction and its speed is zero. The term is also applied to the entire period of low speed near the time of turning of the current when it is too weak to be of any practical importance in navigation. The relation of the time of slack water to the tidal phases varies in different localities. For standing tidal waves, slack water occurs near the times of high and low water, while for progressive tidal waves, slack water occurs midway between high and low water.

Slime—Soft, fine, oozy mud or other substance of similar consistency.

Small Circle—Any plane passing through the earth, but not through its center, produces a small circle at its intersection with the earth's surface.

Solar Day—The duration of one rotation of the earth on its axis, with respect to the sun.

Sound—A relatively long arm of the sea or ocean forming a channel between an island and a mainland or connecting two larger bodies of water, as a sea and the ocean, or two parts of the same body but usually wider and more extensive than a strait. The term has been applied to many features which do not fit the accepted definition. Many are very large bodies of water, such as Mississippi Sound and Prince William Sound, others are mere salt water ponds or small passages between islands.

Sound Signal—A device which transmits sound, intended to provide information to mariners during periods of restricted visibility and foul weather.

Sounding—A measurement of the depth of water.

South Geographic Pole—A reference for specifying a position on the earth's surface, at the south end of the earth's axis. Also called True South Pole.

South Magnetic Pole—The end of the earth's magnetic core opposite the North Magnetic Pole. (Located in Antarctica.)

Special Purpose Buoy—A buoy having no lateral significance used to indicate a special meaning to the mariner, such as one used to mark a quarantine or anchorage area.

Speed (S)—The rate at which a vessel advances relative to the water over a horizontal distance.

When expressed in terms of nautical miles per hour, it is referred to as knots (kn or kt). One knot equals approximately 1.15 statute miles per hour.

Speed Curve—A curve relating the vessel's speed through the water to the engine's throttle setting expressed in revolutions per minute (RPM). See Chapter 5 for details.

Speed LOP—An LOP situated at approximately right angles to the intended track, so named because the EP derived from this LOP provides a good indication of the vessel's SMG.

Speed Made Good (SMG)—Indicates the overall speed actually accomplished relative to the ground along the course line.

Speed of Advance (SOA)—Indicates the speed *intended* to be made relative to the ground along the track line.

Speed of Relative Motion—Apparent speed of the target on a radar display, determined from the relative motion plot.

Speed Over The Ground (SOG)—The *actual* speed made good at any instant in time with respect to the ground along the course being steered.

Speed Through The Water (STW)—The *apparent* speed indicated by log-type instruments or determined by use of tachometer and speed curve or table, at a particular point in time, along the course line.

Speed-Time-Distance—A formula to calculate speed, time, or distance.

Spherical Coordinate System—The system used to define positions on the earth's surface.

Spire—A slender pointed structure extending above a building. It is seldom less than two-thirds of the entire height of the structure, and its lines are rarely broken by stages or other features. The term is not applied to a short pyramid-shaped structure rising from a tower or belfry.

Spit—A small tongue of land or a long narrow shoal (usually sand) extending from the shore into a body of water.

Spoil Area—Area used for depositing dredged materials, usually near and parallel to dredged channels. Spoil areas are shown on charts because these may present hazards to navigation for even the smallest craft.

Spring Tides or Tidal Currents—Tides of increased range or tidal currents of increased speed occurring semimonthly as the result of the moon being new or full. The *spring range* of tide is the average semidiurnal range occurring at the time of spring tides.

Stack—A tall smokestack or chimney. The term is used when the stack is more prominent as a landmark than accompanying buildings.

Stadimeter—An instrument for determining the distance to an object of known height by measuring the angle, at the observer, subtended by the object. The instrument is graduated directly in distance.

Stand of Tide—Sometimes called a platform tide. An interval at high or low water when there is no sensible change in the height of the tide. The water level is stationary at high and low water for only an instant, but the change in level near these times is so slow that it is not usually perceptible.

Stand-on Vessel—That vessel which continues its course in the same direction at the same speed during a crossing or overtaking situation, unless a collision appears imminent. (Was formerly called "the privileged vessel.")

Standard Time—A kind of time based upon the transit of the sun over a certain specified meridian, called the *time meridian,* and adopted for use over a considerable area. With a few exceptions, standard time is based upon some meridian which differs by a multiple of 15° from the meridian of Greenwich.

Standardized Color Coding (Charts)—Standardized colors used to show loran-C lines of position on nautical charts. These color codes for the various secondaries in the loran chain are W=blue, X=magenta, Y=black, and Z=green.

Standpipe—A tall cylindrical structure, in a waterworks system, the height of which is several times the diameter.

Starboard—The right side of a boat when looking forward.

Starboard Hand Mark—A buoy or beacon which is left to the starboard side when proceeding in the "conventional direction of buoyage."

Station Buoy—An unlighted buoy set near a Large Navigation Buoy or an important buoy as a reference point should the primary aid to navigation be moved from its assigned position.

Station Pointer—See three arm protractor.

Stern—The after part of the boat.

Stones—A general term for rock fragments ranging in size from 2 to 256 millimeters. An individual water rounded stone is called a cobble if between 64 to 256 millimeters, a pebble if between 4 and 64 millimeters, and gravel if between 2 and 4 millimeters. These specialized terms of art are used on nautical charts to describe the quality of the bottom.

Stow—To put an item in its proper place.

Strait—A relatively narrow waterway, usually narrower and less extensive than a sound, connecting two larger bodies of water.

Strength of Current—Phase of tidal current in which the speed is a maximum; also the speed at this time. Beginning with slack before flood in the period of a reversing tidal current (or minimum before flood in a rotary current), the speed gradually increases to flood strength and then diminishes to slack before ebb (or minimum before ebb in a rotary current), after which the current turns in direction, the speed increases to ebb strength and then diminishes to slack before flood, completing the cycle.

Submerged Rock—A rock covered at the chart sounding datum and considered to be potentially dangerous to navigation. See also bare rock, rock awash.

Subordinate Current Station—(1) A current station from which a relatively short series of observations is reduced by comparison with simultaneous observations from a control current station. (2) A station listed in the *Tidal Current Tables* for which predictions are to be obtained by means of differences and ratios applied to the full predictions at a reference station.

Subordinate Tide Station—(1) A tide station from which a relatively short series of observations is reduced by comparison with simultaneous observations from a tide station with a relatively long series of observations. —(2) A station listed in the *Tide Tables* for which predictions are to be obtained by means of differences and ratios applied to the full predictions at a reference station.

Swells—After the deep water waves are generated far out at sea, they move outward, away from their wind source, in ever-increasing curves, and become swells.

Swing Ship—A systematic procedure for adjusting a compass and/or developing a deviation curve for a compass aboard a vessel.

Syzygy—Alignment of earth, moon, and sun where the earth, moon and sun are aligned, and the moon and sun are on the same side of the earth. Tides have larger ranges (termed spring tides) when this condition exists.

T

Tachometer—An instrument that indicates the speed of the engine measured in revolutions per minute (RPMs).

Tack—To come about; the lower forward corner of a sail; sailing with the wind on a given side of the boat, as starboard or port tack.

Tacking—Moving the boat's bow through the wind's eye from close-hauled on one tack to close-hauled on the other tack. Same as coming about.

Tank—A water tank elevated high above the ground by a tall skeletal framework. The expression "gas tank" or "oil tank" is used for the distinctive structures described by these words.

Target—Object seen on a radar screen. If the object is known, it is so identified. If not, targets are often given letter designations for plotting purposes, e.g., target alpha, bravo, charlie, delta, etc.

Three-arm Protractor—An instrument consisting essentially of a circle graduated in degrees, to which is attached one fixed arm and two arms pivoted at the center and provided with clamps so that these can be set at any angle to the fixed arm, within the limits of the instrument. It is used for finding a ship's position when the angles between three fixed and known points are measured. Also termed a station pointer.

Thwartships—At right angles to the centerline of the boat.

Tidal Current Tables—Tables which give daily predictions of the times and speeds of the tidal currents. These predictions are usually supplemented by current differences and constants through which additional predictions can be obtained for numerous other places.

Tidal Difference—Difference in time or height of a high or low water at a subordinate station and at a reference station for which predictions are given in the Tide Tables. The difference, when added or subtracted from the prediction at the reference station, gives the corresponding time or tide height for the subordinate station.

Tide—The periodic rise and fall of the water resulting from gravitational interactions between the sun, moon, and earth. The vertical component of the particulate motion of a tidal wave.

Tide Tables—Tables which give daily predictions of the times and heights of high and low waters. These predictions are usually supplemented by tidal differences and constants through which additional predictions can be obtained for numerous other places.

Time Difference—In the loran system, the time difference (in microseconds) between the receipt of the master and secondary signals.

Time Meridian—A meridian used as a reference for time.

Time To Go (TTG)—Calculated time until the next waypoint is reached, obtained by dividing the distance to go by the groundspeed.

Topmark—One or more relatively small objects of characteristic shape and color placed on an aid to identify its purpose.

Tower—A structure with its base on the ground and high in proportion to its base, or that part of a structure higher than the rest, but having essentially vertical sides for the greater part of its height.

Track (TR)—The intended or desired horizontal direction of travel with respect to the ground. (Synonym: Intended Track, Trackline.)

Tracking—Process of moving towards a location by adjusting the heading to compensate for prevailing current so as to travel to the station in a straight line.

Tracking (Loran)—The process of measuring time differences from an acquired master-secondary loran-C pair. The signal-to-noise ratio required for tracking of a preidentified signal is generally less than that required for signal acquisition. For this reason it is sometimes the case that a vessel that has already acquired a loran signal can continue to navigate with this signal although an identical receiver turned on may be unable to acquire the signal.

Transducer—A device that converts one type of energy to another, as a loudspeaker that changes electrical energy into acoustical energy.

Transit—British term for range, see range.

Trawler—A general term to describe a vessel with a displacement or semi-displacement hull designed for long distance cruising. Trawlers often resemble fishing vessels.

Trim—Fore and aft balance of a boat.

Tropic Currents—Tidal currents occurring semi-monthly when the effect of the moon's maximum declination is greatest. At these times the tendency of the moon to produce a diurnal inequality in the current is at a maximum.

Tropic Tides—Tides occurring semimonthly when the effect of the moon's maximum declination is greatest. At these times there is a tendency for an increase in the diurnal range.

True North Pole—The north end of the earth's axis. Also called North Geographic Pole. The direction indicated by 000° (or 360°) on the true compass rose.

True Rose—The resulting figure when the complete 360° directional system is developed as a circle with each degree graduated upon it, and with the 000° indicated as true north. Also called compass rose.

True South Pole—A reference for specifying a position on the earth's surface, at the south end of the earth's axis. Also called South Geographic Pole.

True Wind—The direction from which the wind is blowing.

Turning Bearing—A bearing on a charted object, measured in advance by the navigator, at which the vessel should turn to reach the next leg of the course.

Turning Buoy—A buoy marking a turn, as in a channel.

Twin Propellers (Screws)—A boat equipped with two engines.

Type Of Tide—A classification based on characteristic forms of a tide curve. Qualitatively, when the two high waters and two low waters of each tidal day are approximately equal in height, the tide is said to be *semidiurnal;* when there is a relatively large diurnal inequality in the high or low waters or both, it is said to be *mixed;* and when there is only one high water and one low water in each tidal day, it is said to be *diurnal*.

U

Uncorrecting (A Magnetic Direction)—Converting a true direction to equivalent magnetic or compass direction.

Uncovered—Above water, the opposite of submerged.

Underway—A vessel not at anchor, made fast to a pier or wharf, or aground.

Unmanned Light—A light which is operated automatically.

V

V Bottom—A hull with the bottom section in the shape of a "V."

Vanishing Tide—In a mixed tide with very large diurnal inequality, the lower high water (or higher low water) frequently becomes indistinct (or vanishes) at time of extreme declinations. During these periods the diurnal tide has such overriding dominance that the semidiurnal tide, although still present, cannot be readily seen on the tide curve.

Variable Range Marker—An adjustable range ring in a PPI that can be moved to measure the range of a target.

Variation—The angular difference between the magnetic meridian and the geographic meridian at a particular location.

Varsol—A liquid used in the bowl of a compass to damp the card's excessive motion and reduce response to a slower, more readable, gentle rotation and to lubricate the bearing on the pivot.

Vector—See Scalar.

Very High Frequency Radio (VHF)—Radio frequency of 30 MHz to 300 MHz. The VHF system is essentially a line-of-sight system limited in range to only a little beyond the horizon.

Vigia—A rock or shoal of uncertain position or existence. The same term is used to describe a printed warning to that effect.

Visual Aid to Navigation—An aid to navigation which transmits information through its visual observation. It may be lighted or unlighted.

Voyage Fuel—See Enroute Fuel.

W

Wake—Moving waves, track or path that a boat leaves behind it when moving across the waters.

Watching Properly—An aid to navigation on its assigned position exhibiting the advertised characteristics in all respects.

Water Tower—A structure enclosing a tank or standpipe so that the presence of the tank or standpipe may not be apparent.

Waterline—A line painted on a hull which shows the point to which a boat sinks when it is properly trimmed.

Wave Height—The vertical distance between the crest and the trough of a wave.

Wave Length—The distance between consecutive crests of a wave.

Wave Shape—The height and length of the wave as it travels.

Way—Movement of a vessel through the water such as headway, sternway or leeway.

Waypoint—Arbitrary geographic point entered into a loran set as a reference point for navigational calculations. Typically voyages are organized into a series of waypoints marking the legs of the trip.

Waypoint Sequencing (Route Option)—A feature incorporated into many loran receivers that allows an operator to store a sequence of waypoints in the loran's memory to describe a route. In this mode, whenever the vessel arrives at a waypoint the next waypoint in a prestored route sequence automatically appears on the display screen.

Weighing Anchor—Raising the anchor when preparing to get underway.

Wharf—A man-made structure bounding the edge of a dock and built along or at an angle to the shoreline, used for loading, unloading, or tying up vessels.

Wheel—A circular frame with an axle attached to the rudder of a vessel used for steering. Also a slang expression for a propeller.

Whistle—A wave-actuated sound signal on buoys which produces sound by emitting compressed air through a circumferential slot into a cylindrical bell chamber.

Windward—Toward the direction from which the wind is coming.

Winter Light—A light which is maintained during those winter months when the regular light is extinguished, it is of lower candlepower than the regular light but usually of the same characteristic.

Winter Marker—An unlighted buoy without sound signal, used to replace a conventional buoy when that aid to navigation is endangered by ice.

Withdrawn—The discontinuance of a floating aid to navigation during severe ice conditions or for the winter season.

Wreck—The ruined remains of a vessel which has been rendered useless, usually by violent action, as by the action of the sea and weather on a stranded or sunken vessel. In hydrography the term is limited to a wrecked vessel, either submerged or visible, which is attached to or foul of the bottom or cast up on the shore.

Wreck Buoy—A buoy marking the position of a wreck. It is usually placed on the seaward or channel side of the wreck and as near to the wreck as conditions will permit. To avoid confusion in some situations, two buoys may be used to mark the wreck. The possibility of the wreck having shifted position due to sea action between the times the buoy was established and later checked or serviced should not be overlooked. Also called wreck-marking buoy.

Y

Yaw—To swing off course, as when due to the impact of a following or quartering sea.

Z

Zeroing-in—Approaching a point or object by use of successive approximations such as in tacking.

Selected Symbols, Acronyms & Abbreviations

(Used In This Text or the 1210-Tr Chart)

Shown below is a complete list of symbols, acronyms, and abbreviations used in this text and/or the 1210-Tr chart.. Consult the Glossary for definitions of terms.

ABAND	Abandoned	CG	Coast Guard
ACN	*Advanced Coastal Navigation*	CGAUX	Coast Guard Auxiliary
ADF	Automatic Direction Finder	CH	Channel
Al	Alternating	CMG	Course Made Good
AM	Amplitude Modulation	COA	Course of Advance
ANMS	Automated Notice to Mariner's System	COG	Course over the Ground
		COLREGS	Collision Regulations (NAVRULES)
ASF	Additional Secondary Factor	COP	Circle of Position
ATA	Actual Time of Arrival	CPA	Closest Point of Approach
ATD	Actual Time of Departure	Cup	Cupola
ATE	Actual Time Enroute	cy,cl	Clay
ATON	Aid to Navigation		
BCN	*Basic Coastal Navigation*	D	Distance
bl	Blast	D	Doubtful
brg	Bearing	D	Drift (not preferred)
Blds	Boulders	DBD	Dayboard
BY	Buoy	DBN	Daybeacon
		DEP	Departure
C	Can	dev	Deviation
C	Canadian	DF	Direction Finding
C	Compass	Dft	Drift (preferred)
C	Course	DISC	Discontinued
CAPT	Captain	DIW	Dead in the Water
CBDR	Constant Bearing Decreasing Range	DMA	Defense Mapping Agency
		DMAHTC	Defense Mapping Agency, Hydrographic, Topographic Center
CCA	Current Correction Angle		
CDA	Current Drift Angle		
CDI	Course Deviation Indicator		
CDMVT	Compass, Deviation, Magnetic, Variation, True	DR	Dead Reckoning
		DRM	Direction of Relative Motion

E	East	kHz	Kilohertz
E	Estimated		
EBL	Electronic Bearing Line	L, Lat	Latitude
EBM	Electronic Bearing Marker	LB	Lighted Buoy
ec	Eclipse	LBB	Lighted Bell Buoy
ED	Existence Doubtful	LCD	Liquid Crystal Display
EDT	Eastern Daylight Time	LCDR	Lieutenant Commander
EMER CHAR	Emergency Characteristics	LD	Least Depth
ENR	Enroute	LED	Light Emitting Diode
EP	Estimated Position	LF	Low Frequency
EST	Eastern Standard Time	LFl	Long Flash
ETA	Estimated Time of Arrival	LGB	Lighted Gong Buoy
ETD	Estimated Time of Departure	LH	Light House
ETE	Estimated Time Enroute	LHB	Lighted Horn Buoy
ev	Every	LLNR/LLP	*Light List* Number/*Light List* Page
F	Flashing	LNB	Large Navigation Buoy
F1(2)	Group flashing	LNM	Local Notices to Mariners
FAA	Federal Aviation Administration	Lo	Longitude
FAR	Federal Aviation Regulations	LOP	Line of Position
fl	Flash	LORAN	Long Range Navigation
Fl	Flashing	lt	Light
FM	Frequency Modulation	LWB	Lighted Whistle Buoy
FOG SIG INOP	Sound Signal Inoperative		
FRM	Fixed Range Marker	M	Magnetic
FS	Fog signal	M Board	Maneuvering Board
		m	Meters
G	Gravel	M	Miles (nautical)
G	Green	M	Mud
GDOP	Geometric Dilution of Position	M/V	Motor Vessel
GpFl	Group Flashing	mag	Magnetic
GPH	Gallons Per Hour	MHW	Mean High Water
GPS	Global Positioning System	MHz	Megahertz
GRI	Group Repetition Interval	mi	Miles (statute)
		MLLW	Mean Lower Low Water
HDG	Heading	MLW	Mean Low Water
Hrd	Hard	Mo	Morse Code
ht	Height	Mon	Monument
		MPG	Miles Per Gallon
I	Interrupted	MPP	Most Probable Position
IALA	International Association of Lighthouse Authorities		
IMP CHAR	Aid not displaying characteristics as advertised in *Light List* or Chart	N	North
		N	Nun
		NAVAID	Navigation Aid (ATON)
Irreg	Irregular Light	NAVRULES	Navigation Rules (COLREGS)
ISO	Isophase (equal interval)	NE	Northeast

NM	Nautical Miles	RFI	Radio Frequency Interference
NM	Notices to Mariners	RFIX	Running Fix
NOAA	National Oceanographic and At-	Rks	Rocks
	mospheric Administration	rky	Rocky
NOS	National Ocean Service	RMP	Relative Motion Plot
NTSB	National Transportation Safety	RPM	Revolutions per Minute
	Board	RTPS	Radar Transfer Plotting Sheet
NU	North Up		
NW	Northwest	S/M	Sand over Mud
		S	Sand
OBSC	Observed	s	Seconds
Obstr	Obstruction	S	Set
Oc	Occulting	S	South
ODAS	Anchored Oceanographic Data	S	Speed
	Buoy	SAR	Search and Rescue
OP CONSTSLY	Signal is on throughout 24 hours	SATNAV	Satellite Navigation
Or	Orange	SCD	Secondary Coding Delay
		SD	Sounding Doubtful
P	Pebbles	SE	Southeast
P, POS	Position	sec	Second
PA	Position Approximate	sec	Sector
PD	Position Doubtful	sft	Soft
PPI	Plan Position Indicator	sh	Shells
		SHU	Ship's Head Up
Q	Quick (flashing)	si	Silent
		SMG	Speed Made Good
R	Red	SNR	Signal-to-noise Ratio
R	Relative	SOA	Speed of Advance
Ra ref	Radar reflector	SOG	Speed Over the Ground
RA	Radius of Action	SPM	Single Point Mooring Buoy
RADAR	Radio Detection and Ranging	SRM	Speed of Relative Motion
RB	Relative Bearing	SRU	Search and Rescue Unit
RBn	Radiobeacon	SSG	Student Study Guide
RDF	Radio Direction Finder	STW	Speed Through the Water
RED INT	Aid operating at a lesser range/	SW	Southwest
	intensity than stated in *Light List*	sy, stk	Sticky
REMAINS	Structure remains in area, pos-	T	time
	sibly still standing, and the	T	true
	search for the structure was un-	TB	True Bearing
	successful or search is yet to be	TCPA	Time of Closest Point of Ap-
	made		proach
REMOVED	Old structure located and re-	TD	Time Difference
	moved	TEMP	Temporarily Discontinued
Rep	Reported	TH	True Heading

TR	Track	USPS	United States Power Squadrons
TRLB	Temporarily replaced by lighted buoy	V	Variation
TRSB	Temporarily replaced by a smaller buoy	var	Variation
		VAR	Velocity Along Route
TRUB	Temporarily replaced by an unlighted buoy	VHF	Very High Frequency
		VMG	Velocity Made Good
TSD	Time Speed Distance	VRM	Variable Range Marker
TTG	Time To Go		
TVMDC	True, Variation, Magnetic, Deviation, Compass	W/P	Watching properly
		W	West
		W	White
Unexam	Unexamined	WPT	Waypoint
UNKNOWN	Failed to locate structure during a search of the area	XTE	Cross Track Error
USCGAUX	United States Coast Guard Auxiliary	Y	Yellow
USCG	United States Coast Guard	yd	Yards

Appendix C

Additional
Books and Articles
of Potential Interest

Shown below are a series of additional works on navigation and related subjects that may be of interest to readers of *Advanced Coastal Navigation*. As with other references, some of these present different conventions and/or points of view than those given in the ACN test. Some of the following are out of print, but may be available in libraries or at used or antiquarian bookstores.

The reader may wonder why so many additional references are included. After all, the text has been carefully written, and inclusion of only the standard reference works such as Bowditch should be sufficient. These are furnished here for several reasons:

(i) a professional navigator should be fully familiar with the literature,

(ii) reading additional texts is a subtle review and relearning process, essential to maintaining proficiency,

(iii) each of these references adds to the navigator's cumulative store of knowledge, and finally,

(iv) many of these references offer interesting asides, examples, points of view.

Attwood, E. L. *Theoretical Naval Architecture,* Longmans, Green & Co., London, UK, 1922.

Bok, B. J. and F. W. Wright. *Basic Marine Navigation,* Houghton Mifflin Co., Boston, MA, 1944.

Bradley, A. D. *Mathematics of Air and Marine Navigation,* American Book Co., New York, NY, 1942.

Burch, D. *Fundamentals of Kayak Navigation,* The Globe Pequot Press, Chester, CN, 1987.

Burch, D. *Self-study Course on Coastal Navigation,* Starpath School of Navigation, Seattle, WA, 1984.

Cashman, M. "The Best of Power Navigation," *Ocean Navigator,* No. 4, Nov/Dec 1985, pp. 30, *et seq.*

Childress, L. M. and P. Childress. *A Cruising Guide to Narragansett Bay,* International Marine Publishing Co., Camden, ME, 1990.

Cugle, C. H. *Cugle's Practical Navigation,* E. P. Dutton & Co., New York, NY, 1942.

Defense Mapping Agency. *Handbook of Magnetic Compass Adjustment,* Pub. No. 226, Fourth Ed., Defense Mapping Agency, Hydrographic/ Topographic Center, DMA Stock No. NVPUB226, Washington, DC, 1980.

Delaney, L. E. *Delaney's Simplified Navigation,* Trade Winds Publishing Co., San Pedro, CA, 1947.

DePree, K. "Using Your Loran in the Bahamas," *Ocean Navigator,* No. 15, Sept/Oct 1987, pp. 43, *et seq.*

Devereux, F. L. *Practical Navigation for the Yachtsman,* W. W. Norton & Co., New York, NY, 1972.

Dixon, C. *Start to Navigate,* Adlard Coles, London, UK, 1987.

Ellam, P. *Yacht Cruising,* W. W. Norton Co., New York, NY, 1983.

Frost, A. *The Principles and Practice of Navigation,* Brown, Son & Ferguson, Ltd., Glasgow, UK, 1988.

Garrison, P. *Practical Area Navigation,* Tab Books Inc., Blue Ridge Summit, PA, 1980.

Henderson, R. *The Cruiser's Compendium,* Henry Regnery Co., Chicago, IL, 1973.

Howell, F. S. *Navigation Primer for Yachtsmen,* Imray Laurie Norie & Wilson, Huntingdon, UK, 1980.

Kane, J. D. *Deep Sea Navigation and Pilotage with a Radio Compass,* Martin Publishing Co., Santa Monica, CA, 1966.

Kaufman, S. *Compass Adjusting for Small Craft,* Surfside Harbor Associates, Surfside, FL, 1978.

Kielhorn, L. V. *A Treatise on Compass Compensation,* D. Van Nostrand Co., New York, NY, 1942.

Lewis, D. *We The Navigators,* University of Hawaii Press, Honolulu, HI, 1989.

May, J. M. "Chain Switch Fools Loran Set," *Ocean Navigator,* No. 11, Jan/Feb 1987, p. 7.

McPhee, J. *Looking for a Ship,* Farrar Straus Giroux, New York, NY, 1990.

Mellor, J. *The Art of Pilotage,* Sheridan House, Dobbs Ferry, NY, 1990.

Moore, D. A. *Marine Chartwork,* Second Edition, Stanford Maritime, London, UK, 1987.

Motte, G. A. with T. M. Stout. *Chartwork and Marine Navigation,* Cornell Maritime Press, Centreville, MD, 1984.

Nichols, D. D. *Nichols Distance Off Tables,* Cornell Maritime Press, NY, 1943.

Olson, L. B. *Olson's Small Boat Seamanship,* D. Van Nostrand Co., Princeton, NJ, 1956.

Rogers, J. G. *Origins of Sea Terms,* Mystic Seaport Museum, Inc., Mystic, CN, 1985.

Schlereth, H. "Night Passage to Charleston—Precise Plotting with Lighthouses in a Rewarding Navigational Exercise," *Ocean Navigation,* No. 2, July/Aug 1985, pp. 40-41.

Simonsen, S. T. *Simonsen's Navigation: Coastwise and Blue Water Navigation,* Prentice Hall, Englewood Cliffs, NJ, 1973.

Szczurek, G. D. *Navigation and Coastal Piloting,* Houston Marine Training Services, Kenner, LA, 1988.

Townsend, S. and V. Ericson. *The Amateur Navigator's Handbook, Coastal Navigation Techniques in a Concise and Easy-to-Learn Format,* Thomas Y. Crowell, New York, NY, 1974.

Van Dorn, W. G. *Oceanography and Seamanship,* Dodd, Mead & Company, New York, NY, 1974.

Various. *Great Voyages in Small Boats: Solo Circumnavigations,* John DeGraff Inc., Clinton Corners, NY, 1976.

Various. *Navigation and Operations,* Naval Institute Press, Annapolis, MD, 1972.

Walsh, G. "Coastal Navigation, The Basics: Reckoning Your Speed, The First Step," *Ocean Navigator,* No. 16, Nov/Dec 1987, pp. 57, *et seq.*

Weems, P. V. H. *Marine Navigation,* D. Van Nostrand Co., New York, NY, 1940.

Worth, C. *Yacht Navigation and Voyaging,* J. D. Potter, London, UK, 1928.

Wylie, P. E. *The Essentials of Modern Navigation,* Harper & Brothers, New York, NY, 1941.

Young, H. *Islands of New England,* Little Brown & Company, Boston, MA, 1954.

Index